THE BATSFORD GUIDE TO
THE INDUSTRIAL ARCHAEOLOGY OF THE BRITISH ISLES
General Editor: Keith Falconer

Central Southern England

7 Bristol, Clifton – Goldney House Engine House

The Batsford Guide to
the Industrial Archaeology of
Central
Southern England
AVON COUNTY GLOUCESTERSHIRE SOMERSET
WILTSHIRE

C.A. and R.A. BUCHANAN

B.T. Batsford Ltd · *London*

To The Memory Of Our Parents

First published 1980
© C.A. and R.A. Buchanan 1980

ISBN 07134 1364 6 (cased)

Photoset by Photobooks (Bristol) Ltd, Bristol
Printed in Great Britain by
The Garden City Press
Letchworth, Herts
for the publishers
B.T. Batsford Ltd
4 Fitzhardinge Street, London W1H 0AH

Foreword

Our knowledge, and hence appreciation, of our industrial heritage is, as yet, very inadequate, despite increasing interest in industrial archaeology in the last two decades. This is certainly true of the four counties covered by this volume as there has been until now no comprehensive review of the remains of their industrial past. So many of the crucial processes of industrialization were pioneered in this country and brought about a revolution which has profoundly influenced the foundation and development of all industrialized societies. Its relics are thus monuments of the greatest relevance to our present society. Also of importance and even more vulnerable are the reminders of relatively modern industrial developments only recently made obsolete. These are being erased in a more thorough and systematic fashion, be it in the name of industrial rationalization, urban renewal or land reclamation – even if their preservation is impossible, their passing must be noted and at least recorded.

The pre-eminent place Britain holds in the foundation and continuing development of industrial archaeology is internationally acknowledged. There has been an impressive accumulation of material relating to industrial monuments ever since the phrase 'industrial archaeology' gained general acceptance in the late 1950s. In 1963 Rex Wailes, the noted authority on windmills, was appointed as consultant to the National Survey of Industrial Monuments. This Survey, under the joint aegis of the Council for British Archaeology and the Ministry of Public Buildings and Works sought to identify those industrial sites which merited statutory protection. On Wailes' retirement in 1971 the Survey was based at the University of Bath with a full time Survey Officer and its work continues apace now funded entirely by the Department of the Environment. Further evidence of the growing interest in industrial archaeology is provided by the staggering increase in the number of industrial museums ranging from large company and regional open air museums such as Wheal Martyn China Clay Museum in Cornwall, and Beamish North of England Open Air Museum, to single monument sites preserved by small voluntary trusts. A recent publication lists more than 150 industrial museums and monuments open to the public, most of which have been established in the last 25 years. The present volume provides many spectacular examples of this growing interest in industrial preservation. Recent years have seen the restoration of much of the Kennet & Avon Canal and of its unusual water driven pump at Claverton and its early steam driven pumps at Crofton; the rehabilitation of the City Docks in Bristol as a major amenity area focussed on preserved warehouses, quays, cranes, etc; the conservation of several steam pumps in the Somerset Levels and the rescue from the Falkland Islands of Brunel's ss *Great Britain* and its restoration in its original dry dock in Bristol.

The Batsford series of which this is the fourth English volume, is the first major national series to concentrate on sites themselves as a prime source of evidence of this crucial phase of the nation's development. The Batsford series grew out of informal discussions between Neil Cossons, Director of the Ironbridge Gorge Museum and President of the Association for Industrial Archaeology, Peter Kemmis Betty, Managing Director of Batsford, and myself. It comprehensively covers mainland

Britain with two volumes each on Scotland and Wales, and 13 volumes on England. These volumes systematically list most of those sites where complete or substantial remains can be seen. They will include some 20,000 sites and will thus constitute by far the most comprehensive survey ever attempted in this field. The area covered by this volume does not comprise a readily identifiable region but, as the authors point out, it has recently gained a certain cohesiveness based on the motorway system focused on Almondsbury in the centre of the region. It has a very ancient and distinguished industrial tradition dating back to the Roman mining of lead on the Mendips and iron ore in the Forest of Dean. It was however spared the intensity of industrialization experienced in some other parts of the country such as the Midlands and the North in the nineteenth century. Bristol was for many centuries England's second port while the tributaries of the river Avon and the streams of the Cotswolds and Mendips powered the early textile industry for which the region was renowned. The four counties display a remarkable diversity of industrial monuments reflecting the wide variety of landscapes they encompass. They range from the relics of metal mining on the Brendon and Mendip hills to the peat extraction pits and drainage pumping stations of the Somerset Levels, from the large multi-storey water-driven woollen mills of the valleys around Stroud to the water-powered brass rolling mills of the Avon valley, from the coal tips of the Somerset coalfield to the water meadows of southern Wiltshire. Bisecting the region are three parallel major historic lines of communication. The turnpike road from London to Bath and Bristol with dense networks of smaller independent turnpikes in north Somerset serving the two cities and leaving a rich legacy of toll houses and milestones, the Kennet & Avon Canal with its great aqueducts and flights of locks providing a through route from the Thames to the Severn and Brunel's incomparable Great Western Railway with its massive broad-gauge scale features such as Box Tunnel and the old train shed at Temple Meads.

The task of writing this volume was shared equally by Dr Angus Buchanan an internationally recognized authority on British industrial archaeology and his brother Sandy Buchanan, a prominent member of the Somerset Industrial Archaeology Society. Although both authors have lived for many years in the region and have been familiar with many of the sites described for a number of years, they revisited sites of long acquaintance and sought out a great many new sites to ensure that their guide was thoroughly topical and in doing so they have achieved a balanced presentation of this, the first major review of the region's industrial monuments. It is to be hoped that this volume, and the others in the series, will prove a valuable guide to those wishing to learn more about their industrial heritage and be recognized as a useful tool to those concerned in the conservation and planning of our cultural environment.

Keith Falconer
National Survey of Industrial Monuments
April 1979

Contents

List of Illustrations

WILTSHIRE

Line Drawings

Figure 1   Avon: Bristol, Old Temple Meads Station. This drawing is a cross-section of the original   40
Brunel train-shed, showing the single wide span of the timber-beamed roof. Drawn by Martin
Watts as part of a survey by John Mosse, Architect, for Bristol City Museum.

Figure 2   Avon: Charfield. Elevation of the eastern platform of the station on the Bristol to
Gloucester railway. This is one of the few minor station buildings to survive alongside this main
line. Drawn by Martin Watts.   49

Maps

1   General Map of the Region

Introduction

The four counties which are the subject of this survey do not comprise a readily identifiable region. Without Cornwall, Devon, and Dorset they do not constitute a full 'West Country' or even the 'South-West Region' of modern economic planning policy. With the old Mercian county of Gloucestershire, however, they cannot be described as 'Wessex', despite recent attempts to revive the usage of this ancient region. What we are dealing with is a group of mid-western English counties which have much in common geologically and topographically, but which have quite distinct histories of cultural and industrial development. For this reason it has been decided to treat them separately in the following account, adopting a strictly alphabetical sequence and giving each county its own introductory section.

Our counties are not usually regarded as being amongst the leading industrial areas of Britain. Certainly, there has been a long tradition of continuous industrial activity in cities such as Bristol or Gloucester, while the West of England woollen cloth industry has a venerable history and the lead mining activities on Mendip are prehistoric in origin. But it must be admitted that no part of the region has ever experienced the intensity of industrialization that has been characteristic of some parts of the Midlands and Northern England, and the coal mining district of South Wales, in the last two hundred years. In a sense, however, this makes it all the easier to understand and enjoy the positive contribution of industry to the region. Although a wide range of industries have been active in it, they have tended to mould the landscape gently, without the overwhelming effects of huge mounds of mining waste, furnace slag heaps, and giant factories. It thus remains possible to take a real pleasure in exploring the industrial archaeology of these four counties.

Despite the somewhat arbitrary nature of our region and the comparatively diverse and dispersed quality of its industrial activities, a recent development in the national transport system has given it a cohesion which it previously lacked. This development is the coming of the motorways which has placed one of the major national transport intersections at Almondsbury, in the middle of our region, with the four arms radiating from this crossing of the M4 and M5 motorways encompassing the four counties which are the subject of this study. The result is that the whole area has been integrated to a remarkable degree around this facility for easy movement from one part to another. The motorways have also provided a means of getting an instant impression of the whole region in a way which could only be achieved with difficulty before. It is still customary to regard the motorways as necessary but featureless ribbons of tarmac, taking the line of least resistance from point A to point B without much regard to the pre-existing landscapes. Perceptive motorists are discovering, however, that motorway driving is providing them with an unparalleled opportunity to get the feel of the English landscape as it changes through all its various and subtle mutations. Freed from the anxieties of cross-roads, on-coming traffic, and the frustrations of being held back by vehicles travelling slower than himself, and yet without diminishing his attention to his own traffic conditions, the motorist is finding it possible to observe the nuances of the changing scenery and thus to find a new enjoyment in road travel. In the belief that many of our readers will use the motorways in order to explore the industrial archaeology of the region, we think it will be worth pointing out some of the main landscape features which can be observed from the motorways.

Coming south from Birmingham, the M5 emerges from its difficult two-lane stretch just beyond the Strensham Service Station, where the Ross Spur (M50) loops off to the West. It crosses the Stratford Avon into Gloucestershire at this point, with the serrated line of the Malvern Hills falling away on the right, and Bredon Hill, a dignified 961 ft outlier of the Cotswold escarpment, on the left. Behind Bredon Hill, the main line of the escarpment swings in from the north-east, and remains with the motorway all the way to the Almondsbury intersection, frequently wooded but occasionally revealing a hill-top of bare grassland as at Cleeve Hill, the highest point on the edge (1082ft) with Cheltenham visible beneath it. Passing the tower of Tewkesbury Abbey on the right, the motorway then skirts Gloucester and continues southwards through the Vale of Berkeley, with views out to the Forest of Dean, the prominent copse on May Hill marking its most northerly extension. The River Severn itself can be glimpsed as the road crosses the shoulder of Stinchcombe Hill, jutting out into the plain from the Cotswold edge.

Passing Michael's Wood Service Station, the landscape changes: the Avon County boundary is crossed and the route cuts through the hard sandstone of the Pennant Series as it climbs onto the Ridgeway running south to Bristol, with the Cotswolds receding on the left as Almondsbury is approached. Beyond the intersection, the motorway cuts through the suburban edge of Bristol as it descends to the plain with the industrial development of Avonmouth on the right and the wooded ridge of King's Weston on the left. Then over the Bristol Avon, and the road begins the climb across the Clevedon ridge of mountain limestone, with views out to the estuary over the Vale of Gordano. Descending to the 'levels' of what used to be north Somerset, the motorway approaches the wooded promontory of Worlebury with Weston-super-Mare on its southern slopes, but swings away to slice through the gaps between the isolated peaks which form the western extension of the Mendip plateau. Entering Somerset, the road sweeps across the low-lying and largely reclaimed levels of Sedgemoor. Brent Knoll stands out as a detached hill on the right (457ft), and the ridge of the Quantocks becomes visible beyond as the motorway swings round Bridgwater and on to Taunton. Here the landscape changes again, to gently undulating farmland with rich reddish-brown soil as the road approaches the Devon border.

Only a short stretch of the M4 runs west from Almondsbury in our region, but it possesses the most dramatic features of English motorway engineering in the shape of the Severn and Wye bridges. The road drops fairly sharply from the Ridgeway to the plain of the Severn Estuary, with the towers of the Severn Bridge marking the route ahead. Passing the toll booths and Aust Service Station, it launches out across the estuary, and immediately after making landfall on the Beachley promontory which is the southerly extension of Gloucestershire, the road crosses the River Wye by a second suspension bridge (although of a significantly different design) and so to the Chepstow intersection and the county boundary.

Going eastwards from Almondsbury, the M4 glances past the northern suburbs of Bristol (with the M32 linking it to the city centre) and then crosses the undulating country of the Bristol Coalfield, with at least one derelict coal-mine chimney and a brickworks easily visible on the right of the road. Then the Cotswolds once more come into view ahead, but this time the motorway leaps straight towards them, climbing the edge to the Tormarton intersection for the road to Bath. Proceeding eastwards, it soon enters Wiltshire and traverses the northern section of that county. The chalk plateau of Salisbury Plain which is still the heartland of Wiltshire is not directly accessible from the motorway, but after swinging south round Swindon, with its traditional railway associations and bustling new industry, the M4 climbs up onto the Marlborough Downs and gives the motorist a taste of the rolling yet strangely secretive landscape which is most typical of Wiltshire. Then the route passes into Berkshire and so on to Reading and London.

This motorway itinerary has been described both in order to show how the new transport system has brought the four counties of our region into a more manageable relationship than they possessed before the advent of the motorways, and to help the society outings and family parties whom we hope will be the main users of this book to get to grips with the region. With the needs of such explorers in mind, we have selected the sites mentioned in the following gazetteer from a much larger body of available industrial archaeological material and attempted to keep detailed description down to the minimum necessary for recognition and enjoyment. Our emphasis, in short, has been on establishing the industrial characteristics of the four counties, rather than anything approaching a comprehensive survey.

Our thanks are due to so many people for their assistance, both direct and indirect, that it is impossible to mention them all by name and we trust that we will be forgiven for any apparent discourtesy in this respect. The work done by our colleagues in BIAS and SIAS and by other friends and co-workers in GIAS and the Wiltshire IA societies, has been of enormous value to us, and we have tried to acknowledge our debt whenever it can be done conveniently. For more personal help, on field work and with references of one sort and another, we would like to record our thanks to: Keith Falconer, Martin Doughty, George Watkins, Owen Ward, Roy and Joan Day, John Powell, John Cornwell, WGC Backinsell, DH Warren, MH Jones, AP Ward, C Tilley, G Harding, ID Miles and Mrs Mary Miles. Martin Watts has provided us with some of his excellent line-drawings, as well as advice about windmills. The maps and plans have been compiled and drawn by David Greenfield. Frank Hawtin has supplied us with most of the photographs for Somerset, and Brian Murless has also helped with photographic services. Colin Wilson and his team in the photography unit at the University of Bath have assisted us greatly with the plates for Avon and Gloucestershire. For help in the preparation of the typescript we are grateful to Mrs Judith Burchell and Miss Joanna Valentine.

Collaboration between brothers is not always a successful or harmonious procedure. It is not for us to judge its success or otherwise on this occasion, but as far as we are concerned the experience has been most harmonious and thoroughly enjoyable. We realized at the outset, however, that it would be necessary to define our respective functions so that there would be no confusion as to who was responsible for what. So we adopted a simple territorial division, whereby CA Buchanan has covered Somerset and Wiltshire and RA Buchanan has dealt with Avon County and Gloucestershire. We also decided to deal with the work in as rigorously alphabetical, a manner as was possible. We have endeavoured to make our selection of sites as up to date and as interesting as we could, bearing always in mind that many of the people whom we hope will use this book will have had little previous experience of industrial archaeology. While we have endeavoured to achieve complete accuracy, we have no doubt that blemishes will be found and we will be grateful to readers who take the trouble to correct us so that any future editions can be correspondingly improved.

CAB
RAB

Gazetteer

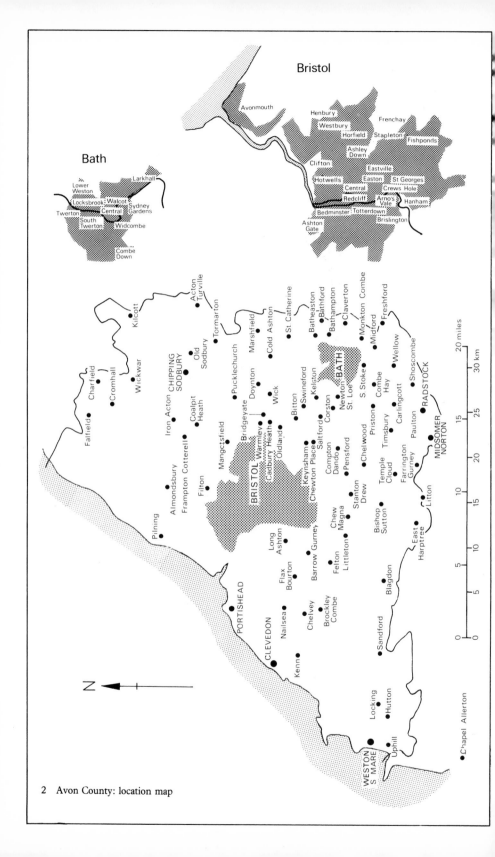

2 Avon County: location map

Avon County

Avon is a new county, created by the Local Government Act of 1972 and brought into official existence on 1 April 1974. It was formed out of the northern part of Somerset and the southern part of Gloucestershire, together with the City of Bristol which had possessed county status in its own right since the fourteenth century. Although the neighbouring counties were thus significantly depleted, the formation of Avon County was a serious attempt to recognize a fact of British regional government – the dominance of Bristol over its immediate hinterland – so that the new county became effectively the Greater Bristol Region. It must be admitted that this has not completely overcome all the anomalies of local government in the area, but that is a political and national problem with which we are not concerned here. For our purposes, Avon County is a compact and heavily populated area representing the Bristol Region, an area in which a tremendous variety of industrial developments has been stimulated by the presence of Bristol with its thriving port and urban market. With a total area of 332,596 acres it is about half the size of Gloucestershire (652,741 acres) but has double the population – 919,600 compared with 487,600 for Gloucestershire (*Whitakers Almanack 1977*, Registrar General's estimates). Unlike its neighbouring counties, in which the effects of industrialization have been somewhat thinly spread, Avon County presents a picture of intense industrial activity. Our treatment of it will need to be correspondingly compressed.

Despite its novelty as an administrative area, the two salient impressions of industry in Avon County are its longevity and its variety. Unlike its sister-city of Bath, Bristol was not a Roman City. The Romans had a packet station at Abonae, now the Bristol suburb of Sea Mills, but they appear to have avoided the marshy ground around the confluence of the Rivers Avon and Frome, where no evidence of Roman settlement has so far been discovered. But ever since a town developed at this point in Saxon England, on the sandstone knoll between the two rivers with a bridge over the Avon and the first wharves of the port of Bristol, there has been an unbroken tradition of urban growth and industrial activity. For a thousand years, at least, there has been continuous industrial development in the Bristol Region. While other medieval towns sank into comparative industrial obscurity, Bristol has maintained its attractiveness to industry, and together with London has been one of a handful of important cities which have preserved their industrial base from the Middle Ages up to the present day, regularly extending it to accommodate new industries and processes. Such longevity is an unusual and important feature, making the industries of Avon County particularly interesting as a subject of historical investigation.

The other outstanding quality of the industries of the Avon County is their remarkable variety. It is only a slight exaggeration to say that Bristol has, over the centuries, had a hand in almost every industrial process that can be named. Of course, the variety of industries being practised at any one time has changed continually, with some always in decline until they eventually disappear while others rise up to take their places. The 'lost industries' of the Bristol Region included the manufacture of soap, glass, pottery, and sugar, all of which have flourished in the past, and all of which have left some traces, albeit very fragmentary in some cases, in the local townscape. The most important contemporary industry is engineering, the county possessing one of the largest complexes of aeronautical engineering in the country, and this is virtually a creation of the present century. This constantly changing variety of industries in the region has meant that Bristol has never been identified with any single industry, as have many of the great industrial cities of modern times, and one beneficial consequence of this has been that the area has never declined. Variety has thus been an important ingredient in the industrial prosperity of Avon County.

At the heart of the industrial activity of the Bristol Region, and a powerful reason for both the longevity and variety which we have noted, has been the prosperity of the port of Bristol. This prosperity has only been maintained by a continuous struggle to improve the port facilities, particularly during the last two hundred years, but although the struggle against the natural problems of the harbour and against mercantile conservatism amongst the policy-makers has been long and sometimes bitter, Bristol has succeeded in keeping its port amongst the leading ports of the United Kingdom. The natural problems have included that of recognizing the inadequacy of the city-centre port facilities of Bristol once the size of ships began to increase significantly in the eighteenth century. The original wharves on the tidal Avon below Bristol Bridge had been improved as early as the thirteenth century by the major earthworks which straightened out the course of the River Frome from its original line along what is now Baldwin Street to a junction with the Avon near the bridge, into the wide trench with new facilities on New Quay and Broad Quay which penetrated deep into the centre of the city. However, this was still a tidal harbour, with ships being carried up the tortuous eight miles from the Severn estuary on what is still one of the highest tidal ranges to be found anywhere in the world. The result was that ships were stranded on the mud and rock of the river trenches twice in every 24 hours.

With comparatively small vessels, such treatment could be irritating but it was harmless. As ships increased in size, however, the possibility of damage by stranding increased correspondingly, and proprietors of large merchantmen began to prefer ports with better deep water facilities like Liverpool and Glasgow. Tardily, Bristol came to terms with the fact that its mercantile pre-eminence on the west coast of Britain was being lost, and undertook a radical reform of the dock facilities. The result was the Floating Harbour of the Bristol City Docks, constructed by William Jessop for the Bristol Docks Company between 1803 and 1809. This scheme converted the course of the Avon and Frome through the city centre into what was essentially an enclosed dock, with permanent high water, and provided for the tidal flow of the Avon by excavating the New Cut across the southern side of the harbour. Unfortunately, the completion of this scheme coincided with the advent of the steamship and a further dramatic increase in the size of vessels. Despite prolonged attempts to keep the city docks up to standard, therefore, Bristol continued to lose trade to its rivals until the final decades of the nineteenth century, when the inevitable trends were accepted and the port of Bristol began the long course of transferring its facilities from the centre of the city to the side of the Severn estuary at Avonmouth on the Avon and at Portishead (and now at Royal Portbury Dock) on the south side of the river.

Although this process is still not complete, virtually the whole of the trade of the port of Bristol is now conducted from the docks around the mouth of the Avon, leaving the City Docks of the Floating Harbour as an obsolete set of water courses and thus as an object of prime importance to industrial archaeologists. Sections of the City Docks have already been lost: two-thirds of the Frome arm of the harbour has been culverted to form the ornamental gardens and traffic roundabouts of the city centre, while the Merchants' Dock in Hotwells has been filled in completely. The only industry still relying on the trade of the City Docks is the local market for sand dredged from the Severn estuary and still brought up regularly into the city. The shipbuilding industry, represented until very recently by the Albion Dockyard of Charles Hill, has now closed down. Nevertheless, it is important to recall the historical function of the City Docks in supporting port industries, both those related directly to the needs of shipping and those derived from commodities brought into the Docks.

Food and drink industries would, of course, be significant with or without the port, and Bristol has possessed the usual array of industries of this sort. Many small grain mills once flourished on the smaller rivers of Avon County, such as the Bristol Frome and the River Chew, draining the northern and southern halves of the county respectively. These were easily converted to such other functions as snuff mills, paper mills, and logwood mills by the stimulus of changing market demand, and several changed their use more than once although most have now become derelict or disappeared. Corn milling itself has tended to become a highly concentrated process, and as far as the Bristol region is concerned most of it is now done in large mills at Avonmouth Docks. Malting barley and brewing beer have also undergone considerable concentration after having been spread widely across the county and especially in the urban centres of Bristol and Bath. Only one brewery remains in action, but that is the large establishment of Courages (until the 1960s, George's Brewery) on the Counterslip close to Bristol Bridge. The region also has various dairies, meat processing, and confectionery industries.

The textile industries have had a long association with Avon County. By far the oldest and most important has been the woollen cloth industry, because, in the early centuries of its development, Bristol shared in the success of the West of England woollen cloth industry, manufacturing fine woollen fabrics from Cotswold wool. Mechanization in the form of water-powered fulling mills began to affect this industry in the later Middle Ages, and caused it to shift eastwards from Bristol towards the fast-flowing streams of the Cotswolds and eastern Mendips. It was here, in the environs of Bath, that the industry prospered until further mechanization and the introduction of steam power brought greater concentration, to the advantage of the Stroud valleys in Gloucestershire and the Somerset and Wiltshire area between Bradford, Trowbridge, and Frome. But the woollen cloth industry retained a base in Twerton, the western industrial suburb of Bath, until the mid-twentieth century, by which time the West of England industry as a whole had declined almost to vanishing point.

The presence of a local coalfield has been until very recently one of the outstanding advantages of Avon County as an industrial region. The coalfield, including the ancient Kingswood mining area and its extension northwards into south Gloucestershire, and the old north Somerset coal measures stretching from Bath in the east through Radstock and Bedminster to Nailsea in the west, occupies the geographical core of the new county of Avon, but it is ironical that the establishment of the county in 1974 coincided almost exactly with the closure of the last two active collieries at Radstock in 1975. Nevertheless, the area of coal mining activity can now be reasonably regarded as the Avon Coalfield, if only retrospectively. From the Middle Ages almost to the present day, this coalfield has provided vital fuel for the wide range of local industries which have developed on and around it. Although much of the consumption was purely local, the possibility of exporting it to neighbouring inland areas encouraged the construction of roads and canals for the purpose, but when railways brought even greater freedom to the inland market for coal, the Avon Coalfield suffered severely from competition with South Wales and the Midlands, and went into the decline from which it never recovered.

Along the eastern edge of Avon County, beyond the geological strata of the coalfield, is the oolitic limestone escarpment of the Cotswolds. The southern extremity of this escarpment around Bath has proved to be the basis of another important extractive industry concerned with exploiting the stone as a building material. Bath stone has been quarried and mined in this area for many centuries, but particularly since the great building boom in Bath of the eighteenth century. Like local coal, Bath stone became a staple bulk commodity on the canal network, being used extensively in London and elsewhere. It is a type of stone which has proved itself to be ideal for fine ashlar masonry, in which the blocks are regularly jointed with thin bands of mortar, and thus superbly appropriate to the classical style adopted in the construction of Georgian Bath. Other local stones which have been worked in the region include pennant, a fine-grained grey sandstone once worked in the Frome valley near Stapleton, but now only available from the Forest of Dean. Carboniferous limestone is still worked for roadstone and lime in the county, and fuller's earth is still being extracted from shallow mines at Combe Hay, near Bath. Avon County also possesses one of the few known workable deposits of celestine, a strontium mineral used in flares and fireworks, at Yate.

While the Cotswolds form the eastern edge of Avon County, the southern rim runs along the Mendip Hills, a plateau composed largely of carboniferous limestone which has been economically important in the history of the region as a source of lead and zinc. Mendip lead played a significant part in the industry of Bristol, where it was converted into sheeting, piping, and lead shot. The process of making lead shot by pouring molten lead down a shot tower was discovered in Bristol and when the original tower was demolished a few years ago, a new modernistic shot tower was erected in the city centre to perform the same simple process.

During the eighteenth century, lead was replaced by zinc as the most important metal being extracted from the mines of Mendip. This was because calamine, an ore zinc, was easily available around Shipham at a time when the young Bristol brass industry required it as a raw material in order to produce the alloy brass by mixing zinc with copper. The copper was imported from Cornwall, but it gave a great boost to the brass mills which sprang up along the River Avon from the first brass works at Baptist Mills to Conham, Keynsham, Saltford, Kelston, and Weston (Bath), to have a reliable local supply of calamine. Both the mining activity and the brass mills suffered in the nineteenth century from Welsh competition, and the industry went into a long decline, the last brass mill closing at Keynsham in 1927. The most ambitious of all the local brass works was that established by William Champion at Warmley in the mid-eighteenth century. Although this soon got into financial difficulties and was taken over to be converted to other uses, the site still possesses some tantalizing clues to its existence as a brass factory.

Iron has been worked in various ways in Avon County. Valuable deposits have been found in conjunction with the coal measures and have been mined at Iron Acton, Frampton Cotterell, and elsewhere. Many small foundries flourished in the towns, and during the nineteenth century a substantial iron works developed at Ashton Gate, near Bedminster. Pin making became a significant industry in Kingswood, Bitton, and other places, originally encouraged, like shoe-making, as an industry for female labour on and around the coalfield. Some local foundries developed into significant engineering firms, like Stothert & Pitt of Bath who acquired a specialist reputation as manufacturers of pumps and cranes. Other engineering enterprises started out in response to the need for new machines, railway locomotives and rolling stock, automobiles, aeroplanes, and engines. The huge modern engineering complex at Filton, devoted to the manufacture of airframes and aero engines, began in 1910 with an attempt to improve the traffic of the Bristol Tramways by establishing there the British & Colonial Aeroplane Company. This and other large engineering enterprises make a substantial contribution to the modern prosperity of Avon County.

Historians of Bristol industry are invariably obliged to resort to a large miscellaneous category in order to include some of the many industries which have flourished in this area of very varied industrial development. Soap making, for instance, was an early Bristol industry to take advantage of local coal and other raw materials. This industry reached the peak of its prosperity in the nineteenth century, when the Christopher Thomas factory was built on Broad Plain to manufacture Puritan Soap. Like other once-dispersed industries, however, this has been a victim of twentieth-century rationalization and concentration, and has disappeared from the region. The same has happened with glass making and pottery, both of which have made a distinguished contribution to the history of industries in the Bristol region, but have now been completely extinguished. Paper-making, which developed in the region from the sixteenth century, could well have gone the same way, except for two significant developments. One was that, in the national rationalization of large-scale board manufacture, Bristol was chosen as one of the centres where the industry could most usefully be encouraged. The result has been the growth of large board-mills like that at St Anne's in Crew's Hole. The other development has been the related success of Bristol as a centre in the paper and board packaging business, promoted partly by the needs of tobacco and other consumer product industries but also by the enterprise of individuals such as ES & A Robinson in the mid-nineteenth century. The result has been that certain specialized types of paper production remain as important industries in the area, even though many small paper mills have gone out of business and disappeared. One high-quality specialization to survive has been the 'Bible paper' manufactured by the Bathford Paper Mill, east of Bath.

Where a population is comparatively scanty, there is little demand for such facilities as water supply and sewage disposal, but once the population becomes dense and predominantly urban as it is in Avon County, the provision of public services has to be regarded as a category of important industries in its own right. Water supply became a matter of urgent public concern in both Bath and Bristol in the middle of the nineteenth century and led to very significant industrial investment in reservoirs, mains, and pumps in order to ensure a supply of good quality water to urban residents. Even earlier, from 1818, both cities had begun to acquire gas companies providing the innovation of gas lighting in both streets and private houses. Somewhat later, provision was made for networks of sewers and sewage treatment plants (although Bristol continued to rely on the tidal Avon for the removal of its effluent into the present century), and for the supply of electricity (beginning in the 1890s with companies in both Bristol and Bath) and for urban transport services, to which the new electricity supply made a distinguished contribution for half a century in the shape of the electric tramcar. All these public services have undergone drastic changes in recent decades which has made the study of their industrial archaeology a matter of some urgency.

Transport, of course, is not merely a matter of public service and local enterprise: the transport revolution which has accompanied the rapid industrialization of the last two hundred years has brought radical transformations in the transport facilities of Avon County as of the rest of Britain. The roads were the first to feel the impact of these changes. Bath was amongst the first places in the country to take advantage of the turnpike legislation to improve its roads in the early eighteenth century, and Bristol followed soon after. The most important link was the west–east road between the two cities, and continuing to London, but many other roads benefited from the investments and enterprise of the local turnpike trusts, and many relics of this activity can still be observed in the form of mileposts, turnpike houses, and in the alignment of modern roads.

The most important artery of transport, at least for bulky commodities, in Avon County in the eighteenth century, was the River Avon, and in 1727 the Avon Navigation undertook the improvement of this waterway from Bristol to Bath, resulting in a greatly improved facility for moving coal and stone in particular. The great age of canal construction which began in the second half of the century did not at first make much impact on Avon County, but eventually John Rennie's Kennet & Avon Canal, completed in 1810, made a very significant improvement in the transport links between the County and the inland areas to the east. The branch canal and associated tramways of the Somerset Coalfield maintained the supply of coal into this inland network, and other tramways were constructed to convey Bath stone from the hill-top mines around the city to wharves on the canal system.

The coming of the railways disrupted both the turnpike roads and the canal companies so badly that the turnpikes were taken over by the county authorities and most of the canals were taken over by the railways. The Great Western Railway, engineered by I.K. Brunel on his controversial broad gauge, came to dominate Avon County and took over both the Kennet & Avon Canal and the useful coal tramway, the Avon & Gloucestershire Railway, which had linked the collieries of Warmley and Oldland with the navigable Avon. The tramway was closed and the canal allowed to decline into insignificance. But the GWR did not have everything its own way in the county, because the Midland Railway managed to buy out the majority interest in the Bristol & Gloucestershire Railway, and in time brought an alternative, narrow gauge, route from the north, with a loop to a new station in Bath (now Green Park) linking with the Somerset & Dorset Junction Railway and thus opening up a north–south route from Birmingham through to the south coast. However, the GWR remained the leading railway of the county (despite its conversion to the narrow gauge), with its key route from London through the Box Tunnel and Bath to Bristol, and extended thence to Weston-super-Mare, Exeter and the far west, and with its splendid station at Temple Meads, Bristol, which despite congestion and successive extensions remains one of the most interesting groups of railway buildings in the country. Nationalization and rationalization has brought simplification of the railway system, in Avon County as elsewhere, causing the reversion to the original GWR main east–west line, although the later Badminton line to the Severn Tunnel is also still open to express traffic and provides part of the north–south link also on the line up to Gloucester. Most of the lesser stations have disappeared, together with the old signalling equipment and signal boxes, but much remains of interest to the industrial archaeologist.

In reviewing the transport history of Avon County, however briefly, it is appropriate to mention shipping and aircraft. Despite its long tradition of maritime traffic, Bristol has done surprisingly little to preserve this aspect of its heritage. The Floating Harbour of the City Docks is now receiving attention as an amenity and a heritage feature, but it is too early to predict that the result will be entirely satisfactory. In the heart of the City Docks, however, the outstanding feature is the ss *Great Britain*, being steadily restored to something approaching her original splendour in the dry-dock in which she was built and from which she was launched in

1843. The near-miraculous sequence of events by which this broken and rusting iron hulk was brought back to Bristol in 1970 was the result of private initiative and resources, and although she was warmly welcomed home by the people of Bristol, the city officials have been somewhat slower in recognizing the immense value of this asset now restored to Avon County. The *Great Britain* remains for the moment the only vessel of any size for which any deliberate conservation effort has been made in Bristol. As far as aircraft are concerned, the situation is no better. A Boxkite is preserved in the City Museum, and the British Aircraft Company still use the great hangar constructed after World War II to accommodate the *Brabazon*, the still-born giant of the piston-engined era. But no other attempt has yet been made to conserve in any local collection specimens of the many distinguished machines made in Bristol aircraft factories.

Conservation policy, in short, is still in a somewhat indeterminate condition so far as industrial monuments are concerned in Avon County. There is a good City Museum in Bristol, with a new industry and technology section opened in a dockside transit shed in 1978, and Bath is acquiring an industrial museum as a largely private venture in the Camden Museum (there is still no general museum of Bath history– an extraordinary omission for such a tourist-orientated city). The local industrial archaeological society, BIAS – Bristol Industrial Archaeological Society – was formed out of a Bristol University Extra Mural Class in 1967, and is a vigorous society with its official base at Bristol City Museum. Despite its title, BIAS defined its sphere of influence effectively as that which was later chosen as Avon County, so it can claim to be a genuine county venture. But, with these exceptions, there is still a great deal to be done in Avon County towards distinguishing the priorities of conservation and industrial preservation. It is much to be hoped that the new county authority will apply itself urgently to these matters in order to ensure the proper valuation of the industrial heritage in a region which possesses such an enormous wealth and variety of industrial monuments.

ACTON TURVILLE

A Cotswold Village close to Badminton Station and Park, possessing a neat two-storey stone **Toll house** (ST808808) at the junction of roads to Chipping Sodbury, Malmesbury, and Chippenham. The building has a half-hexagonal front, with a clock and space for a toll-board on the foremost face. It is roofed with limestone tiles.

Badminton Station (ST810812) survives on the main-line railway just north of the village: the platforms are intact but the buildings are dilapidated.

ALMONDSBURY

Although this village has given its name to the busy M4–M5 motorway intersection, it is tucked away under the Ridgeway and comparatively isolated from traffic. The major industry is the **Cattybrook Brickworks** (ST590833), the largest and now the only active brickworks in the region. It was developed to provide brick for the construction of the Severn Tunnel in 1873–1886, and the bright red bricks were widely used in Bristol industrial buildings.

BARROW GURNEY

This straggling village has two small farm mills, **Lower Barrow Mill** (ST523686), and **Upper Barrow Mill** (ST529681) on the stream (the Land Yeo) running down its narrow valley. But the major feature of the village is the **Water Treatment Station** (ST537678) set up there by Bristol Waterworks Company. There are three substantial storage reservoirs alongside the A38, receiving water from Blagdon Reservoir and elsewhere, and then a battery of filtration beds and equipment for ensuring the purity of water distributed from this point to the public water mains. There is a small collection of relics assembled at the Treatment Centre by the late Mr F.C. Jones, who was a local historian and employee of the BWW Co, but it is not normally open to the public.

BATH CITY

With its long tradition of being a spa-town, based upon its extraordinary and geologically puzzling hot springs, and going back at least to Roman times, Bath is not an obvious candidate for industrial archaeological interest. It is still primarily known as a tourist centre, with its Pump Room, Roman Baths, Medieval Abbey Church, and gracious Regency terraces, all built in the mellow, honey-coloured, Bath stone. But behind this façade there is plenty of evidence of busy industrial activity, based both on indigenous resources like wool, coal, and stone, and on engineering and other processes which have been introduced to the city and have acquired firm roots there.

Central Bath The River Avon flows strongly through the city, and the old weir at Pulteney Bridge at one time sustained two watermills – **Town Mill** and **Bathwick Mill** (ST 753649): the former has now been obliterated by the North Parade Gardens

except for a fragment (with a label on it) preserved amongst some bamboo shoots; and Bathwick Mill has more recently been cleared out by the flood control works which renewed the weir in 1971 and installed the counter-weighted sluice on the site of what used to be the tail-race for the mill. The River Avon also provides a reason for several notable bridges, in addition to the three-span stone arched **Pulteney Bridge**, built in 1774 by Robert Adam in the favourite Palladian style with small shops along both sides: **Victoria Bridge**, (*Plate 1*) (ST 741650) constructed by James Dredge in 1836 on novel suspension principles, whereby the load on the bridge platform was evenly distributed by increasing the angle between the suspender rods and the catenary cable as they approached the centre of the 150ft span, still stands today as a footbridge; and **Cleveland Bridge** (ST 753 657), although unobtrusively strengthened below its deck to take heavy road traffic, presents the appearance of a cast-iron bridge with the name of its maker, W. Hazledine (1827), cast on a plate in the railings, and with quaint and now unoccupied lodges at both ends. **The Guildhall** (ST 751649), in the centre of Bath, provided the reference point for the Bath Turnpike Trust, one of the earliest road-improving trusts in the country, with many milestones preserved on the roads radiating from Bath and with a few of these possessing terminus stones where the juris-

1   Bath Central – Victoria Bridge

diction of the BTT ended and showing a hand pointing out the distance from the Guildhall. The Railways brought two stations to Bath. **Bath Spa Station** (ST 753643) opened when the Bristol to Bath section of the Great Western Railway began carrying passenger traffic on 31 August 1840: the line was opened through to London on 30 June 1841. I.K. Brunel designed the station with an all-over roof, rather like his terminus at Temple Meads, which was later converted to its present double platform, each with its own awning. The station has been modified in other ways: the signal box above the down-line platform, the through lines between the existing platform lines, and a third platform tucked alongside the London end of the up-line platform, have all been removed, and the platforms have been extended at both ends. But the main façade to the station, designed by Brunel in Bath stone and a modest Jacobean style, has not been significantly altered. **Bath Green Park Station** (*Plate 2*) (ST 745647) was opened on 20 July 1874. It was then named Bath Queen Square Station, being changed to its present style in 1951. It provided a double terminus, for the Midland Railway branch from Mangotsfield (opened

1869) and the Somerset & Dorset Joint Railway (opened through to Evercreech Junction in 1874). There were three pairs of rails under the central arch of the train shed, with small supporting arches over the platforms on either side. This graceful structure is a miniature St Pancras and as a provincial railway monument it is quite outstanding. But it is now used as a car park, and both the train shed and the fine Georgian-style frontage are now decaying while their future is debated. The lines running into Green Park have been lifted, but those through Bath Spa Station now carry the High Speed Inter City 125 mph trains on the main Western Region of British Railways from Paddington to Bristol.

Combe Down Due south of the centre of Bath, Combe Down occupies the centre of the ridge running from High Barrow Hill at Haycombe in the west to Bathampton Down in the east. The area is now dominated by suburban development, with an important Ministry of Defence (Navy Department) establishment in Combe Down itself, and the new University of Bath on Bathampton Down. Historically, however, it has been significant as the major source of the

2 Bath, Central – Green Park Station

outstanding natural resource of Bath stone. The relics of many stone quarries can still be discerned, especially where the roads climbing the hill cut into the edge of the escarpment just below the summit, for it was here, 20–30ft below the level of the hill top, that the best building stone was located. This is in the form of a thick bed of the Greater Oolite. However, to exploit fully the natural qualities of this stone it was necessary to mine it, and to weather it gently on exposure to the outside air. As a result, the hill top under Combe Down is honeycombed with stone mines, the full extent of which is not known. But some of the gallery entrances can still be seen off Combe Road (e.g. at ST756623). The excellent stone available here was first exploited commercially by Ralph Allen in the first half of the 18th century. He used it to construct his nearby mansion at Prior Park, and sponsored the construction of a tramway to convey the stone down to the River Avon at Dolemeads. The tramway (*Plate 3*) has disappeared, but its alignment coincided with that of Ralph Allen's Drive and Prior Park Road for most of its course (Ref: Sir Arthur Elton: 'The pre-history of railways', *Proc. Som. A.N.H. Soc.* (107) pp.31–59, 1963). Also in Combe Down, and particularly unexpected in a residential district, is the **de Montalt paper mill** (ST763619). This flourished briefly in the first half of the 19th century but then became a laundry before being abandoned for industrial purposes. The buildings are now largely derelict but still impressive, with a stone chimney standing strangely aloof amongst the surrounding trees. The mill was originally water-powered, possessing a large overshot waterwheel supplied by a piped conduit from the springs above the mill.

Larkhall The last eastern suburb of Bath on the London Road, just before the junction with the Stroud Road (A46), and near the point where the Swainswick Brook runs into the River Avon from the north. There is a mill site at **Lambridge** (ST762666), but little of interest remains. However, at Bailbrook, where the A46 enters Bath, there is an attractive small **toll house** (ST763673).

Locksbrook Chosen as the site of their gas works in 1818 by the Bath Gas Light

3   Bath, Combe Down – Ralph Allen Tramway, Prior Park

Company, (ST737652) this suburb to the west of the Royal Victoria Park became the centre for the subsequent development of the gas supply industry in Bath, although it spread across the River Avon to the adjacent land on the south bank, where the large gas holders were constructed. The gas works have been transformed in the last decade by the cessation of coal gas manufacture and the consequent demolition of the battery of vertical retorts. But several of the older retort houses survive for the time being, as does the modest office block on the Upper Bristol Road.

Lower Weston Separated from the 'village' of Weston by the complex of the Royal United Hospital, this area on the north bank of the River Avon benefited from proximity with the industrial community of Twerton on the south bank. When the Avon Navigation improved sailing conditions on the river in 1727 they excavated the Weston Cut to enable barges to negotiate the two weirs at **Twerton** (ST725648). The artificial island thus created acquired the nickname of Dutch Island on account of its association with the brass mill of Nicholas Graef, who died in 1743. Nothing remains of this industry except the street name Brass Mill Lane, and the island is now used as an open-air store, the only building of significance being the **five-storey spinning mill** which is the only surviving fragment of the woollen cloth industry that once flourished in and around Twerton. The north-facing front of this building is alongside the Weston Cut, and is distinguished by a long attic window. The original **humped bridge** over the Cut also survives. Other industries have since been attracted to this part of Bath, including **maltings** (ST724650).

Sydney Gardens This attractive public park has twice suffered desecration by transport improvements: once by the construction of the Kennet & Avon Canal, completed in 1810, and then by the Great Western Railway a generation later. One can only imagine the outcry if a contemporary proposal should be made to cut a road through it . . . But to be fair, it must be said that both the canal and the railway responded to the challenge to provide proper architectural and amenity consideration to their works. As a result, the canal makes a very graceful traverse through the Gardens, with

two short tunnels and **two neat cast-iron foot-bridges** (bearing plates: *Anno Domini 1800*). It has been surmised that the sections for these bridges, like those for the similar but smaller bridges over the Widcombe locks, had been made locally by Stothert's, but it now seems likely that George Stothert acted as the agent for Coalbrookdale castings (Ref. H. Torrens: *History of Stothert & Pitt*). The towing path is not accessible from the Gardens, but can be reached from either end. At the western end, the canal tunnel runs under **Cleveland House** (ST758653), which was built as the headquarters of the Kennet & Avon Canal Company. A persistent legend claims that there was a trap door allowing direct communication with passing barges, but at the speeds then current this seems somewhat superfluous. The railway cutting through the Gardens was provided with appropriate architectural, and almost theatrical, form by I.K. Brunel, to whom the Brunel Society erected a plaque here in 1977. Also worthy of interest in Sydney Gardens are the cast-iron public lavatories, as such structures are becoming something of a rarity. So are the handsome **Penfold pillar boxes** (*Plate 4*) on Pulteney Street nearby.

South Twerton An amorphous area of Victorian industrial and domestic development running (ironically) east of Twerton itself rather than south. It is of industrial significance because of the spread of **Stothert & Pitt** from Newark Foundry (ST746644) just below Churchill Bridge on the Lower Bristol Road (built in the 1850s when the firm moved from its earlier home in Newark Street, where the bus station has been built), taking in several premises as far as Dutch Island in Lower Weston (*q.v.*). This important Bath engineering firm has a long tradition of manufacturing cranes and pumps. Two small steam engines made by the firm were presented to the University of Bath on permanent loan in 1977. Other industries in South Twerton include printing (**Pitmans Printing Press** (ST737648) was established on the Lower Bristol Road in the 1880s, although the existing buildings are mainly from the 1920s), furniture manufacture, and **brick works** (ST733644), although the site has now been landscaped and redeveloped.

Twerton Originally Twiverton (see the Harcourt-Masters maps of the Bath Turnpike Roads in 1784, in Somerset County

4   Bath – Sydney Gardens, Penfold Pillar Box, Pulteney Street

Record Office), this village to the west of Bath has now been firmly included within the city as a residential and industrial suburb. The bend of the Lower Bristol Road in the centre of the village (now cut off by the realignment of the road made necessary by Brunel's railway) has a defaced milestone marking the second mile out of town. The village was once an important centre of the woollen cloth industry, and traces of weavers' cottages can still be discerned, running at right-angles to the river. The River Avon had two weirs at Twerton, now replaced by a single flood-control gate, and each of these had a mill at both ends. On the Twerton side, these were textile mills for most of their lives – latterly the factories of Isaac Carr & Co and of W.&R. Cook, most of which were demolished in 1964. Furniture manufacture is currently an important industry in Twerton, with **Arkana Ltd** occupying a substantial red-brick factory which was once (incredibly) the home of an early aircraft company (ST 730 647). Also worth mentioning are the remains of the coal mine at **Pennyquick** (ST 714 644). **Walcot** Walcot was once an important industrial area, close to the centre of Bath and stretching out along Walcot Street, Ladymead, and the London Road. It retains many signs of this past activity, and also a few small industries survive. There is, for example, still a small iron foundry at work between Walcot Street and the River Avon, next to the **Tramway Depot and Generating Station** (ST 752 653) which is a decaying red brick building now used as a store by the South Western Electricity Board. There have been substantial breweries and maltings in the area, but little is left of any significance. **Widcombe** This village south of the River Avon was associated with the woollen cloth industry and possessed a number of small mills on the stream coming down from Lyncombe. However, little survives of these, and by far the most important industrial monuments in Widcombe now are those associated with the Kennet & Avon Canal. The canal made its junction with the River Avon, and with the Avon Navigation to Bristol, in the middle of the village, at a spot in Dolemeads close to the terminus of the stone mine tramway from Combe Down, where there was a stoneyard and workshops and a wharf with cranes for loading the stone onto barges. The canal ascends a flight of

seven locks (now reduced to six as a result of road improvement schemes, with one new lock – the second in the series – serving as a double-lift lock), which have been restored to working order and their side-ponds put back into good shape. Alongside the first lock (*Plate 5*) in the series is a small **pumping station** (ST 754 643), used to restore the water to the top of a flight, with a square-built engine house and stone chimney. Another chimney-like column alongside the middle lock in the series (ST 758 645) is probably only decorative. Over the third and sixth locks (allowing six in the flight) there are small iron **footbridges** bearing the name Stothert. By the top lock is a **lengthman's house**, and here the canal starts its long stretch to Bradford-on-Avon without further change of level. Near the top lock, also, **Baird's Malting** (ST 758 647) has been very pleasantly converted into flats and studios as a successful piece of adaptive re-use, retaining the unmistakable configuration of a small malting with its kiln attached. Another feature of Widcombe is the **footbridge** over the River Avon (ST 753 643), connecting the village with Bath Spa Station. This wrought-iron girder bridge was built in 1877, replacing a less substantial structure which collapsed into the river in June 1877 as a result of over-loading during the first centenary show of the Bath & West Agricultural Society on Beechen Cliff. The new bridge uses the masonry piers of its predecessor and retains the toll house from which it acquired its nickname as Halfpenny Bridge.

BATHAMPTON

A village two miles east of Bath, with an old church, farm, and barn between the Kennet & Avon Canal and the main line railway, but otherwise spreading up the slopes of Bathampton Down to the south in a rash of suburban development. There is a **weir** on the River Avon at the bottom of Mill Lane, with a mill site at both ends, and with what remains of both now incorporated into restaurants (ST 774 670). The road crosses the river at this point by one of the few surviving toll bridges in the region, to link up with the London Road near Batheaston. Up on Bathampton Down to the south is plenty of evidence of **stone quarrying and mining** (ST 777 653), and from these workings a

5 Bath, Widcombe, – Entrance Lock to Kennet & Avon Canal

tramway or **plateway** (some grooved stone sleeper blocks are still *in situ*) ran down the slope north-eastwards towards Holcombe Farm, where there was a **wharf** on the canal (ST783659). There is still a wooden **swing-bridge** across the canal at this point.

BATHEASTON

This is quite a substantial village on the London Road two miles out of Bath, at the point where the St Catherine's Brook enters the River Avon. The village has grown greatly as a result of becoming a dormitory suburb for Bath. It has had industrial associations, but these have now been largely lost. The mill site at **Bathampton weir** (*q.v.*) (ST774670) is now a restaurant, and there is another mill site on the St Catherine's Brook (ST779679). Incredibly, William Smith, the famous pioneer geologist, conducted a trial colliery excavation searching in vain for coal close to Batheaston Church.

BATHFORD

Bathford straggles round the northern shoulder of Bathford Hill, above the confluence of the River Avon and the By Brook, and in the angle between the Bath–Bradford-on-Avon road (A363) and the old London Road over Kingsdown (now bypassed by the modern A4 route through Box). On the By Brook stands **Bathford Mill** (ST790671), still operating as a paper mill manufacturing high quality Bible paper, but no longer using water power or steam power (a fine steam engine was removed from the mill recently and acquired by Wendron Forge Museum in Cornwall). An earlier industry in the village was that of stone mining, of which extensive workings are still visible near the top of Bathford Hill, although now much overgrown by forest plantation. The tower of **Brown's Folly** (ST795661) marks the centre of these operations.

BISHOP SUTTON

A substantial village, close to the Chew Valley Lake reservoir. There was a Coal Pit (ST583 592) here, but much of the site has been built on by recent residential development. **Bishops Sutton Mill** (ST585595) was a steam-driven corn mill.

BITTON

Bitton is on the A431 road, about half way between Bristol and Bath, and near the confluence of the southward-flowing River Boyd with the River Avon. The valley of the Boyd is known as Golden Valley, probably on account of the prosperity once derived from its coal mines, for it forms the eastern boundary of the once-flourishing Kingswood Coalfield. The **Golden Valley Mill** (ST682 697) is a substantial establishment built as a paper mill but now manufacturing plastics. The mill pond, an octagonal brick chimney bearing the date 1880, and a fine wrought-iron entrance bearing the name of the mill survive. Upstream on the River Boyd, two smaller **watermill sites** may be discerned (ST686704 and ST688710). Like many villages in the ancient Kingswood Forest, Bitton supported a thriving pin-making industry as an adjunct to coal mining, and the remains of one **pin-factory** survive (ST682695) as the upper floor of a row of cottages on the right-hand side of the road from Bristol. The coal mining sites near the village are not of any distinction, but there is a spoil heap of one of the **Golden Valley collieries** on the west side of the River Boyd about one mile north of Bitton (ST685705).

BLAGDON

One of a string of villages at the foot of the north-facing escarpment of the Mendip plateau, Blagdon has one industrial monument of some significance: **Blagdon Pumping Station** (ST503600). The valley of the River Yeo at Blagdon was chosen by the Bristol Waterworks Company for the site of its major reservoir in 1889. The pumping station, at the western end of the Blagdon Lake thus formed, was completed in 1905, with two redbrick wings around a central chimney, a boiler house, and various settling basins and ancillary buildings. There were two Woolf compound beam engines in each wing of the engine house, of which one pair (in the south wing) have been preserved: they were made by Glenfield & Kennedy Ltd., of Kilmarnock in 1902 (hp 21in × 5ft 3in: 1p 34in × 7ft: drop valves; 2¼ mgd at 17rpm) and stopped working in 1955. The brick chimney has been truncated.

BRIDGEYATE

Half a mile to the north of this settlement on the A420 road from Bristol to Chippenham via Tog Hill, is **Webb's Heath Colliery** (ST680738), of which more survives than most of the collieries that once dotted this part of the Kingswood Coalfield. It still possesses an engine house, chimney, and spoil heap.

BRISTOL CITY

As Avon County is, practically speaking, the Greater Bristol Region, and as the City of Bristol is still the industrial heart of the county, it will be realized that the city contains a large proportion of all the industrial monuments in the county. For convenience in surveying them here, these features are grouped according to the main geographical areas of the city, although the monuments of the Bristol City Docks and Floating Harbour have been extracted for separate treatment under the heading Bristol Port.

Arno's Vale   On leaving the inner-city at Totterdown, the Bath Road swings eastwards past Arno's Court and Arno's Park and then climbs up Kensington Hill to Brislington. Opposite the Court, at the foot of the hill, Bristol Tramways constructed the **Brislington Tram Shed** (ST612715), with an ornate entrance opening into a yard from which a fan of tram lines turned right into the sheds: it is now used as a bus depot. The entrance should not be confused with the nearby **Arno's Vale Arch**, now derelict but previously giving access to the part of the Arno's Court estate containing the bizarre stables and out-buildings known as **the Devil's Castle** (ST612717), built largely of the black slag blocks cast from the copper furnaces of the Bristol brass industry. •

Ashton Gate   One of the best-preserved specimens in the county, **Ashton Gate Toll house** (ST573717) is a two-storey semi-circular fronted building with cast-iron columns supporting the veranda. It has been empty for some years.

Ashley Down   This Victorian suburb of Bristol is dominated by the austere mass of **Muller's Orphanage** (ST599755), consisting of five major buildings in pennant sandstone. Begun in 1849 as an orphanage by the German evangelical philanthropist George Muller, these buildings received financial support from many sources, including Muller's compatriot and successful industrialist Conrad Finzel, the sugar manufacturer. The buildings were acquired by the local authority in the mid-20th century and now house the Brunel Technical College.

Barton Hill   Barton Hill developed as an industrial suburb on the eastern edge of Bristol in the 19th century, when the **Great Western Cotton Factory** (ST610727) was built there alongside the Feeder Canal in 1838. The large five-storey fire-proof construction spinning block, faced in pennant sandstone, was demolished in 1968. The weaving shed is still in use for small industrial purposes, and the decorative gateway on Great Western Lane survives. The factory is significant in the industrial history of Bristol because it placed it firmly on the map of cotton-manufacturing districts in Britain. It also represents one aspect of the efflorescence of Bristol's industrial activity in the late 1830s and 1840s associated with the *Great Western* railway and steamship, and, of course, with I. K. Brunel. The firm eventually got into financial difficulties and closed after World War I although it reopened briefly as an artificial silk factory from 1926 to 1929.

Bedminster   Immediately south of the New Cut, this part of Bristol developed rapidly in the 19th century with the growth of the large tobacco factories of W.D. & H.O. Wills. These have now been vacated as the firm (now part of Imperial Tobacco) has moved out to brand new buildings at Hartcliffe, on the site of the old Whitchurch Aerodrome. **Bedminster No.1 Factory** (ST587717) was equipped with Belliss & Morcom high-speed steam engines providing power and exhausting into process and steam heating systems, and other Wills factories possessed similar equipment because the use of process steam made these engines very economical. Bedminster was also the site of several collieries, in a westward extension of the Kingswood Coalfield: most of these have been lost under urban development, but note the remnants of **South Liberty Colliery** (ST565701) and **Dean Lane Colliery** (ST584 717).

Brislington   See **Arno's Vale** for tramways depot.

Central Bristol, 'Brycgstow' or 'the site of the bridge' derives its name from the original bridge at the lowest bridge-point over the tidal River Avon, still eight miles from the Severn Estuary, between the sandstone bluffs on which the early townships of Bristol and Redcliff stood. The present **Bristol Bridge** (ST590728) is a three-arch masonry bridge designed by James Bridges and opened in 1768. It has a 55ft semi-elliptic central span supported by two 45ft semi-circular arches, but widening was carried out in the 1870s, with pillars inserted outside the piers to carry the extension of the roadway, and this alteration, with subsequent modifications, has obscured the classical outline of the bridge. From the bridge, High Street leads up to the cross-roads (High Street – Broad Street – Corn Street – Wine Street) which is the traditional centre of Bristol and the site of **Bristol Cross**. It is a sad comment on the attitude of Bristolians towards their heritage that they scrapped this medieval relic in the early 19th century, although it was rescued by the antiquarian Sir Samuel Hoare who re-erected it near the entrance to his home at Stourhead Park (ST777340). A later replica was also abandoned, but on this occasion the upper section was preserved in a corner of Berkeley Square (ST580731). Around Bristol Cross stood a selection of the old parish and guild churches of Bristol, several of which can still be seen. And on Corn Street, outside the classical Exchange (John Wood the Elder, 1740–3) stand the **Bristol Nails** (ST589730), four brass pillars topped by a flat circular table on which, before the construction of the Exchange, it was customary to pay 'on the nail'. Of the four, two are Elizabethan and the others early 17th century. Corn Street drops gently to Baldwin Street, which follows the line of the early city wall, and probably the course of the River Frome before this was straightened for the port improvement of the 13th century. Beyond Baldwin Street was an area of marshland which was progressively reclaimed as the city expanded. An early piece of this expansion was King Street, which possesses the oldest theatre in Britain in the **Theatre Royal** and a venerable hostelry in the **Llandoger Trow**, both with industrial associations. The theatre, described by Pevsner as 'a most valuable document of English theatrical history' (*Bristol*, p.416), now incorporates the **Coopers' Hall**, a grand

Palladian building for an important Bristol Guild (William Halfpenny, 1743–4). And the three-gabled timber-framed public house was closely associated with the traffic on nearby Welsh Back. There are also some small but nondescript warehouses on King Street, and beyond it is Queen Square, a piece of 18th-century town planning desecrated by a 20th-century main road cutting diagonally across it. The Square contains the **Custom House**, a modest building of 1836, and the much more ornate offices built for the **Port of Bristol Authority** in 1889 but now vacated in favour of new offices at Avonmouth. Between Queen Square and the Llandoger Trow is the spectacular brick edifice of Pearce's **Welsh Back Granary** (*Plate 6*) (ST589126), one of the outstanding industrial buildings in the centre of Bristol (Ponton & Gough,1869). Its exotic brickwork is eloquent testimony to the confidence of the Bristol commercial classes in the second half of the 19th century, and although no longer a granary it is a hopeful example of adaptive re-use as the bottom floors have been leased by a nightclub. A contrasting style of Bristol commercial architecture, but no less typical, is that of the pennant-sandstone faced warehouses in the vicinity of Queen Square. The finest and best conserved of these is **Bush's Warehouse** (ST586725), standing at the junction of the Avon and Frome arms of the Floating Harbour, a five-storey building dating from the 1830s when it was a tea warehouse: it has passed through several successive uses and has recently been reconditioned as the Arnolfini Gallery. On the other side of Prince Street is the **Seed Warehouse**, at the end of The Grove, another pennant-faced structure with internal cast-iron columns, somewhat marred by modern window frames. Except for this and the **Hole-in-the-Wall Restaurant** at the other end of the row, The Grove has lost all its traditional wharf-side buildings. Across the Frome arm of the Harbour (St Augustine's Reach) is Canon's Marsh, a part of central Bristol which has only been reclaimed for industrial use in the last century. And already the goods railway terminus and marshalling yard, opened in 1906, has been abandoned to leave a large car-park and an early reinforced concrete shed (ST583724). Next door to this site was **Canon's Marsh Gas Works**, (ST581724) developed as a rival enterprise to

6   Bristol, Central – Pearce's Welsh Back Granary

the Bristol Gas Company in 1828, but later merged and now almost entirely derelict: the retort houses are ruinous, and the office block has been largely demolished. From here it is a short step across Deanery Road to **Brunel House** on St George Street behind the Council House (ST582728): built as a hotel for passengers between the Great Western Railway and the steam ship *Great Western*, it has survived precariously in other uses. Across Park Street, on Denmark Street, is the headquarters of **Harveys Wine** (ST585728) with a grim pennant-sandstone bonded warehouse and an attractive cellar museum of the wine industry (open by appointment only). Passing the Colston Hall on Colston Street brings one to Perry Road, and at the junction of the two streets some fragments survive of an important intersection and shed on the **Bristol Tramways** (ST586732). From this point it is possible to descend by **Christmas Steps**, a quaint survival of a fragment of ancient Bristol, to the old walled city which can be re-entered through the gate below St John's Church and thus by Broad Street back to the central crossroads.

Clifton Clifton was developed as a select residential suburb to Bristol, mainly in the early 19th century. It occupies the gentler slopes of the limestone ridge to the north of the ancient city, with the precipitous Avon Gorge forming the Western boundary and the open expanse of Durdham and Clifton Downs preserved on the top of the plateau. To the industrial archaeologist, the glory of Clifton is the **Clifton Suspension Bridge** (ST564 731). Built to the design of I.K. Brunel, who won the competitions held in 1829-31 to decide on a bridge across the Avon Gorge, the enterprise ran out of money and remained incomplete in his lifetime, to be finished in 1864 as a memorial to the great engineer. The final design differed slightly from Brunel's plans, particularly in the addition of a third wrought-iron chain to the two on each side from which the suspension rods are hung. But the main features are as Brunel intended them to be, and the bridge has been maintained in excellent condition although it is not open to very heavy vehicles. Above the bridge, on Clifton Downs, stands **Clifton Observatory** (ST566733), now a *camera obscura* giving, on a fine day, a wonderful panorama over the city, but originally a

windmill built as one of two such towers in a snuff factory in the 18th century. **Victoria Pumping Station**, Oakfield Road (ST577 737) is part of the network of pumping stations provided by Bristol Waterworks Company. It has had successive generations of steam engines, of which some parts remain in the shape of a Hathorn Davy inverted vertical triple expansion engine of 1912, but the station is now electrically powered. It pumps water up to the water tower on Clifton Down. Another feature in Clifton of great industrial archaeological interest is in private grounds and not normally accessible: this is the **Goldney House Engine House** (*Plate 7*) (ST574726), of which it may be said that the building is probably the oldest steam engine house surviving in the country. It is a circular tower, built in the 1760s by Thomas Goldney to accommodate a small Newcomen-style atmospheric engine which pumped water up a tank at the top of the tower, from which it gravitated into the fantastic gothic grotto still surviving beneath the adjoining ground.

Crew's Hole Immediately to the east of the central city area of Bristol, the River Avon emerges from a marked valley. This is nothing like as distinctive as the Clifton Gorge to the west of the city, but it is nevertheless distinctive and has considerable industrial archaeological interest because it has become an area of industrial dereliction, by-passed by modern industry. However, there are modern enterprises in the area – notably St Anne's Board Mill and Butler's Tar Factory – but most of the sides of the valley have been neglected and possess fragments of earlier processes. The **chimney on Trooper's Hill**, dominating the valley on the north side, is the most prominent feature (ST628732): this is at the end of a flue, now largely overgrown, from a copper works in Crew's Hole. Further evidence of this copper industry is apparent in the copper slag blocks used in buildings in the area, and particularly in the other **chimney at an old colliery site** in the bottom of the valley (ST629728). On the north bank of the Avon, in Crew's Hole, are the remains of a small pottery, with two kilns: this was **Amatt's Pottery** (ST626731). A more ancient establishment, **Brislington Pottery** dating from 1650, (ST621727), is commemorated by a plaque in St Anne's

Board Mill. Crew's Hole also possesses fragmentary remains of lead-smelting works and a large chemical works manufacturing alkali at **Netham Alkali Works** (ST617727).
Easton   An inner suburb of Bristol, possessing in **Baptist Mills** (ST602744) one of the earliest sites of the Bristol brass industry. It was here that Abraham Darby I learnt his craft before moving to Coalbrookdale and the iron industry in the first decade of the 18th century. With redevelopment and flood-control works on the Bristol Frome, little remains of the mill site.
Eastville   A Victorian suburb of Bristol, and the site of **Stapleton Road Gas Works**, the largest and best equipped coke gas works in the region until the transformation of the gas industry by oil-based processes and North Sea Gas made most of the plant redundant (ST606748).
Fishponds   Until the end of the 1960s, **Pountney's Bristol Pottery** was still active on Lodge Causeway (ST628753) but the site of this, the first and last of Bristol's important potteries, has now been redeveloped.
Frenchay   North of Bristol, the River Frome runs along a steep-sided and wooded valley which is an important and attractive feature. This valley provided some quarries for the widely-used pennant sandstone, and also supplied water power for a series of small mill sites. Those in Frenchay included **Cleeve Mill** (ST644777), a grist mill which became an iron mill manufacturing agricultural implements to 1885; **Frenchay Flock Mill** (ST642773), built as an iron works in 1761 but subsequently converted, and **Frenchay Mill** (ST638773), last used as a corn mill about 1905. Frenchay itself, above the valley on the north side, preserves much of its character as a village, with its green and a number of distinguished buildings.
Hanham   Modern Hanham is a Bristol suburb astride the A431 road to Bath, but most of the interest in the parish is in the valley of the River Avon, where there is a low **weir and lock** on the Avon Navigation (ST648700). A mile downstream from here is the likely site of the **Hanham Abbots Brass Works** (ST635718) below Conham, and near the same point descended the incline from **Hanham Colliery** (ST638721), of which some buildings survive including a beehive-shaped powder house.
Henbury   A pleasant residential suburb of

Bristol. The River Trym flows through the parish, once providing water power for **Combe Dingle Mill** (ST557774) and also for **Stratford Mill** (ST562784) in the grounds of Blaise Castle Park, although this is strictly a museum feature as it was moved when its original site was inundated by the Chew Valley Reservoir.
Horfield   A 19th-century northern extension of Bristol, Horfield possesses few buildings of interest except the **prison** (still in use) and the barracks (now demolished). But it does have a **tram shed** (ST594764), now well adapted to other purposes, and on the corner of Horfield Common there is a rather distinguished **cast-iron urinal** (ST595768).
Hotwells   Attempts to develop the tepid springs of Hotwells as a spa in the early 19th century failed. But it provided a terminus for the Bristol Port Railway & Pier at **Clifton Station** (ST565729) (later renamed Hotwells), now almost entirely obliterated by the modern Portway. Also, the **Clifton Rocks Railway** ran on a 1 in 2·5 gradient from Clifton through solid rock to Hotwells, where the dilapidated entrance can still be seen alongside the Portway. The tunnel was opened to traffic in 1893 and struggled on to 1934: it was used in World War II as an air raid shelter.
Redcliff   Redcliff was originally a rival township to Bristol, standing across the River Avon on the sandstone ridge to the south. The 13th-century port improvements united the two developments, and thereafter Redcliff grew as an important industrial section of Bristol. This small part of inner Bristol has thus experienced successive stages of concentrated industrialization and redevelopment, with only a few fragments currently surviving of earlier phases of this process. At the heart of Redcliff stands the noble parish church of **St Mary's** (ST591 723), which may rightly be regarded as in part an industrial monument because it was built largely out of the profits of the late-medieval woollen cloth industry. This industry declined from the 16th century, but there is a fine pennant-sandstone warehouse, the **Wool Hall** (*Plate 8*) still standing (ST593726). This is near the church of St Thomas à Becket, another of the cluster of ecclesiastical buildings in Redcliff. Other industries which once flourished in the area

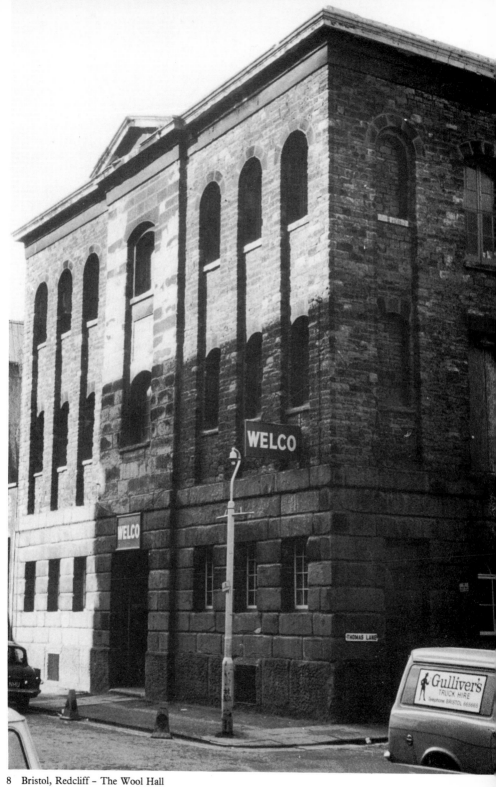

8   Bristol, Redcliff – The Wool Hall

but have now disappeared almost without trace include **pottery** (sites have been excavated near Temple Church, but there are no surface remains), **glass** (with the substantial fragment of the **Redcliff Glass Cone** (*Plate 9*) – ST593723 – now incorporated as a restaurant in the Dragonara Hotel), **sugar refining** (with a fragment of the great 19th-century **Finzel's Sugar Refinery** on the Counterslip surviving in Courages' Brewery – ST592729) and **rope making** (with no visible remains). **Lead shot making** originated in Redcliff, being first made by William Watts in the **shot tower** opposite St Mary's (ST590723) in 1782. But the building was demolished in the interests of road-widening in 1968, although not before a brand new shot tower had been constructed to replace it (ST595729) at the Cheese Lane establishment of Sheldon Bush & Co. Redcliff has a collection of buildings associated with the public service industries, including the **Temple Back Retort House** (ST596726), the first base of the Bristol Gas Light Company in 1816 (an outer wall and the stump of a chimney are incorporated in a modern factory on the south side of the Floating Harbour); **Temple Back Power Station** (ST594728), completed in 1893 as the Central Electricity Lighting Station as

the lettering on the pediment of this brick building still boldly declares; and **Bristol Tramways Power Station** (ST593729) a distinguished brick and masonry building completed around 1900 and now incorporated in Courages' Brewery. There are also some substantial offices and warehouses, including **Redcliff Back Warehouses** (ST591727) and the **WCA Warehouse** (ST591725) (Western Counties Association) on the side of the Floating Harbour. The ancient street pattern of Redcliff was disrupted in the second half of the 19th century by the appropriately named **Victoria Street** cutting through to Temple Meads Station. Most of the fine Victorian buildings on this street have been victims of either wartime bombing or post-war redevelopment, but a few fragments remain together with some attractive details of the earlier Redcliff around St Thomas and Temple Churches. For all its successive mutilations, Redcliff still contains much fascination for industrial archaeologists including such bizarre details as the length of tram track which speared into St Mary Churchyard in a World War II blitz and has stuck there ever since.

St George A Victorian suburb of Bristol, built as the city spread eastwards onto the Kingswood Coalfield. The district contains

9 Bristol, Redcliff – Truncated Glass Cone

many relics of the coalfield, including some of the buildings at **Whitehall Pit** (ST618738 – Church Lane off Foxcroft Street) and the site of **Speedwell Pit** (ST625746), now largely redeveloped. At Beaconsfield Road (ST623 735) is the building of the original **Bristol Tramways Power Station**.

St Philips One of the earliest industrial suburbs of Bristol, St Philips lies between Old Market and the River Avon. It contains the **Avon Street Gas Works** (ST601725), the main centre of coal gas manufacture in Bristol between 1821 and 1879: some of the horizontal retort houses have been adapted to other uses and two gas holders are still in use. Also the distinguished 'Bristol Florentine' brick mass of **Christopher Thomas' Soap Factory** (*Plate 10*), built in the 1880s and now converted to offices and showrooms (ST597729); the less conspicuous jumble of buildings at **Horton Street Flax factory** (ST598730), with a boiler house and chimney; and part of the **Old Market Sugar Refinery** in Jacob Street (ST597731). During

the 19th century industry spread into the flat ground of St Philip's Marsh, between the River Avon and the Feeder Canal, and although this area retains little of historic interest, the site of **Avonbank Power Station** (ST608725) still possesses some of the functional buildings constructed in 1902 to house the generators of the expanding electricity supply industry.

Stapleton A village east of Bristol, now absorbed in the expansion of the city, but like Fishponds a mile further out, still preserving something of its village character, particularly in the parts of the parish in the Frome valley, where the series of mill sites continues from those in Frenchay (*q.v.*) with **King's Mill** (ST631767) – little above ground except the 10ft weir, but the site has been extensively excavated in recent years – (see *BIAS Journal 4* 1971); **Witherlyas Mill** (ST629765) – otherwise known as Snuffy Jacks, with very little to be seen; **Whitwood Mill** (ST625765) better known as Parker's Mill, with the shell of some buildings and a waterwheel surviving

10   Bristol, St Philip's – Christopher Thomas' Soap Factory

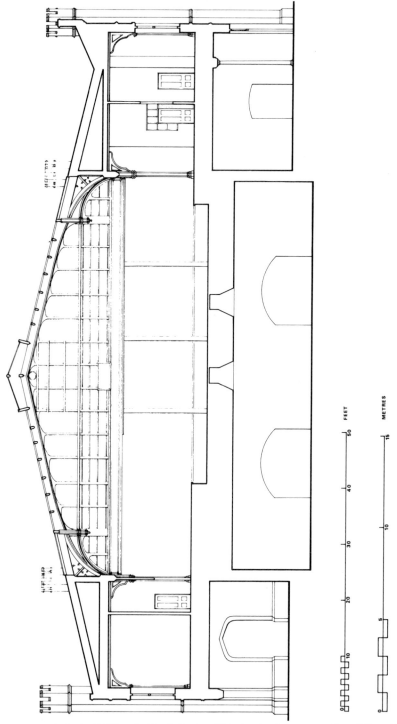

Figure 1   Avon: Bristol, Old Temple Meads Station. This drawing is a cross-section of the original Brunel train-shed, showing the single wide span of the timber-beamed roof. Drawn by Martin Watts as part of a survey by John Mosse, Architect, for Bristol City Museum.

in a recreational area (there is also the flywheel of a supplementary steam engine); and **Lathbury Mill** (ST618759), below Wickham Bridge, with a weir and ruinous buildings remaining.

Temple Meads Strictly speaking a part of Redcliff, this field by the River Avon assumed significance when I. K. Brunel chose it as the site for his original terminus to the Great Western Railway in Bristol. This building, **Old Temple Meads Station** (*Fig 1*) (ST595724) is still virtually intact in the form it was completed in 1840, and survives as the oldest intact main-line railway terminus in the world. This gives some indication of the outstanding importance of this structure with its timber-roofed mock-hammer beamed train shed and neo-Tudor façade. It is now recognized as a Grade I listed building, and even though it is now used as a car park there is hope for its eventual restoration to a more dignified function. Just across the main approach road to Temple Meads Station are the **Bristol & Exeter Railway Offices** (ST596724), built very soon after Old Temple Meads (1852) in a neo-Jacobean style. Nor should the present **Temple Meads Station** (ST597725) be overlooked: built by Sir Matthew Digby Wyatt in 1878, this has an impressive iron-construction train shed following the curve of the line in the right angle between the original juxtaposition of the GWR and B & E lines. The façade, with its rough-hewn dolomitic conglomerate, is also quite imposing. Beyond the main train shed, further platforms were added in another extension to the station made in 1935. The whole complex of buildings makes this one of the most interesting and important sites in the possession of British Rail. There is also a fragment of a **tramways depot** and track alongside the main station approach and Old Temple Meads.

Totterdown The nondescript area across the River Avon from Temple Meads is Totterdown. The junction of the two roads leading into Bristol from Bath and Wells respectively was until recently graced by a very elegant **cast-iron fingerpost** (ST599 718) which was removed to permit road-widening and put into store until it can be replaced.

Westbury This self-contained village on the River Trym to the north of Bristol has been enveloped in 20th-century surburban expansion. It contains little of industrial significance, but one curiosity is the **Westbury Tram Shed** (ST573766), a small tram shed at the junction of Grange Road and Westbury Road which has now been incorporated in a garage.

BRISTOL PORT

The port has been a feature of Bristol from its earliest existence as a town down to the present day. It has been intimately related to the River Avon, although over the centuries this relationship has changed, as the great tidal range of the river, which was initially an advantage in bringing vessels eight miles upstream to the inland wharves below Bristol Bridge, gradually became a disadvantage. The growing problem of accessibility for large ships was partially overcome by converting the city-centre reaches of the Avon and its tributary the Frome into permanent high-water dock which became known as the Floating Harbour (because boats floated in it at all stages of the tide) or as Bristol City Docks. The latter designation became normal once the necessity for deep-water docks at the mouth of the river led to the construction of such facilities at Portishead and Avonmouth in the 1870s. Although subsequent attempts were made to maintain the viability of the City Docks, the main centre of activity of the Port of Bristol shifted remorselessly towards Avonmouth, and in the last decade the virtual closure of the City Docks has been accompanied by the opening of the large new Royal Portbury Dock on the south side of the river mouth, and also by the completion of the Avonmouth Bridge which has placed the river-mouth docks in a most convenient proximity to the motorway network. Nevertheless, important monuments to the earlier stages of the Port of Bristol remain, and the City Docks in particular survive as the largest single industrial artefact in the region requiring sympathetic conservation. In surveying these features, we follow a topographical rather than an alphabetical pattern, beginning at the mouth of the River Avon and working upstream.

Avonmouth The first **Avonmouth Dock** (ST512780) was completed in 1877 and **Portishead Dock** (ST475770) in 1879. Both were plain rectangular basins, with wharves around the sides, and both were built by private companies which were subsequently taken over (1884) by Bristol Council. Portishead Dock has not developed greatly, but Avonmouth Dock has been extended and in 1908 a large new basin, the **Royal Edward Dock** was opened just to the north of it (ST510788). It was around this complex on the north bank of the river that the main industrial development occurred, and during the 20th century the suburbs of Bristol have stretched out to absorb it into Bristol City. Nevertheless, the south bank was chosen for the new venture, the **Royal Portbury Dock** (ST500770), opened by the Queen in 1977 in the course of her Jubilee celebrations.

The Avon Tideway   **Pill** (ST526761) is at the southern end of the **Lamplighter's Ferry**, one of the traditional river crossing points now made redundant by Avonmouth Bridge. **Pill Creek** has long been known as a base for pilots whose services are essential on all ships coming into the port. The **Powder House** (ST537765) is best approached from the river: this was the wharf and warehouse where ships were intended to deposit explosives before proceeding up into the City Docks. **Sea Mills Dock** (ST549759), at the mouth of the River Trym on the north bank of the Avon, is the site of the oldest port facilities in the region, as this was the Roman packet station of Abonae. The surviving masonry walls, however, date only from the 18th century, when a premature attempt was made to develop this dock as an alternative to the wharves in the city centre. Near the entrance to the City Docks, the roadways approaching **Rownham Ferry** (ST567723) can be seen in the mud at low tide. **Ashton Swing Bridge** (ST568721) was a double-deck bridge, with a road on top and a railway on the lower level. It was built in 1906, but the road has now been replaced by the Cumberland Basin flyover, and although the bridge is retained to give limited rail access to the southern side of the Floating Harbour, it is no longer swung.

The New Cut   The most laborious part of the construction of the Floating Harbour on the scheme planned by William Jessop and supervised by him between 1803 and 1809 was the excavation of the $1\frac{3}{4}$ mile **New Cut** from Ashton Gate to Totterdown to carry the tidal flow of the Avon past the enclosed docks. This involved slicing through a sandstone ridge, and a great mound of spoil

was dumped on the south bank, along which Coronation road now runs. There are several bridges over the Cut, including **Vauxhall Footbridge** (ST567721), designed to swing like Ashton Bridge, but the cessation of traffic on the Cut made this unnecessary; **Wapping Footbridge** (ST585721), a graceful small suspension bridge; and the two double bridges carrying the main roads at **Bedminster Bridge** (ST590720) and **Bath Bridge** (ST597722), both of which were originally the sites of single span bridges known respectively as Charford's Bridge and Hill's Bridge.

Cumberland Basin   William Jessop provided the Floating Harbour with an entrance basin, excavated out of Rownham Mead and named **Cumberland Basin** (ST568723). This originally had two entrance locks from the river and one junction lock between the Basin and the Floating Harbour. The **Old North Entrance Lock** was replaced in 1873, so that the only remaining fragment is a curved masonry wall across what was once the mouth to the lock. Outside this is the **Gridiron**, a framework of large beams on which small craft are able to settle at low water to have their hulls inspected or to be painted. The present **North Entrance Lock** (*Plate 11*) which came into service in 1813 and which has remained the main entrance to the Floating Harbour ever since, was designed by the Docks Engineer Thomas Howard to smooth out the sharp angle at which ships had previously been required to turn in order to enter the Harbour. The lock gates are of a conventional mitre gate arrangement, but they were amongst the first to be operated by hydraulic power. The original **South Entrance Lock** was separated by a narrow central pier from its slightly larger neighbour. This pier was one of the limiting factors influencing I. K. Brunel when he was invited to submit designs for a new lock to replace it: his plan envisaged the use of single-leaf caisson gates which would be housed in recesses on the southern side of the lock to relieve the load on the pier. This design was accepted and completed, after considerable delays, in 1848. The **Brunel Lock** was an imaginative and carefully built structure, but it was always handicapped by its awkward angle of entry and towards the end of the 19th century it was phased out of use. It is now sealed with a dam across the middle, and

11   Bristol Port, Cumberland Basin – The North Entrance Lock to the City Docks

the gates have been scrapped, but at low water it is still possible to see clearly the masonry structure of the outer half of the lock, with the gate recess, hinges, and chain-channels. To complete his design, Brunel provided a swing bridge which demonstrates an early stage in the evolution of the engineer's wrought-iron tubular bridge structure which received its final consummation in the Royal Albert Bridge over the Tamar at Saltash. This **Brunel Swing Bridge** was later moved by Howard to bridge his new North Entrance Lock, and may still be seen on the south side of that lock. But a replica was subsequently made to take its place and it is this **South Entrance Lock Bridge** which, truncated and no longer able to swing, crosses the lock. The whole assembly of locks and bridges can be seen from the modern **Cumberland Basin Flyover** which crosses the locks. At the upper end of the Cumberland Basin, Jessop built only one **Junction Lock**: this is the southern lock, now sealed and used as a mooring for small craft. Its gate recesses

are still visible (there were three pairs of gates, one being for tide gates to restrain the highest tides from entering the Harbour). The lock is now the only one surviving from the original design of the Basin, so it gives an interesting indication of the maximum size of ships able to enter harbour. There is a terrace of attractive **dock cottages** alongside the lock built by the Bristol Docks Company for its employees in 1832. **The North Junction Lock** is now the only effective link between the Basin and the harbour. It was built by Thomas Howard in 1871, with three sets of mitre gates like its older neighbour, but these were the first to be hydraulically operated in the Port. The power was supplied from the **hydraulic engine house** (*Plate 12*) on the northern edge of the lock: a neat Italianate structure in pennant sandstone, it stands dilapidated and urgently requiring sympathetic re-use. Both the entrance locks were crossed by the railway which came in over the Ashton Bridge to reach the northern side of the Floating Harbour and the Canon's

12 Bristol Port, Cumberland Basin – The old Hydraulic Engine House

Marsh terminus in 1906. The two lock bridges were dismantled after the railway closed in 1965, but the brick buttresses can still be seen.

The Underfall Yard Jessop had achieved permanent high water in the Floating Harbour by building a dam across the River Avon at Rownham. This dam was originally an 'overfall' allowing surplus water to run off over the top, but when I. K. Brunel was consulted about the serious silting problems in the Harbour in the 1830s he recommended converting it into an underfall with culverts under the dam which could be used for scouring silt from the harbour as the tide fell in the New Cut outside. When this conversion had been completed it was found possible to build up the area of water behind the dam, and on this 'made ground' was established the **Underfall Yard** in the 1880s. The **Underfall Dam** (ST572721) is now scarcely visible under Cumberland Road and the railway which crosses it, but the four culverts (three small, for water control, and one large, for scouring silt) still operate beneath it: they are controlled from the building on the left of the main entrance to the Yard. The main function of the Yard was to accommodate the **engineering workshops** of the PBA (Port of Bristol Authority). These consist of a building with two parallel bays: the southern bay contains a small Tangye horizontal steam engine and a Cornish boiler in a room at the west end, driving through belts and shafting the machine tools in the remainder of the building. Although subsequently re-equipped, several of the machines installed in the original array of the 1880s remain, including a Whitworth planing machine and a long-bed gap-lathe by Kendal & Gent. The northern bay of the building is the forge, with blacksmiths' equipment and a steam hammer. The whole assembly of machines and equipment is a fascinating exercise in the history of engineering. Ship repair work was carried out at the Underfall Yard, and there are still sheds and a bay with a ramp running down into the water for this service. Across the bay is the present **hydraulic engine house**, a red-brick building with a short tower to house the accumulator, although this has been replaced by an accumulator in an open gantry alongside the tower. This engine house was constructed in 1887, when the demand for hydraulic power was spreading

rapidly around the Floating Harbour, making the first engine house alongside the Junction Lock inadequate. But the original steam engines were replaced in 1906 by three electric ram pumps by Fullerton, Hodgart & Barclay, and these machines are still at work although their duty has been greatly reduced in recent years. The engine house has an attractive gilded galleon vane. The remainder of the Underfall Yard site is occupied by a terrace of **BDC houses** where Cumberland - Road becomes Avon Crescent, and the **Nova Scotia Public House** on the Cumberland Basin corner of the site.

The Floating Harbour The result of the scheme completed by William Jessop in 1809 was to introduce sinuous fingers of permanent high water into the centre of the city of Bristol. Although parts of this pattern of water surfaces have been lost by unimaginative urban development such as that responsible for covering much of the Frome arm of the Harbour to make the flower gardens of the modern city centre, most of it still remains, posing problems for conservationists and planners alike. So far no satisfactory scheme has emerged for the re-use of the water area and attendant wharves, warehouses, transit sheds, and dockyards. Proceeding up the Harbour from Cumberland Basin, the main features are: **Merchants Dock** (ST573724), filled in as recently as 1967 after years of relative disuse; the adjacent **Hotwells Dock**, still doing business in the sand trade; the **Albion Shipyard**, (ST576 724), until recently the busy premises of Charles Hill & Sons Ltd, but now cleared of most of its equipment and leaving only derelict slipways and buildings and an empty dry dock; the **Great Western Dry Dock** (ST578724), built (or at least extended) in the 1830s to accommodate the steam ship *Great Britain*, the brain-child of I. K. Brunel and the first large iron ship as well as the first large screw ship in the world, and now almost miraculously restored to her birth-place after leaving the Floating Harbour for the first and last time in 1844 and returning after a most remarkable career in 1970 (*Plates 13 & 14*); **Canon's Marsh Wharves** and bonded warehouses (ST584723), including the circular base of a crane; the **Heavy Lift Fairbairn Steam Crane** (ST586722) installed on a semi-circular promontory on the Wapping Wharf on the southern side of the

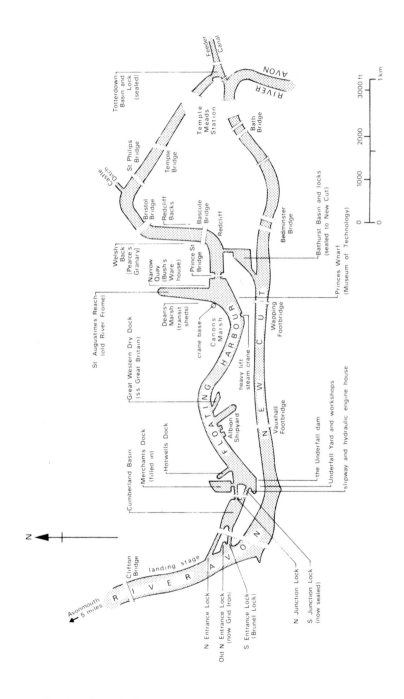

3 Avon County: Bristol City Docks

Harbour by Stothert & Pitt, the Bath crane engineers, in the 1870s; the Frome arm of the Harbour, or **St Augustine's Reach**, now terminating with Neptune's statue (ST585 728), lined on the west by transit sheds and on the east by the wharves of Narrow Quay which possess some attractive old bollards; **Prince Street Bridge**, a swing bridge with its own hydraulic engine and accumulator tower (ST586723) between two masonry abutments which once provided a means of sealing off one half of the Harbour from the other for separate scouring; the **Bathurst Basin** (ST587721), which was an essential feature of this divided scouring operation because it provided its own entrance and junction locks from the New Cut, but the entrance lock is now sealed and silted while the triangular Basin itself has become a mooring for small ships; and **Welsh Back** (ST589725) with its transit sheds leading up to Bristol Bridge, providing the effective termination for sea-going traffic.

The Feeder Canal A vital element in the scheme for the Floating Harbour was a supply of fresh water. Some of this came from the River Frome, but this became seriously polluted by sewage so that the BDC was compelled to divert the Frome in the 1820s through a culvert under the Harbour directly into the New Cut. The main source of fresh water was the River Avon, and to ensure a reliable supply from a point above high-tide level, the Feeder Canal was built from Netham to the head of the Floating Harbour at Totterdown, a distance of just over a mile. **Totterdown Lock** (ST599722) gave direct entrance to the canal from the New Cut, at the basin outside the Floating Harbour: it was firmly sealed in World War II to prevent the drainage of the Harbour by a direct hit on the lock. It had a lock-keeper's cottage which also served as a toll house until it was demolished in 1966. The Feeder Canal gave convenient water access to a number of industrial enterprises, including the fine fireproof cotton mill of the **Great Western Cotton Factory** (see Bristol City, Barton Hill), but is now little used except for the occasional pleasure boat. **Netham Weir** (ST617725)

13 Bristol Port – The Floating Harbour, SS *GREAT BRITAIN* soon after her return to Bristol, 1970

still serves to divert a flow of water along the Canal. It was raised in height on the recommendation of I. K. Brunel, and has been subsequently modified. The weir marks the effective limit of normal tides on the River Avon, and can thus also be regarded as the last feature of the Port of Bristol.

BROCKLEY COMBE

There is a ruinous **windmill tower** (ST473 661) in the upper corner of a forestry plantation above this valley. It is masonry built with slightly tapering sides.

CADBURY HEATH

A brick engine house and other buildings here formerly belonged to **Brook Pit** (ST669 721), one of the more recent collieries of the Warmley district. It is alongside the Warmley to Willsbridge road, and is now owned by Bristol Waterworks.

CARLINGCOTT

There is a **watermill** site here on the Cam Brook (ST695584).

CHARFIELD

There was a **pin mill** north of the village (ST722930); two five-storey stone buildings survive with a date stone '1829' but have now been converted to other uses. Half a mile downstream is **Huntingford Mill** (ST717 936), with two overshot internal waterwheels still working a few years ago, but the mill has now been converted into a restaurant. The small brick buildings, trimmed in stone, of **Charfield Station** (*Fig 2*) (ST723922) survive on the east side of the track, almost alone amongst the lesser stations on the main line between Bristol and Gloucester. There is also a large derelict **Brickworks** (ST721926) in the village.

CHELWOOD

A pleasant village on the Somerset coalfield, there are several small colliery sites in the area, including **Frys Bottom Pit** (ST630 604), with an overgrown spoil heap above the alignment of the Bristol–Radstock railway.

14   Bristol Port – The Floating Harbour, SS *GREAT BRITAIN* undergoing restoration

S. GREAT BRITAIN

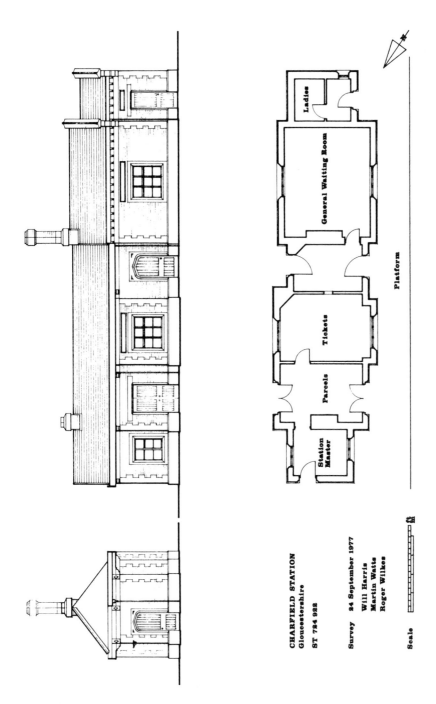

Figure 2   Avon: Charfield. Elevation of the eastern platform of the station on the Bristol to Gloucester railway. This is one of the few minor station buildings to survive alongside this main line. Drawn by Martin Watts.

CHELVEY

Chosen as the site from which to extract water from wells by the Bristol Water Works, **Chelvey Pumping Station** (ST474679) has had several sets of engines before the present electric pumps, and the 1923 engine house still contains a Lilleshall inverted-vertical triple expansion steam engine.

CHEW MAGNA

This village has become an attractive dormitory community for Bristol executives, with a good selection of interesting buildings. There is a substantial **watermill** (ST577629) at Tun Bridge with an undershot wheel on its south wall, manufacturing cattle-feed. There was a small **gas works** (ST577633) run virtually as a one-man enterprise before nationalization, but the site has recently been redeveloped. On the hill south-west of the village at Blackmoor are the fragmentary remains of a Bristol Waterworks **pumping engine house** (ST552632). This is alongside a waterworks conduit running underground, but nearby it crosses a small valley by an impressive **aqueduct** (ST548641).

CHEWTON PLACE

The **watermill** site here (ST656670) was once a logwood mill, and the edge-runners can be seen in front of the building which is now a private house.

CHIPPING SODBURY

Once an important local market town with a fine wide main street, Chipping Sodbury is losing some of its character with the development around it of the new residential community of Yate-Sodbury. There is a **toll house** (ST725838) on the B4060 north of the town, a two-storey structure in local stone with a half-hexagonal front and Gothic detailing.

CLAVERTON

A village conveniently bypassed by the Black Dog Turnpike Road from Bath through Limpley Stoke to Warminster (the A36). Ralph Allen (the 18th-century Bath landowner and entrepreneur who promoted the local stone-mining industry) is buried in the churchyard, but his manor house was replaced by the early 19th-century **Claverton Manor** on the hill above the village, now the home of the American Museum in Britain. Below the village, across the main road, the Kennet & Avon Canal, and the Railway, is **Claverton Engine House** (*Plate 15*) (ST791644), a superb industrial monument recently restored to working order to pump water from the River Avon into the K & A Canal. It is a water-powered double beam engine, designed by John Rennie and installed in 1810. There is a long undershot wheel in the shed at right-angles to the narrow engine house, driving the cast-iron beams through the connecting rods and with a flywheel. The engine was essential for maintaining the water level in the canal on the long reach between Widcombe and Bradford on Avon. The lane down to the engine house crosses the canal by a neat stone bridge typical of the K & A. Note also the **wooden swing bridge** opposite Warleigh Wood (ST787633).

CLEVEDON

Carefully developed as a discreet Victorian seaside resort by the major landowners, the Eltons of Clevedon Court, this town preserves something of the select flavour of that period. The resort possessed no natural beach or anchorage, so the construction of **Clevedon Pier** (ST400719) in 1869 was an event of considerable local importance. This slender pier, delicately balanced on wrought-iron arches, celebrated its centenary in 1969 but got into difficulties the following year when two of the arches collapsed into the sea during loading tests. So far, the escalating costs of rehabilitating the structure have defeated the efforts of local enthusiasts, but it is undoubtedly one of the most important piers in the country and well deserves a major preservation effort. (Ref. *BIAS Journal 2*, 1969)

COALPIT HEATH

Despite its evocative name, this village is now largely a dormitory suburb for Bristol. But the name records the fact that there were important collieries in the area, the largest of which was **Frog Lane Pit** (ST687814), with a few surviving surface remains. Another mining site and railway alignment on Ram

Hill possesses a **Haystack Boiler**, once used as a water tank in a now derelict railway engine house (ST682795), but this is on private property and not easily accessible.

COLD ASHTON

A strangely isolated little village five miles north of Bath, in the angle of the A46 and A420 roads. In the steep valley below the village, at the head of the St Catherine's Brook flowing southwards to Batheaston, there are some fragmentary watermill remains: e.g. **Cold Mill** (ST760721); **Paper Mill** (ST761711) (see St Catherine's).

COMBE HAY

Although only three miles from the centre of Bath, this village in the valley of the Cam Brook has an atmosphere of deep rural seclusion. However, the fact that the Somerset Coal Canal passed through the village, making its transition from one level to another 130ft above it, gives the village great industrial archaeological significance. The flight of 22 **canal locks** (ST743605) can still be traced in a tight horseshoe bend up the tributary valley to the north, and **Caisson House** (ST741603) marks the basin at the end of the upper level, from which the celebrated and mysterious 'caisson lock', and subsequently an inclined plane, attempted to transfer barges to the lower level before the company resorted to conventional locks (see *BIAS Journal 2* 1969, and *BIAS Journal 8* 1975: also K. Clew – *The Somersetshire Coal Canal*, 1970). At the other end of the village was a short section of **canal tunnel** (ST728 599), but most of the route has been obliterated here by the engineering of the Limpley Stoke to Hallatrow Railway, which followed the line of the Canal as closely as possible, and, more recently, by local authority tipping.

COMPTON DANDO

In rolling countryside on the edge of the

15   Claverton – Kennet & Avon Canal Engine House

North Somerset Coalfield, this village has a **watermill** site (ST686485) with **colliery** remains in the vicinity (ST652662). Also near the village is another watermill site, **Tucking-mill** (ST658637) the name indicating a relationship with the woollen cloth industry. To the west of the village, at Woolard, are the substantial ruins of a **Tannery** (ST634644), behind the house called Old Tannery.

CORSTON

A small village four miles west of Bath on the Lower Wells Road of the Bath Turnpike Trust (the four-mile post stands just outside the village).

CROMHALL

A copse on a spoil heap marks the site of **Cromhall Engine Pit** (ST688891) on Cromhall Common, the most northerly colliery of the South Gloucestershire and Bristol Coalfield.

DOYNTON

The **watermill** (ST719743) remains as a store.

EAST HARPTREE

The village lies on the steep north slope of the Mendip plateau, near the Chew Valley Lake. It was the centre of one of the ancient mineries by which lead mining was administered on Mendip, and on Smitham Hill above the village are the remains of one of the 19th-century **lead works** (ST557546), including the only surviving lead works chimney on Mendip. The chimney and its adjacent pool in Frances Plantation are actually over the county boundary in Somerset, but the remains of the flues and piles of waste fall mainly in Avon.

FALFIELD

A **windmill tower** (ST684928), is just visible through trees on the ridge to the west of the M5 motorway immediately south of junction 14.

FARRINGTON GURNEY

Old Mills Colliery (ST654551) was one of the last to close in the North Somerset Coalfield. Its conical spoil heap remains, and the double horizontal steam engine made by William Evans of Paulton in 1861 has been preserved for re-erection in the Bristol City Museum.

FELTON

The **windmill tower** (ST515649) on Felton Common has been converted into a private residence.

FILTON

This industrial and residential suburb to the north of Bristol is now the home of the giant British Aircraft Corporation and of Rolls Royce Aero Engines, with the associated Airfield. These industries are here because Sir George White, a director of the Bristol Tramways Company, established the British & Colonial Aeroplane Company at Filton in 1910 in order to bring traffic to this terminus of the tramway system. The area has relics of earlier industries in south Gloucestershire, including **Harry Stoke Drift Mine** (ST619 786), the last working coal mine on the Bristol Coalfield.

FLAX BOURTON

Kingcot Watermill (ST517698) is now part of a farm building with the pond and watercourses filled in, but the internal breast wheel is still intact.

FOXCOTE

This small village, on the southern slopes of the Wellow Brook valley, has the remains of a **watermill** (ST715558) and a **colliery** (ST711 552). The latter was approached by a railway incline from Writhlington, and this alignment can still be traced, with a 'pug mill' in the adjacent wood providing evidence of a brick-making industry associated with the colliery.

FRAMPTON COTTERELL

Straddling the Bristol Frome in its upper reaches, this village had a **watermill** near the Church, the site of which can still be discerned (ST667822). In the eastern part of the village, on top of the hill, is the tapered masonry tower of a **windmill** (ST673814) and an adjacent chimney suggesting supplementation by steam power at some stage in its history. This part of the village also has a **hat factory** (ST667815), consisting of two three-storey mill buildings in pennant sandstone, now largely derelict. The village is firmly within the Bristol Coalfield, so that there are many old mining sites in the vicinity, including one **iron mine** (ST669819) since converted into a source of water supply with a pumping house at the top of the shaft, and with a fragment of embankment surviving to the north from the railway connecting the mine to the line at Iron Acton.

FRESHFORD

Freshford is a substantial village in the south-eastern corner of Avon County. It is on a ridge on the western side of the Limpley Stoke valley, close to the confluence of the River Avon and the Somerset Frome: the Kennet & Avon Canal is on the opposite side of the valley here, but the Railway from Bath to Westbury passes close to the village and still provides a small station. The most distinguished industrial building in the village is **Dunkirk Mill** (ST785595), well up on one of the hillsides to the south: the shell of this late 18th-century woollen cloth mill is intact, although the floors have collapsed: there is a wheel pit fed from a pond above the mill, and also a steam engine house and chimney adjacent. The **watermill** buildings at the bottom of the hill, on the River Frome (ST787596), have been converted into a modern rubber processing factory. There are other buildings of interest in the village, including a **brewery** (ST789602) and some **clothiers houses** (e.g. ST791601), and also some unusual shop signs like the lion above the door of a shop in the main street. At Iford Manor, a mile south-east of the village, is an elegant two-arch **masonry bridge** with a statue of Britannia surmounting the central pier (ST800589): there is also a small **watermill** converted into a house with the mill race still running underneath.

HUTTON

A village under the northern edge of the Mendips where these approach the sea at Weston-super-Mare. There is the tower of a **windmill** (ST361589) at the east end of the village, now a private residence.

IRON ACTON

Despite its name, Iron Acton is associated more with coal mining than with the iron industry, and there are remains of collieries scattered in the fields around the village. The place-name Engine Common to the east of the village is a reminder of this mining activity, and there are some sections of a **tramway embankment** which linked the mines with the main Bristol & Gloucester Railway at ST703852. The village is close to the head of the Bristol Frome, which nevertheless provided power for **Cog Mill** (ST665828), now a farm, **Algar's Manor Mill** (ST667832), now part of a private house but with edge-runners by the door, and **Nibley Mill** (ST692824), part of a farm with some used grindstones outside.

KELSTON

Under the distinctive Kelston Round Hill, marking the southern extremity of the Cotswold escarpment, this village is 3½ miles from Bath. Much of it was designed as an estate village for the house in Kelston Park. Down by the River Avon is **Kelston Mill** (ST694680), where a substantial brass mill was built in the second half of the 18th century, deriving water power from the weir between the mill and the village of Saltford across the river. The site is now ruinous, although partially redeveloped (and mutilated) as a marina. The outstanding features are the two annealing furnaces (*Plate 16*) which are important in brass works because the metal hardens on being worked and requires frequent re-heatings to keep it malleable. These two towers and that at Saltford Mill are probably now unique. It seems likely that the low-lying nature of the Kelston site made it liable to frequent flooding (there are some flood marks carved on the masonry) and that it did not remain long in production (Ref. Joan Day: *Bristol Brass*).

KENN

Out in the Levels between Clevedon and Weston-super-Mare, this village possesses a

16 Kelston – Annealing Furnace, Kelston Brass Mill

windmill tower (ST411696), visible to the west of the M5 motorway.

KEYNSHAM

Emanuel Bowen's 1760 map of Somerset describes this village as 'proverbially called Smoky Canesham, from its being a Foggy Smoky place', which probably reflects the considerable industrial activity of the period. He also notes the 'snake stones' found in the stone quarries here: these are ammonites or fossil shells abounding in the liassic limestone which provides the major building material in the village. Situated half-way between Bristol and Bath, Keynsham has managed to preserve something of its identity as a separate township, having been helped in this by the opening of the Keynsham Bypass for the A4 Trunk Road but hindered by a rash of modern development in and around the village. Two distinguished bridges over the Avon and the Chew were washed away in the disastrous flood of 10 July 1968 and have been replaced by functional modern structures. The major industry in Keynsham during the 18th and 19th centuries was the **brassworks** (ST658689). This large establishment was the centre of operations for the Bristol Brass Company (later known as Harfords) until this closed in 1927. It was just above the County Bridge and the confluence of the Avon and the Chew, with a weir providing power for eight waterwheels. Most of the buildings have been demolished as the site has been acquired by a paper mill, but the elegant house with its bell-tower survives near the entrance, and a section of the wharf on the river-front. A smaller **brass mill** (ST657686) stood on the River Chew, and the 15ft undershot waterwheel has been preserved as a feature in the public park. The next industrial site up the Chew is **Albert Mill** (*Fig 3*) (ST656679), a fine three-storey structure in the local lias stone, with two large breast wheels, one internal and the other on the south wall of the mill. This mill was last operating as a logwood mill, chipping and crushing tropical hard woods to extract dyes from them. This work stopped in 1964, since when the building has been used as a warehouse although the logwood machinery has been preserved. The mill was the subject of a BIAS Survey (Ref. *BIAS Journal 7*, 1974). Apart from these processes, Keynsham has supported several other industries. It is on the northern edge of the North Somerset Coalfield, with remains of pits still visible such as those of **Charlton Bottom Pit** (ST638685). A **chemical works** was built by the River Avon to manufacture polysulphates (ST666691), but has been converted to other processes. **Fry's Chocolate Factory** moved out from the Pithay in central Bristol to Somerdale (ST658695) in the 1920s, having a rail connection to the main Bristol–Paddington railway cutting across the northern edge of the village, with a small and much neglected **railway station** (ST657689). There have also been lime works, tanneries, and ochre factories in the vicinity. The village still has a selection of interesting buildings off the main street, including the Church (with remains of an abbey) and some nonconformist chapels.

KILCOTT

In Lower Kilcott, beneath the Cotswold edge in the north-east corner of Avon county, is a small farm **watermill** (ST786893) which has been restored to working order. It has a high-breast waterwheel, *c.*14ft diameter and 3ft wide, with an unusual combination of cast-iron and wrought-iron spokes. The wheel drives a single set of stones.

LITTLETON

On the upper reaches of the northern branch of the River Chew, above Chew Magna, there are two watermill sites: **Littleton Mill** (ST556638), still in use as an ochre mill, and **Powdermill** (ST551643), where the buildings have been incorporated in a farm but once housed a gunpowder mill. There is a substantial masonry-lined basin at the end of a leat, with the remains of a grinding shop on the north side. On the south side is the shell of a **clock tower** (*Plate 17*), an important feature in a process requiring careful timing.

LITTON

On the border between Avon and Somerset, but strictly in the former, **Sherborne Paper Mill** (ST585551) is a shell of a small mill, now used as a barn, on the River Chew.

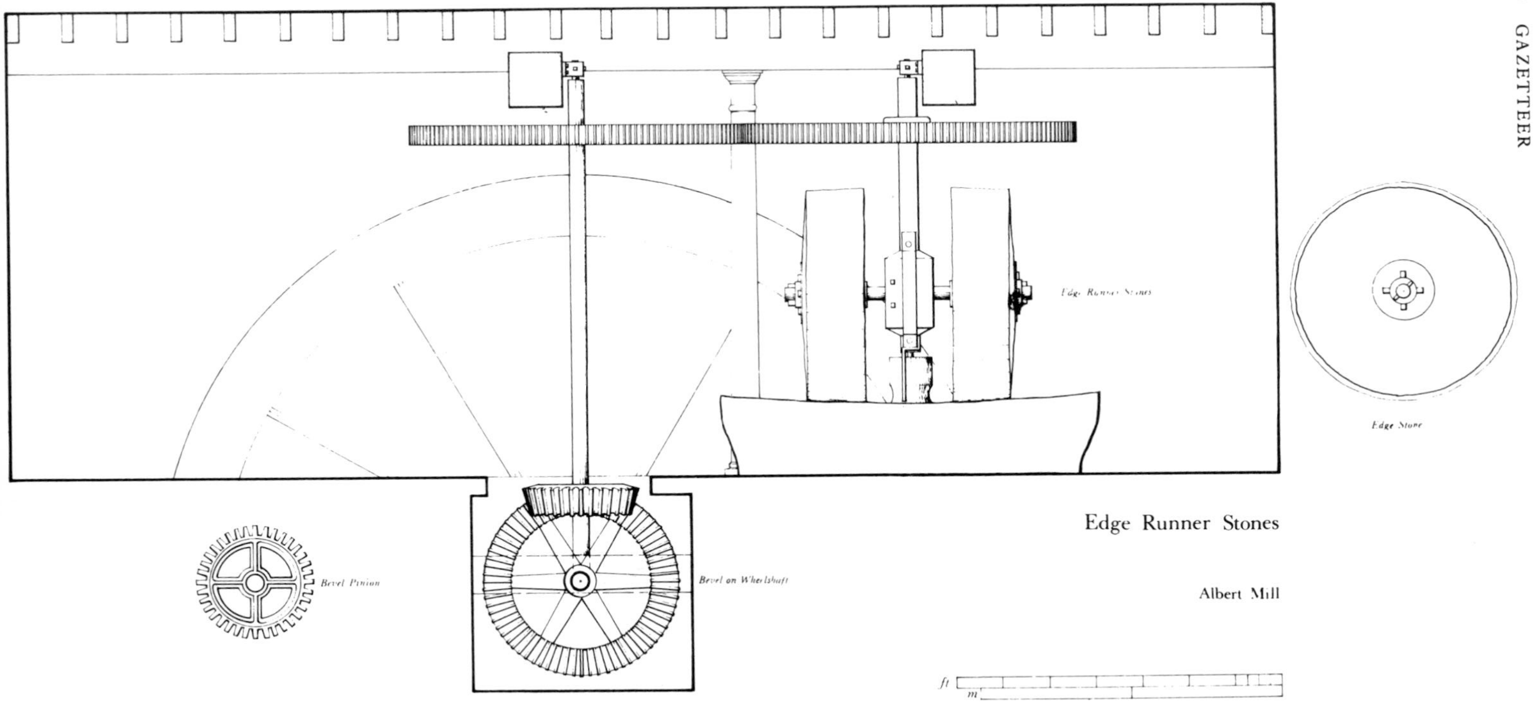

Figure 3 Avon: Keynsham. The edge-runners for crushing logwood to make dyestuffs are still in place in the Albert Mill, and capable of being driven by water-power although they are no longer in use. Drawn by Martin Watts.

LOCKING

A village to the west of Weston Airport, with a **windmill tower** (ST359617) on its northern fringes, near the railway.

LONG ASHTON

This straggling village has become in effect a suburb of Bristol. The ridge of carboniferous limestone to the north has been quarried for lime: a **limekiln** survives at the side of the B3128 road (ST543712): and has also been excavated for ironstone, with the remains of an **iron mine** (ST535709).

MANGOTSFIELD

Absorbed into Bristol by the urban expansion of the last 100 years, Mangotsfield developed as a village on the Kingswood Coalfield and retains fragments of its origin in colliery sites such as **Staple Hill Pit** (ST654759) and **Church Farm Deep Pit** (ST668763). It was also an important railway junction between the Bristol–Gloucester line and the Midland branch to Bath, but its attractive **railway station** (ST664753) with curved platforms was demolished when both these lines fell under the Beeching Axe in the 1960s.

MARSHFIELD

Now that it has been bypassed by the A420 road from Bristol to Chippenham, Marshfield has recovered much of its rural isolation and dignity. It has little of industrial interest, but note the **toll house** (ST772737) at the western end of the village, and in the St Catherine's Valley to the south is the site of **Ayford Mill** (ST776708).

MIDFORD

Until quite recently, this hamlet on the B3110 road from Bath to Norton St Philip and Warminster had a remarkable crossing of two railway viaducts, a canal, a road, and the Midford Brook. The Somerset Coal Canal has virtually disappeared, but a small **aqueduct** survives (ST757605) bringing an abortive branch-canal from Radstock over the river. This branch was replaced by a tramway, parts of the alignment of which can still be traced although now liable to be

confused with those of the Somerset and Dorset Railway. This railway was responsible for the surviving **viaduct** in Midford (ST761 605): the other, belonging to the Limpley Stoke – Hallatrow railway, has been demolished. There is a **watermill** (ST763606) on the Wellow Brook, and a **malting** alongside the main road (ST764602).

MIDSOMER NORTON

A coalmining village which has adjusted itself with difficulty to life without the coal mines. **Norton Hill Pit** (ST669541) was the largest in the district and was active until 1966. It has left an extensive spoil heap on the hillside south of the village.

MONKTON COMBE

A neat village standing on the north side of the Midford Brook, shortly before this joins the River Avon in the Limpley Stoke Valley. The substantial **watermill** (ST775615) was a flock mill and has now become a warehouse and display area. Another mill site was **Tuckingmill** (ST765616) at the bottom of Horsecombe Vale, close to the **Viaduct** of the Somerset & Dorset Railway: the name suggests an association with the woollen cloth industry, but in recent years the site has been used for water works and fullers earth works. Near the same point is the cottage in which William Smith, pioneer geologist and surveyor of the **Somersetshire Coal Canal**, is supposed to have lived while working on the canal. The alignment of the canal itself can be traced through the valley, even though in places it was overlaid by the Limpley Stoke–Hallatrow railway. As the alignment approaches the main Avon valley, the canal and railway diverge, the latter swinging south to join the Bristol–Westbury line, and the canal bending north to a junction with the Kennet & Avon Canal in a Basin to the west of the **Dundas Aqueduct** (ST785626). This is one of the most splendid monumental features on the British canal system, with a single masonry arch over the River Avon and two supporting arches. The Coal Canal entered the Basin through a lock, the top stones of which mark out a rose garden in the cottage standing beside it. A hand crane made by Acramans of Bristol and a small warehouse are on the wharf. At the eastern (Wiltshire)

17   Littleton – Clock Tower, Gunpowder Mill

end of the aqueduct, the alignment of a tramway incline can be discerned, bringing stone down to the canal from quarries at Conkwell.

NAILSEA

This rather drab mining village has been much extended in recent years by new housing developments which have converted it into a dormitory suburb for Bristol. It is in the middle of a small coalfield, quite separate from the main North Somerset field, and although the quality of coal produced here was poor, it was good enough to provide the fuel for the glass industry which was established here in 1788 by J. R. Lucas, a Bristol glass manufacturer who built a **glass factory** in Nailsea (ST478709) with two glass cones and ancillary buildings, a few traces of which survive. There are also a few colliery sites still visible: **Grace's Pit** (ST458700), with derelict buildings on Engine Lane, **Old Church Road Pit** (ST477698), with a derelict engine house in the garden of a private house, and **Backwell Common Pit** (ST479691), which possessed a large Cornish-style engine house until it was demolished recently.

NEWTON ST LOE

This village three miles west of Bath is largely an estate village for the Gore-Langton family who owned Newton Park House in the 19th century. The village stands upon a ridge above the Avon valley, and at the foot of this ridge the Bath Turnpike Trust met the Bristol Turnpike Trust at what is now the **Globe Inn** (ST701652). In the 18th century, this building was at the centre of coal mining activity, with 'Mr. Harrington's Coal Works' busy both in the meadows alongside the river and on the slopes of the ridge to the southeast, in both of which places dark spoil marks can still be discerned when the land is newly ploughed. It seems likely that much of the actual spoil was used in the embankment carrying the first stage of I.K. Brunel's Great Western Railway from Bristol to Bath: one of Brunel's ornate **tunnel porticos** can be seen in the parish (ST719652). Also in the parish is a **watermill** (ST716649) on the Priston Brook, and the spoil heap of **Pennyquick Pit** (ST713645) which was active until the mid-19th century.

OLDLAND

Oldland is part of the sprawling settlement that occurred over the Bristol Coalfield from Kingswood to Bitton. In **California Pit** (ST665715) it possesses the remains of a significant colliery, with spoil heap and buildings now owned by Bristol waterworks. But by far the most interesting feature of the area is the **Avon & Gloucestershire Railway**, a horse-drawn tramway running from Mangotsfield to the River Avon at Keynsham. In Oldland, the tramway linked with the California Pit by a short incline (ST668709) and ran along an embankment into a deep rock cutting and eventually into a **tunnel** at Willsbridge (ST666706). This marked a considerable advance on the previous engineering standards of such mineral tramways. **Willsbridge Mill** (ST665 707) has a substantial dam and mill pond, although damaged in the 1968 floods: it was an iron-rolling mill, later converted into a grist mill.

OLD SODBURY

On the A432 road from Chipping Sodbury is a **toll house** (ST750816). The name Hartley House is incised into the panel where the toll-board would have fitted, and it is now used as a café.

PAULTON

Situated on the ridge between the Cam and Radstock Brooks, Paulton has a continuing record of involvement in engineering and printing industries. The major industrial monument of the village, however, is the **canal basin** (ST657577) near Goosard Bridge on the road to High Littleton. The outline of this double basin at the terminus of the Somersetshire Coal Canal with a bridge and some ancillary buildings still standing, can be discerned even though they have been dry for many decades. The route of the railway which replaced the canal, running from Limpley Stoke to a junction with the Bristol-Radstock line at Hallatrow, ran to the north of the canal at this point so that the canal works were not mutilated by it.

PENSFORD

Pensford is dominated by two industrial

monuments: the **viaduct** (ST618638) which carried the Bristol-Radstock railway high over the River Chew, and **Pensford Pit** (ST618625), the spoil heap from which falls into the valley to the south of the village. This colliery was one of the most prosperous in the district until its closure in 1958. It boasted possession of the first pithead baths in the country, and the red brick winding house still stands. **Pensford Mill** (ST618637) was acquired by the copper and brass industry in the 18th century, as was **Publow Mill** (ST625642) nearby. Fragments of both sites survive.

PILNING

Pilning is the small settlement close to the eastern entrance to the **Severn Railway Tunnel** (ST545855). It is also close to an earlier route across the treacherous Severn Estuary, the railway which ran out onto a pier at **New Passage Hotel** (ST544865) to link by boat with a pier at Black Rock on the opposite shore. The masonry footings can still be seen at the landward end of the New Passage pier, as can the alignment of the railway.

PORTISHEAD

There was little to Portishead before the Bristol & Portishead Pier & Railway Company opened its broad gauge branch in 1867 (**station** at ST467766) to be followed by the construction of Portishead Dock in 1879 (see **Bristol Port**). Various schemes had been put forward to make the **pier** (ST477775) a terminus for Atlantic passenger traffic, so that ships would not need to navigate the Avon, but they did not come to anything. Previously, the village had possessed a **tidemill** (ST648766), now the White Lion Inn with millstones used decoratively, and a **windmill** (ST458767), the tapering tower of which has been incorporated into a Golf Club house. Portishead is now dominated by the large **power stations**, the only electricity generating plant left in the county except for the atomic station at Oldbury.

PRISTON

A secluded village five miles south-west of Bath, Priston has a **watermill** (ST695615) about a mile to the north of the village which

has been in existence at least since 1086, when there was a reference to it in Domesday Book. The present mill structure is probably 18th-century, but the 22ft pitch-back metal waterwheel is more recent, dating from the mid-19th-century. The grinding machinery is kept in working order and produces flour for a local market. The miller appreciates the publicity value of a working watermill and runs a small shop for visitors on the premises (Ref. *BIAS Journal 7* 1974). Priston is on the edge of the North Somerset Coalfield, and one mile south of the village are the fragmentary remains of **Priston Pit** (ST693 595), although it is closer to the hamlet of Tunley than to the village.

PUCKLECHURCH

Off the main roads to the east of Bristol, and just south of the M4, the substantial village of Pucklechurch is curiously isolated. Once the site of a Royal Hunting Lodge in the Kingswood Forest, it later developed through proximity to profitable coal mines at **Parkfield Pit** (ST690777), with a brick chimney still standing adjacent to the motorway; **Brandybottom Pit** (ST682553), with a masonry chimney still marking its position; and **Shortwood Pit** (ST681765). There is also a **toll house** (ST686757) at the junction of the B4465 and Siston Lane.

RADSTOCK

Pevsner describes Radstock as 'really desperately ugly', and there is certainly not a great deal to be said for this compact little colliery town jammed into the bottom of five converging valleys, at least so far as architectural distinction is concerned, although the Waldegrave family which owned most of the local coal mines did invest in some modest town buildings in the mid-19th century. There is a **watermill** (ST689546), with a small external overshot wheel incorporated in a farm, but most of the industrial archaeology of the town is associated with the coal mining industry. The last mines to close in the North Somerset Coalfield (in 1973) were **Kilmersdon Pit** (ST687538), one mile south of Radstock and with a gravity-operated incline linking it to the Bristol-Frome railway line, and **Writhlington Pit** (ST706553): both these had steam engine houses, although the engines had been replaced by electric winders before closure. Earlier mining sites are **Old Pit** (ST686555), on the lane from Radstock to Clandown, **Middle Pit** (ST687553), with buildings and chimney adapted to other uses, **Ludlow's Pit** (ST693548), south of the Frome road at the bottom of the hill, and **Wellsway Pit** (ST681546), north of the Wells Road with overgrown spoil heaps and engine house. The large spoil heaps left by **Tyning Pit** (ST696553) and **Clandown Pit** (ST681558) are also prominent features of the area, although they are quickly becoming overgrown. The latter site, at Clandown, was the scene of a remarkable experiment in economic pit operation, the 'Clandown Pass-by', designed to make it possible to operate two cages in a narrow shaft (Ref. *BIAS Journal 9* 1976). The convergence of two railways in the centre of Radstock – the Somerset & Dorset line from Bath to Shepton Mallet, and the Bristol to Frome line – with adjacent stations and level crossings in the centre of the town, was another unusual feature. Both railways have now closed and virtually disappeared, although some of the undistinguished **station buildings** of the S & D survive (ST689800), including an engine shed. The S & D followed the alignment of the mineral tramway connecting Radstock with the Somersetshire Coal Canal at Midford (*q.v.*) and from Radstock a fan of tramways fed this from the coal mines of the neighbourhood. Part of the alignment up the valley to Clandown is still recognizable.

ST CATHERINE'S

Although there are few houses to this village, it boasts a church attached to the fine Elizabethan mansion of St Catherine's Court. Some of the mills in the upper reaches of the St Catherine's valley come within Cold Ashton and Marshfield (*q.v.*), but the **watermill** downstream from the Court (ST782697) is also a recognizable site.

SANDFORD

Sandford Hill on the north edge of the Mendip plateau has been extensively mined and quarried over several centuries. Alongside the modern roadstone quarry (ST421580) are three substantial **limekilns** in one batch each

approximately 22ft high. The quarry was linked to the Cheddar Valley and Yatton railway by means of a short inclined plane which was working within living memory. The north side of the hill is scarred by the grooves and drifts of **mine workings**. Many were dug for lead, but some appear to have been worked for ochre (e.g. at ST429593).

SALTFORD

The older part of the village of Saltford is down by the River Avon, cut off by the main Bristol–London railway line from the modern development through which the A4 Bristol to Bath road passes. There are two weirs, one at either extremity of the village: the upper one providing power for **Saltford Brass Works** (ST687670), a remarkably complete site, with a small annealing tower and iron waterwheel together with several buildings now adapted as a boat store (Ref. *BIAS Journal 9* 1976); and the lower weir serving another **watermill** (probably once a tucking mill – ST692 679) where the Avon Navigation Lock and Public House now stand. The main function of this lower weir was to provide power for **Kelston Mill** (*q.v.*) on the opposite side of the river. In addition to the main railway line, which runs in a cutting through most of Saltford, there is a derelict **railway bridge** over the river (ST688674) which carried the Midland branch line from Mangotsfield to Bath. On the main A4 road through Saltford, once part of the Bristol Turnpike Trust road to Bath and London, there is a **toll house** (ST689663).

SHORTWOOD

Shortwood is a hamlet on the B4465 road from Bristol to Pucklechurch. **Shortwood Pit** (ST681765) was one of the Pucklechurch group of collieries (*q.v.*): it was also known as Lapwater Pit. The most significant feature in Shortwood is the **brickworks** (ST679769), now derelict but still complete, with claypit, mixing and drying sheds, and Hoffman Kiln (Ref: *BIAS Journal 8* 1975). Now owned by the Ibstock Brick (Cattybrook) Company, it is due to be demolished but has been made the subject of a short film by the University of Bath Educational Services Unit.

SHOSCOMBE

There is a small **aqueduct** near this village (ST728566) carrying a stream over the tramway (and later the Somerset & Dorset Railway) between Midford and Radstock.

SOUTH STOKE

An attractive village just south of Bath overlooking the Midford valley. There is a substantial **tithe barn** (ST747612) next to the Church, with a semi-circular annex indicating a horse-wheel house, probably a cider press. There is also a **brewery** (ST748 613) in the village, with long vaulted bays, now converted into a private house. The hillside to the west of the village has been mined extensively by **fullers earth works**, most notably at ST735612.

STANTON DREW

This small village on the River Chew is chiefly famous for its Neolithic stone circles. But it also has a **watermill** site (ST595635), now converted into a private house. And in its **toll house** (ST596636) it possesses the most distinguished of these features in the region: a hexagonal two-storey thatched building with white rendered walls at the junction of the B3130 and the lane into the village. Nearby, at Stanton Wick, there was a **glassworks** (ST613620) which has left an indication of its existence in the name of Glasshouse Farm. Like the Nailsea Glassworks, with which it was closely associated, the advantage of this site was the proximity of cheap coal, in this case available at **Bromley Pit** (ST607618) marked by a spoil heap and the embankment of a tramway to Pensford.

SWINEFORD

A hamlet on the north bank of the River Avon between Bitton and Kelston, this became the base of the **Swineford Copper Mills** (ST691689), a substantial group of buildings established in 1840, with two undershot waterwheels still in position. The buildings were converted to a flock mill and are now used mainly for storage.

TEMPLE CLOUD

On the A37 road south from Bristol to Wells,

this village possesses a **watermill** site (ST617 575), now incorporated in Mill Farm, on the headwaters of the Cam Brook.

TIMSBURY

Timsbury is typical of the villages which began as mining communities on the North Somerset Coalfield and have now mellowed into dormitory suburbs for Bath and Bristol. It is built largely with the local white lias, but otherwise it has no buildings of any distinction. There are, however, a considerable number of mining sites in the vicinity, of which only a few are worth mentioning: **Lower Conygre Pit** (ST674583) has left a spoil heap south of the village, on the lane to Radford, and **Upper Conygre Pit** (ST667 588) a spoil heap at the north end of the village, near the junction with the Farmborough road. **Radford Pit** (ST663577) has a spoil heap which is prominent from the line of the **Somersetshire Coal Canal**, which is here approaching its terminus in the Paulton Basin (*q.v.*). The alignment of the canal and the Limpley Stoke–Hallatrow railway which succeeded it can be seen from the bridge in Radford, where there is also a **watermill site** (ST672578).

TORMARTON

Now Junction 18 of the M4 Motorway with the A46 Bath to Stroud Road, the village itself is set back in the angle between the two highways. But it has a neat **toll house** (ST757784) near the entrance to Dodington Park: it is an irregular eight-sided design in Cotswold stone with two storeys, now in good condition.

UPHILL

Uphill is a southern extension to Weston-super-Mare, where the last finger of the Mendip Hills points to the sea and Brean Down. On the top of the ridge is a **windmill tower** (ST317583) now used as an observation platform. **Bleadon & Uphill Station** (ST325577) on the main Bristol–Exeter line was a typical small railway station, occupied as a railway museum for a time after its closure.

WARMLEY

This village on the A420 due east of Bristol, is

in the middle of the Bristol Coalfield. It was also chosen as the site of his major **Spelter Works** (ST668728) by William Champion in the mid-18th-century, and this establishment became one of the largest industrial undertakings of its period, producing brass from copper and zinc. The office block remains, and also Champion's mansion (now council offices) but most of the site has been cleared. **Warmley Tower** (ST667727) was probably a windmill used in the factory but the waterwheels have disappeared, the pond has been drained (although part of the copper slag block statue of Neptune survives) and most of the artisans' houses of the period have gone. Part of the site was converted into a pottery manufacturing industrial earthenware, but this, too, has now been closed. The area conveys an impression of rather messy dereliction and redevelopment, which is a pity considering the great significance of this plant in the history of the British brass industry and of the Industrial Revolution in general. There are many colliery sites in the area, such as **Siston Common Pit** (ST669739) and the **Avon & Gloucestershire Railway** can still be traced as it swings southwards across Siston Common and past Warmley Church (not to be confused with the line of the Mangotsfield to Bath railway, now also derelict).

WELLOW

An attractive village on the north side of the Wellow Brook valley. A **watermill** (ST741 581) has been neatly converted into a private house. There is a pack horse bridge over the river at this point. The Somerset & Dorset Railway passed through the village, as did the tramway linking Radstock with the Somersetshire Coal Canal at Midford. The tramway was designed as a canal and part of it was excavated as such, including the **canal tunnel** which survives (ST743584) 405ft long under the main road and a corner of the parish church yard: sealed at one end, it is still accessible (with permission) through a farmyard at the south end. Wellow possesses a good collection of old, well preserved, buildings. There is also a **steam mill** (ST739582) and a **fullers earth factory** (ST741582).

WESTON-SUPER-MARE

This 19th-century seaside resort has managed to maintain its image as an attractive yet somewhat select holiday place. There has never been much industry associated with the town, although the Bristol & Exeter Railway brought a loop off its main line into the town, and much useful traffic with it. There is no tradition of a fishing village: the vast stretch of level sand and mud made anchorage difficult until the construction of **Birnbeck Pier** (ST308624). The **Grand Pier** (ST317614), on the other hand, is purely ornamental as far as marine traffic is concerned. There was a plan in the mid-19th century to develop a deep-water anchorage on **Brean Down** (ST285593), which continues the line of the Mendip Hills out into the Bristol Channel towards Steep Holm, and some masonry relics of this scheme can still be seen although they should not be confused with the later installation of a **gun battery** on the end of the promontory (ST280593). On Worlebury Hill to the north of Weston, a **windmill tower** (ST352632) with white plastered walls and castellations provides a good landmark.

WICK

On the A420 road from Bristol to Chippenham where this crosses the River Boyd, this straggling village has two watermills. The upper one, the **Ochre Works Mill** (ST706 731), produces colour from ochre quarried in the vicinity. The lower mill is **New Mill** (ST695725), an animal-feed mill which used a turbine in its final phase of operation as a watermill. At the southern end of the village, the Bath Turnpike Trust 'Wick and Abson' road ended where it joined the main road, the point being marked by a characteristic BTT **terminus stone** (ST711727).

WICKWAR

A compact village on the B4060 road between Chipping Sodbury and Wotton-under-Edge, Wickwar is at the north portal to the Charfield **railway tunnel** (ST724889). The buildings of the small **brewery** in the village (ST723886) are still intact.

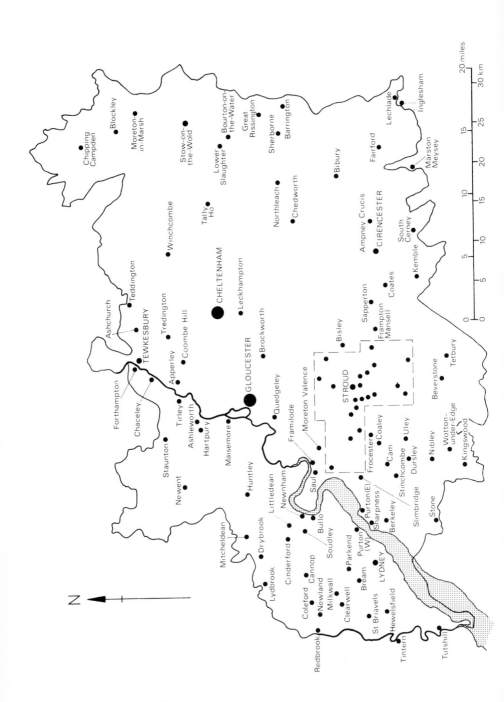

4 Gloucestershire: location map

Gloucestershire

The English shires were formed as administrative units during the centuries of the Anglo-Saxon settlement. Some of them were 'kingdoms' like Kent or Sussex, but the larger kingdoms such as Mercia and Wessex were sub-divided or 'shorn' into smaller areas, and these 'shares' became the shires, with the Normans later taking them over and re-styling them 'counties', representing the domain of a *Comte* or Count. Gloucestershire was formed in the tenth century as a shire of the kingdom of Mercia, probably as a means of levying soldiers against Danish aggression, and it was certainly well established by 1016, when the name 'Gloucestershire' was first recorded in the Anglo-Saxon Chronicle. The name of the city of Gloucester itself is much older, deriving from the British 'Caer Gloui', the 'splendid city', which became the Roman 'Glevum' and the Saxon 'Gleauanceaster'.

The shire of which Gloucester thus became the shire-town seems to have been a largely arbitrary area, comprising most of the southerly land-holdings in Mercia, so that it was defined on the west by the River Wye, along the eastern side of which the Mercian king Offa had built his renowned earthwork or 'dyke' to keep the Britons in Wales, and on the south and east by the area of West Saxon occupation. On the north, the most arbitrary of all its boundaries separates the shire of Gloucester from the other shires of the Mercian midland kingdom, based on Hereford, Worcester, Warwick, and Oxford. The area enclosed by these boundaries was some 800,000 acres, but this was substantially reduced in the county reorganization of 1972 which transferred South Gloucestershire, roughly south of the Little Avon, to the new county of Avon.

Although in many respects Gloucestershire is a midland county, it is unique amongst the midland counties in having in its heart a great tidal estuary which has enabled it to maintain two major ports: historically, Bristol, until the city received independent county status in 1373, and Gloucester itself. The River Severn and its estuary, however, is not a division in the county as much as a highway defining the Vale of Severn, the continuing plain from Bristol to Tewkesbury which forms the central region of the traditional three regions of Gloucestershire: Forest, Vale, and Wold. To the west of the Vale is the Forest, the triangle of land between the Wye and the Severn forming the ancient Forest of Dean. And to the east of the Vale are the Wolds, the low limestone plateau of the Cotswold Hills, presenting a continuous 50-mile front – The Edge – to the Vale of Severn, but dipping away gently eastwards into the neighbouring counties of Oxfordshire and Wiltshire.

These topographical divisions of the county reflect the underlying geological differences. The oldest rocks in the county are those on the west, where an outcrop of old red sandstone and carboniferous limestone encircles the coal measures of the Forest of Dean coalfield. The youngest rocks are those on the east, where the extensive plateau of oolitic Limestone dips below the clays of Oxfordshire and the chalk of Wiltshire. In between, the soils of the Vale of Severn are derived largely from the fertile clays of the Triassic series, with soft sandstones like the new red sandstones adding a distinctive colour to the soil of the Leadon valley, where the Vale opens out into Herefordshire and Worcestershire.

Geological differences accounted largely for variations in vegetation, with the primaeval forest being thickest in the Vale and thus deterring settlement until techniques had been developed to clear the trees and till the heavy clay soils. The first systematic settlement in Gloucestershire was thus on the wolds, where there was no thick forest cover and the lighter soils responded to the simple 'scratch-ploughing' techniques of the early farmers. Physical evidence of this settlement survives in abundance, with about 50 long barrows scattered across the Cotswolds (*Finberg* 1955 p.22) and many smaller barrows and earthworks representing the Neolithic, Bronze, and Iron Ages, of the first 2000 years BC. Roman settlement seems to have followed the pattern of existing cultivation, to judge from the alignment of the Fosse Way along the Wolds and the abundance of rich Romano-British villa sites like that at Chedworth. The apparent wealth of the area in Roman times, indeed, justifies the traditional adage, 'Scratch Gloucestershire and find Rome'. Cirencester, the Roman Corinium, grew to become the second city after London of the Roman province of Britain, and had already at this early stage become a centre of cloth manufacture.

When the Anglo-Saxons eventually broke through into the Gloucestershire area after the Battle of Dyrham in AD 577, the prosperous town and villa life of the Wolds was extinguished for several centuries, but on the other hand they also brought to the district for the first time a mastery of heavy-ploughing techniques which enabled the Vale to be cleared and farmed. This change, of course, took time, but gradually the prosperity of the area revived, although spread more uniformly than it had been previously. It has been observed that, when the Normans came to England, they found an old country, well settled and ordered. This could certainly be said for Gloucestershire. Almost 20 years after the Norman Conquest, and half a millenium after the Battle of Dyrham; King William I held his court in Gloucester at Christmas, 1085, and gave the momentous order which resulted in the following year in the Domesday Survey. Extrapolation of the detailed evidence compiled in this survey has made it possible to determine that the Domesday population of Gloucestershire was substantial, with many villages and small towns distributed fairly evenly over the county except for the Forest of Dean, which had acquired the status of a Royal Forest and was valued for its hunting, timber, and iron resources.

The pattern which emerges from even a cursory survey of Gloucestershire in Saxon and Norman times is of a predominantly rural county, with its main wealth derived from its agriculture. To a remarkable extent, this remains the pattern to the present day. Admittedly, Gloucester and Cheltenham are now substantial urban areas with important industries, and there are many smaller towns of significance. But farming is still the most pervasive occupation of the county, and if the Forest of Dean is excepted it is true to say that Gloucestershire has only had one major industry and that that industry was derived in the first place from its land or, more particularly, from the backs of the sheep which grazed upon its pasture land. The wool and woollen cloth industries have been of tremendous importance in the economic history of the county and have made, as we will see, the outstanding contribution to its industrial archaeology, but territorially their extent has been very limited, following a process of rapid concentration in the valleys of the fast-flowing rivers, and especially in the western valleys in the vicinity of Stroud. Even the exception of the Forest of Dean does not involve a significant modification to this generalization, for although the iron and coal industries of Dean have been important and have supported subsidiary industries in Gloucester and elsewhere, they have not been on a scale comparable with that of the woollen cloth industry, and their physical remains are certainly less tangible.

The industrial archaeology of Gloucestershire is thus of a somewhat limited and elusive quality. It is limited both territorially and regarding its subject matter, and it is elusive because, in the towns and villages of the Cotswolds where the cloth industry once flourished it is now difficult to find traces under the veneer of recent prosperity and tasteful conversions by which many mills and other small industrial buildings have lost all their original character. The problem here is not so much loss due to the comprehensive redevelopment of an urban area, but the more subtle qualitative change deriving from the conservation and 'improvement' of the Cotswold townships and villages. Many of these have acquired a new lease of life in recent decades. The woollen cloth industry, to which most of them owe their origin, has disappeared with virtually no trace except perhaps a mill site, tell-tale water courses, and a public house with an ancient name. Even the farms which sustained them have tended to become well-organized gentlemen's estates employing much less labour than in earlier years, and in some cases have become absorbed in the parkland of gracious country houses. The old village livelihoods have thus declined, and in some cases the villages have themselves disappeared or acquired a decidedly run-down appearance.

But their accessibility from Oxford and even from London and Birmingham has made these villages attractive to a new class of resident: the well-heeled industrialist, businessman, or administrator with his family, seeking the comfort and seclusion of a country home. New building has been severely restricted by the planning legislation so that existing cottages acquired social cachet in what the housing agents have come to call the Cotswold Stone Belt that would have amazed farm labourers who once occupied them. Once purchased, it has been possible to gut these cottages, equipping them with new interiors, central heating, drains, and every modern convenience, without infringing the planning regulations. In the course of this restorative process, the fabric of the villages, – including many old mill buildings, forges, bakeries, wool houses and other centres of rural industry – has been made good for many more years, while an aura of countryside calm has been carefully fostered. Many of these villages look better built, more trimmed and manicured, than they have ever done before. But the price has been a loss of the traditional life that once gave vitality to the villages, replacing it by a sort of well-turned-out sterility which is nice for the occupants and for the tourist gazing from his coach window, but is far removed from the human activity with which they were once animated. As far as the industrial archaeologist is concerned, these villages are of little interest, despite the survival of mill buildings and other structures. Very few have consequently been included in the following gazetteer.

The Gloucestershire woollen cloth industry has left an impressive collection of industrial monuments. These range from the large mills of the Stroud valleys to the abundance of smaller buildings for ancillary processes – dyehouses, teazle-houses, drying sheds and so on – and between them several varieties of smaller mills and the elegant houses built by wealthy clothiers for their families, and the more functional housing occasionally provided for their workers. It is not practicable within the scope of the following gazetteer to provide a comprehensive list of all these remains. Our approach has been frankly selective, aimed at spotlighting the more significant monuments, and those which add an interest to places where it might not otherwise be expected. For a more detailed account of the leading mill sites, and for a treatment of their development over time, the reader is referred to Dr Jennifer Tann's pioneering survey of *Gloucestershire Woollen Mills* (Newton Abbot 1967).

On the opposite side of the county, the Forest of Dean poses a different set of problems for the industrial archaeologist. The monuments of the Forest industries do not generally have the solidity of the woollen mills of the Cotswold valleys, and are frequently very elusive, tending to merge back rapidly into the Forest once work has ceased. The industries thus share the strangely remote quality of the Forest of Dean, isolated as if by choice as well as by topography, withdrawn upon itself, with its many acres of varied woodland interspersed by random clearings with groups of buildings in reddish-coloured stone which have an ineffably untidy and dilapidated appearance even when they are structurally sound. In this curiously featureless landscape, the industrial monuments need to be sought with particular patience and persistence.

The industries of the Forest of Dean have traditionally been those based upon the exploitation of its natural resources – wood, stone, iron and coal. Having been a Royal Forest since 1016, Dean provided a vital ingredient in national power in the shape of timber for the navy. The woodland has on several occasions been badly depleted by excessive demands for timber, but it has then been revived by reafforestation and careful silviculture.

Stone is still quarried extensively in the Forest, although the operations are frequently, like those at the large Bixhead Quarry between Coleford and Cannop, so hidden in the woodland that the visitor is scarcely conscious of their existence. Geologically, the Forest is a triangular-shaped basin, with a rim of older rocks – mainly carboniferous limestone and old red sandstone – surrounding a plateau of coal seams which has been deeply eroded by north–south valleys. Amongst the coal seams lies a massive bed of pennant sandstone, and it is this which is quarried at Bixhead and elsewhere as a durable building material. The older rocks of the periphery have also been quarried intermittently for lime (as at Symonds Yat) and for roadstone (especially in the Wye valley in the St Briavels area).

Ironstone, located particularly in the 'crease limestone' of the carboniferous series, has provided the basis for the most famous of all the Forest industries, the mining and working of iron. Some of the earliest workings for iron ore have left the weird landscape of the 'scowles' near Bream and in other places round the edge of the Forest, and these were almost certainly Roman in origin. The later iron miners sank shafts to reach the ore at deeper levels, and it has been estimated that the Forest had yielded a total of iron ore in excess of 10,000,000 tons by the time that the last commercial mine ceased operating in 1945. Most of this was smelted in the Forest, using locally produced charcoal in the early bloomeries and charcoal blast furnaces up to the eighteenth century, and coke from local coal in the subsequent coke-fired blast furnaces. Fragments of charcoal blast furnaces survive, that at Guns Mill being a particularly early specimen, and several coke blast furnaces, with that at Whitecliff (Coleford) being the most complete. Most of the Forest iron seems to have made its way to the market as cast-iron, but some was refined into wrought-iron and steel such as that produced in the nineteenth century by the Mushet family in their Darkhill and Titanic workshops in Milkwall. Tinplate was also produced, especially in the Lydbrook valley and Cinderford.

The other traditional industry of Dean has been coal mining, which was probably worked in small quantities from Roman times, like iron ore. The first evidence of trade in Forest coal, however, dates from the thirteenth century, since when there has been on unbroken record of coal extraction, maintained at present by the last dozen or so Free Miners. The Free Miners were originally both iron and coal miners who had rights to mine specific 'gales' within the Hundred of St Briavels (roughly coterminous with the present Forest of Dean), these rights being jealously maintained in special courts. Most of their operations were (and are) small scale family affairs, but the amalgamation of 'gales' made possible larger mines such as those which flourished for a time at the beginning of the present century. But in the Forest of Dean, more quickly than in other coalfields, the remains of old coal workings are quickly lost under the growth of new woodlands, and it is difficult to find any significant remains of the industry other than those colliery waste tips such as New Fancy, south of the Speech House Hotel, which have been deliberately preserved as a tourist attraction. The most interesting evidence of coal mining is the activity of the remaining Free Miners, but as these change their location from year to year, the explorer must seek local guidance about where to find them.

Other industries have come to the Forest of Dean as the traditional processes have disappeared or changed their character. Modern development has been encouraged at Lydney, which has always been the best natural outlet for the Forest, and also at Cinderford and Coleford. Modern engineering firms, manufacturers of building materials, paper mills and various chemical processes, have taken over from the old industries, in some cases reoccupying old buildings, but more usually creating new complexes of sheds which, however unlovely, are highly functional. This process of industrial change is not, of course, peculiar to the Forest, but has occurred throughout the county, so that Gloucester and Cheltenham now have flourishing new industrial estates, and many of the old woollen mills of the Stroud valleys and elsewhere have now been occupied by engineering, chemical, and other firms. Such new industries rarely have much to interest the industrial archaeologist, so that no attempt has been made to cover them in this account except in so far as they have occupied or adapted older industrial premises.

The development of industry in Gloucestershire, in Forest, Vale, and Wolds, has been closely related to the development of transport facilities. The first highway in the county was the prehistoric Ridgeway, running along the edge of the Cotswolds between the settlements of the first farmers in the region. The Roman Fosse Way followed a very similar route, reflecting the Romano-British prosperity of the Wolds, but the Romans also pushed roads westwards to the Severn, at Sea Mills (Abonae) in the south, now in Avon County, and to Gloucester (Glevum) in the north, and thence along the coastal route into South Wales. And the Romans also linked Abonae and Glevum with the first road to penetrate the forest of the Vale, while they drove another road inland from Lydney, through the east section of the Forest of Dean, to their iron-working centre at Weston-under-Penyard (Ariconium). A section of this has been revealed at Blackpool Bridge which demonstrates, by its choice of a carefully graded curve across the river, that the Romans did not *always* build their roads in a straight line.

The Romans also drove a road north from Gloucester, through Worcester to Droitwich (Salinae) which was already famous as a source of salt, and in the subsequent centuries, when the Roman road system fell into disuse, other tracks developed in order to distribute this valuable commodity from the Droitwich area. One of them, Salter's Way, is still marked on the 1″ OS maps, climbing the edge of the Cotswolds near Winchcombe and proceeding thence in a south east direction. There were similar tracks established by drovers operating between Wales and London, and by clothiers and packmen traversing the Wolds in search of raw materials and customers. Generally speaking, nothing survives of these medieval roads except the clues implicit in an occasional place name.

The rising pace of industrialization in the eighteenth century brought new transport initiatives in Gloucestershire. For centuries, the Severn had been the main artery of trade through the county from Bristol to Gloucester and beyond as far as Coalbrookdale, to which the Bristol brass manufacturer Abraham Darby had moved to set up his renowned ironworks in 1708. The easy communication by means of the navigable Severn had been an important factor influencing his choice of site, and the river course was gradually improved by the Severn Navigation and provided with quay facilities at Ashleworth, Tirley, Chaceley, and Forthampton (Lower Lode). The other major river of the county, the Wye, was also important as a natural waterway, providing an outlet from Lydbrook, on the north edge of the Forest of Dean, and with wharves at Redbrook and Brockweir (St Briavels). The first canal in the county was the Stroudwater, opened to Wallbridge Wharf in Stroud in 1779 after many false starts and abortive schemes. This broad canal (its 13 locks were 15½ feet wide and 72 feet long, designed to accommodate Severn trows). Ten years later, in 1789, the Thames & Severn Canal was opened between Stroud and Inglesham, on the Thames, a distance of 29 miles involving a tunnel of 3,817 yards through the Cotswold escarpment at Sapperton. Its locks were narrower but longer than those of the Stroudwater, to suit the Thames barges (12¾ feet by 90 feet).

The next step in the canal network of the county was the construction of the Gloucester & Sharpness Canal (originally the Gloucester & Berkeley, but the decision to shorten it by terminating at Sharpness changed this). Work began on this in 1794 and was completed in 1827. It was built as a wide canal (90 feet) for 16 miles, with no locks except the entrance lock at Sharpness and that at Gloucester, and until the construction of the Manchester Ship Canal it was the largest in the country. While this was under construction, the Herefordshire & Gloucestershire Canal was begun in 1796, although this was even longer in reaching completion, which it did not do until 1845, by which time the canal boom was over and attention was switching to railways. The Coombe Hill Canal, a broad canal 2½ miles long, was built to connect the Severn with the Cheltenham road in 1796/7 (it was abandoned in 1876), and in 1813 the Lydney Canal made a new cut between Lydney and the Severn, with excellent harbour facilities in its new tidal basin. Pidcock's Canal had already been cut by 1800 to extend the accessibility of the forges in the valley above Lydney to small tub boats.

Of these canals, only the Gloucester & Sharpness remains in business, and some of them have virtually disappeared although the exercise of tracing their courses remains an attractive task for industrial archaeologists. They were all victims of the competition from the railways from the 1840s onwards, although before that decade many tramroads had been built in various parts of the county to supplement the waterways. The principal tramroads were the Gloucester and Cheltenham Railway, completed in 1811 to convey stone from the Leckhampton quarries to Gloucester docks; the Forest of Dean Tramroad, opened as a plateway in 1809 to connect Cinderford with the Severn estuary at Bullo Pill, making the tunnels at Soudley and Haie amongst the earliest railway tunnels in the world (the line was subsequently changed to broad gauge in 1854 and to standard gauge in 1872: it was closed in 1969); the Monmouth Tramroad, opened in 1812 to connect Coleford with the Wye Navigation at Monmouth via Redbrook; and the Severn and Wye Railway and Canal Company, opened in 1810 and connecting Lydney with the Wye at Lydbrook through the heart of the Forest of Dean. There were also many shorter branches, such as the Purton Steam Carriage Road which tried to provide a steam-powered outlet from the Forest of Dean at Purton.

It was the advent of steam traction which converted the tramroads from useful supplements to the waterway network into active rivals, as the new railways of the 1840s and subsequent decades aimed at replacing the canals and in many cases transformed the tramroads into full railways. The first such railway to enter the county was the Birmingham & Gloucester in 1840, reaching Cheltenham (Lansdown

Station) in June and Gloucester by the end of the year (the original terminus was replaced by Eastgate Station in 1896). The Bristol & Gloucester Railway was opened to the Central Station, Gloucester, in 1844, as a GWR broad gauge line, causing formidable transhipment problems in the arrangements between the two main stations in the city. The Midland Railway acquired control of both companies in 1845-6, and had by 1854 built their own standard gauge through-route between Birmingham and Bristol. The Cheltenham and Great Western Union Railway was authorized in 1836, but was acquired by the Great Western Railway in 1843 and completed through to Cheltenham (from Swindon through Kemble, Stroud and Gloucester) as a broad gauge line in 1847. The South Wales Railway then took the GWR broad gauge system on to Chepstow and Swansea in 1852, acquiring an interest in the Forest of Dean Tramroad *en route*. Three minor railways completed the railway network of the county: the Banbury and Cheltenham District Railway (opened 1887 and acquired by the GWR 1897), the Midland and South Western Junction Railway (running north–south from Andoversford through Cirencester to Cricklade in Wiltshire, opened in 1884), and the Severn Bridge Railway (linked Berkeley and Sharpness with the South Wales Railway and Forest of Dean lines with the opening of the Sharpness Railway Bridge in 1879). These minor railways have all been closed except for a few links with the main lines, but the main lines themselves remain much as the nineteenth-century engineers constructed them, although all now operating on the standard gauge and shorn of most of their branches and virtually all their smaller stations.

The revival of road traffic with the advent of the internal combustion engine brought about a rapid decline in the importance of the railways, causing the abandonment of lesser lines and the curtailment of services. The result for the industrial archaeologist is that the remnants of old railways can be identified in many places, especially in the Forest of Dean. The main Swindon to Stroud line had branches from Kemble to both Cirencester and Tetbury until the 1960s, and these alignments are still clearly visible, including some deserted signal boxes and a virtually complete station building in Cirencester, currently serving as a bus station. On the other side of the transport coin, the revival of the road system has brought the motorways to Gloucestershire, and serves to remind the traveller of an earlier road network provided by the turnpike trusts of the county which has left many handsome turnpike toll houses and a lot of milestones set out in different styles according to the taste of the individual trust. The A46 along the Cotswolds from Bath to Stroud, for example, possesses a good set of milestones and a number of well-preserved toll houses. At Butterow, near Stroud, the toll house preserves an unusually fine specimen of a toll-board setting out the tolls for different kinds of traffic.

It will be apparent from this brief review of the industrial and transport history of Gloucestershire that, even though the industrial activity in the county has been diverse and somewhat localized in its effects, producing little to compare with the landscapes created by intensive heavy industry in the Midlands and elsewhere, it is still a very rewarding subject for industrial archaeological investigation. The Cotswold valleys have been marked, and occasionally embellished, by every stage in the development of the wool and woollen cloth industry, while the Forest of Dean has been worked over many times by the various industries which have consumed its raw materials. Elsewhere, the proliferation of rural crafts and urban industries, working local materials like stone and leather or producing food and drink for an expanding population, have made a more transient but often significant contribution to the landscape of physical monuments with which industrial archaeology is concerned, while the web of roads, waterways, and railways has been woven across the face of the county, leaving its own landmarks to industrial change. This whole complex fabric, with its attendant social pattern of houses both great and small, churches and chapels, public houses and clubrooms, is available for examination by the discerning and sympathetic eye. Out of its study there should emerge an understanding of the processes by which modern industrial society has been moulded.

AMPNEY CRUCIS

The **watermill** (SP065017) in this village is one of the more pleasant adaptations of a Cotswold mill into a house. The external 10 ft diam. iron breast wheel is still in position.

APPERLEY

A small village on the east bank of the River Severn north of Gloucester, with a Severn Navigation **coal wharf** (SO854283) which still possesses an inn called The Coal Man.

ASHCHURCH

This village has become a rather dreary mill town serving the large Dowty establishment nearby. **Northway Mill** (SO920348), on the Carrant Brook to the north-west of the village, is a substantial building with an external waterwheel; it can be glimpsed from the south-bound carriageway of the M5. A mile upstream on the Carrant Brook is Aston on Carrant, with an **old forge** (SO945346) which is now a nicely restored thatched cottage with no industrial significance. Between here and Ashchurch the minor road crosses the British Rail main line running due north–south by a manned **level crossing** (SO926342) with a lodge like that of a road toll house.

ASHLEWORTH

A village on the west bank of the River Severn north of Gloucester, distinguished by a fine church and magnificent **tithe barn**, now owned by the National Trust. There was a small **quay** beside the river (SO818251) and a ferry operated by the Severn Navigation. The Boat Inn is a house with a bowed addition onto the quay. There is also a small brick storehouse.

AVENING

The A434 road from Tetbury to Nailsworth descends into a steep Cotswold valley and turns a sharp bend in the middle of this village. On the small brook below the road is a four-storey building, once a **cloth mill** (SO883981): a stone structure dating from the early 19th century, later converted into a flour mill.

BARRINGTON

Great Barrington is a surprisingly dilapidated village, unlike most of its spick-and-span neighbours in the Windrush valley. There is a small **mill** on the river (SP210131).

BERKELEY

Between the medieval castle and the modern atomic-fuelled power station is the village of Berkeley, and there is a **watermill** (ST676991) here where the Little River Avon becomes the tidal Berkeley Pill. The present building is probably of early 19th century date. Originally a fulling mill, it was converted to oil-seed crushing and later became a flour mill.

BEVERSTONE

A small village with a romantic **castle ruin** (ST861939) in private ownership and not accessible. But it is possible to see from outside the garden a small drystone bridge crossing the dry moat: this has a single pointed arch, partially collapsed on one side.

BIBURY

Bibury has become something of a show-village, set in the shallow but steep-sided valley of the River Coln, and with its main street open on one side to the fast-flowing clear water of the river. William Morris called it the most beautiful village in England. The main item of industrial interest is **Arlington Mill** (SP114068), a high, buttressed, building adapted as a private museum to display mill machinery and equipment. The internal waterwheel has been replaced as an effective part of this display. Historically, the village was an important centre of the Cotswold woollen cloth industry, and the highly picturesque cottages of **Arlington Row** (SP 115067) were associated with this industry. They were reputedly built before 1500 and partially occupied in the 17th century as a factory, giving the name Rack Isle to the field in front of them where the cloth would have been 'tentered' in the open air.

BISLEY

An isolated Cotswold village on the plateau, about two miles north of Chalford and the Golden Valley. The village has a curious double **lock-up** (SO 903060) in the centre. **Stancombe toll house** (SO 897069) about a mile north-west of the village, is a typical two-storey turnpike building, in good condition despite conversion to domestic use.

BLOCKLEY

This well-kept village straggles along the side of a hill. There is a long two-storey **mill** building converted into a house on the hillside near the church (SP 165350), with a pond intact behind it. Also another **mill** on the stream near Northwick Park (SP 174358).

BOWBRIDGE

Bowbridge is almost a suburb of Stroud, providing a link between that town and Thrupp in the Golden Valley. There is a group of buildings surviving from **Bowbridge Mills** and dyehouses (SO 857043), although they have been so modified that it is not easy to work out their relationships. Nearby, the stretch of the **Thames and Severn Canal** at Bowbridge has been 're-stored' by constructing a concrete dam shaped like lock-gates to provide a pleasant amenity. The adjacent circular-weir canal overflow has also been rebuilt and supplied with a protective cage.

BOURTON-ON-THE-WATER

A somewhat jazzed-up village to accommodate the thriving tourist industry. But it possesses a most attractive central feature in the shape of the River Windrush flowing through the middle, with streets on both sides opening onto it and with several low bridges for roads and pedestrians. The two-storey stone, slate-roofed, **mill** (SP 166207) has been converted into a motor museum.

BREAM

Bream is an untidy township in the Forest of Dean, on the western fringe of the coal basin and adjacent to iron outcrops in the carboniferous limestone. The latter are responsible for the dramatic remains of early workings, known as **Devil's Chapel Scowles** (SO 607046). These are tortuous open-cast excavations from which iron was probably extracted in Roman times. They are now heavily overgrown, which increases their bizarre appearance but means also that they should only be explored with great caution. Evidence of more recent iron working can be found in the Oakwood valley on the opposite side of Bream, where the 19th century **Bromeley Hill Furnace** (SO 601062) is set into the north side of the valley just below the point where the road from Orepool crosses it. This was a coke furnace, which according to Hart (p. 150) has been out of blast since 1871. The remains are very ruinous, but a section of the inner wall of the furnace can be distinguished amongst the rubble, with the charging point about 40 ft above the casting floor. Nearby, under the road, is a masonry-lined adit, with traces of some sleeper blocks carrying a tramway into it. Beyond the road is a **mill**, now a public house, and further up the valley Hart locates the Oakwood Foundry. Going down the valley from the road, a track leads to a complex of 19th-century buildings now used as a **chemical factory** (SO 604067). It seems likely that this group of buildings once formed part of the Flour Mill Colliery.

BRIMSCOMBE

This is a sorry story. Brimscombe once boasted a thriving inland port, serving the Thames and Severn Canal just above its junction with the Stroudwater Canal. There was a substantial basin where the barges moored, with an island in the middle used as a coal store. On the northern side of the basin there was a handsome range of stone-built offices and warehouses. Left empty for several years after the basin had been filled in, they were eventually demolished to make room for a new factory, and the whole site has now been so mutilated that it is difficult to imagine the role once performed there for the industries and communities of the Golden Valley. Part of the four-storey **Brimscombe Port Mill** (SO 869023) survives with additions and water tower. A clump of trees in the car park shows the position of the island in the basin which was the coal store. A little way upstream, **Bourne Mill** (SO 873022), was a cloth mill converted into a walking-stick factory and a much altered stone building survives. In the tributary valley of the Toadsmoor Brook, entering from the north is **Markhall Mill** (SO 877023), a three-storey building in red brick, and a two-storey **corn mill** (SO 878027) with water courses intact.

BROCKWORTH

Five miles south-west of Cheltenham, the village is off the Cheltenham to Stroud road (A46), on which there is a **turnpike toll house** (SO 891152).

BULLO

Just off the main A48 road between Blakeney and Newnham, **Bullo Pill** (SO 691099) is a derelict and overgrown tidal basin with a ruinous entrance lock from the River Severn.

CAINSCROSS

A mile west of Stroud, Cainscross is at an important route intersection in the busy lower valley of the River Frome. The **lock** on the Stroudwater Canal here (SO 835048) has been made into a waterfall. There is a **crane** with a 20 ft wooden jib on a neighbouring wharf (SO 834048).

CAM

Cam possesses one of the few remaining working woollen cloth mills in Gloucestershire: the **Cam Mill** factory (ST 754999) of Hunt & Winterbotham, occupying an old four-storey stone mill, with brick water tower and clock, and with new weaving sheds and other buildings adjacent. There are also some terraces of workers' houses close to the mill. The water-powered fulling stamps were removed from this mill to be stored in Stroud Museum.

CAMBRIDGE

The River Cam from Uley and Dursley passes under the A38 at Cambridge. From here to the Gloucester and Sharpness Canal 1½ miles away, the river has been canalised to form a narrow **branch canal** (SO 739051–748040).

CANNOP

Cannop is essentially a cross-roads in the middle of the Forest of Dean. But a careful examination of the surrounding woodland will show that it is the centre of several significant Forest industries. In the first place, there are several large colliery remains in the area, such as that at **Wimberry Slade** (SO 607124), with an older **drift mine** (SO 600121) and a tramroad. The **New Fancy Colliery** (SO 628096), on the road south from the **Speech House Hotel** (SO 620120) – itself a point of historic interest, as the traditional meeting point of the Verderer's Court for maintaining the law and custom of the Forest – has now been most pleasantly redeveloped by the Forestry Commission as a tourist attraction, with an informative viewing-point established on top of the colliery waste heap. Back at Cannop itself, there is a **wood distillation factory** (SO 609114) still in business, while a mile to the south, below the Cannop Ponds, is a **stone cutting factory** (SO 608100) which derives its raw material from the extensive **Bixhead Quarries**, in the woodlands to the west (SO 598108). A thick stratum of pennant sandstone outcrops along this ridge and has provided one of the main sources of building stone in the Forest. **Cannop Ponds** are themselves artificial reservoirs for iron foundries lower down the valley towards Parkend. The alignment of the **tramway** down the Cannop valley from Lydbrook in the north to Parkend in the south can be traced in several sections.

CHACELEY

A secluded village on the west bank of the

River Severn with a **Severn Navigation quay and inn**, now a clubhouse (SO865297).

CHALFORD

Chalford stands at the head of the industrial development of the Golden Valley of the Stroud River Frome. The valley continues eastward for three miles, but when first the main-line railway and then the Thames and Severn Canal leave it by tunnels to the south, the valley turns northward becoming increasingly enclosed and inaccessible. Chalford itself clings to the steeply falling northern side of the valley, but the industrial complex associated with the village is in the valley bottom where the main road from Cirencester (A419) drops down from the east. The **canal round house** (*Plate 18*) (SO892024), one of the best preserved on the canal, may be taken as the centrepiece of this complex. The surrounding buildings were clearly associated with the woollen cloth industry in their heyday, but all of them have now changed function and even the designations are confusing. Adjacent to the round house is **Chalford Mill** (SO892025) with a mill pond feeding an internal waterwheel pit. Below this is a **water pumping station** (SO892025) utilizing the strong supply of fresh water. Upstream is the site of **New Mill** (SO894025), a three-storey stone structure with water tower and clock, standing on a site which is being redeveloped as an industrial estate. The river here has been largely culverted and the area has lost most of its historical character. About a mile downstream from the round house, but still in the parish of Chalford, is **St Mary's Mill** (SO886023), one of the best specimens of 19th-century cloth mills to survive in the district. Stone built, with five storeys, the factory now produces walking sticks for a world market, and has preserved both a waterwheel and a steam engine, although neither are now used. It has been described as 'one of the most well-documented mill sites in Gloucestershire' (Tann pp. 186–9). Much of the course of the Thames and Severn Canal has been obliterated in the lower part of Chalford in the interest of road widening, but above the road some fair stretches remain including a **bridge** (SO902024) with an inscription on the keystone: 'Clows Engin. 1785' commemorating Josiah Clowes,

Engineer to the Canal Company. Crossing the railway on the approach to St Mary's Mill there is a neat **keeper's lodge**.

CHEDWORTH

A Cotswold village off the Fosse Way, and chiefly famous for its fine **Roman villa**, now owned by the National Trust (SP053134). This is some way out of the village, as is also **Stowell Mill** (SP081129), now a somewhat derelict farm store with little to show of industrial interest.

CHELTENHAM

Cheltenham preserves the character of the handsome spa town which developed at the end of the 18th and beginning of the 19th century, drawing some of the aristocratic clientèle away from Bath. Comparison with Bath is apt because both towns were seeking to provide leisure facilities for the wealthier classes, and were successful with very similar formulae which included mineral spring waters, assembly rooms, and plenty of amenities for gambling, promenading and dancing. Cheltenham rose in fashion thanks largely to the favour bestowed on it by George III, but a generation later both Bath and Cheltenham were eclipsed by the Prince Regent's liking for Brighton, and the future trend towards seaside leisure resorts was then firmly established. The town differs from Bath in being flat, so that it lacks any distinct topographical features, and it also lacks a great church in the centre, although the parish church, hidden mostly behind the Promenade, is set in a pleasant churchyard with some of the flamboyant Dragon and Onion lamp-posts which give a fine decorative flourish to the street furniture of Cheltenham. Another striking difference from Bath is that the buildings on the elegant crescents and terraces are almost all stuccoed. that is, the stone is faced in a smooth cement mixture, which can then be treated in a variety of colours according to taste. Architectural detailing thus relied more heavily than in Bath on the **ornamental ironwork** (*Plate 19*) used in profusion for balconies, window-boxes and other wall-fittings. This ironwork constitutes a feature of considerable industrial archaeological interest, and has been the subject of a specialist study by Miss

19 Cheltenham – Ornamental Ironwork

Amina Chatwin (*Cheltenham's Ornamental Ironwork*, Cheltenham 1974). Another aspect of the ironwork street furniture to be found in Cheltenham are some hexagonal Penfold pillar boxes. Apart from the ironwork, industry cannot be said to have made much impact on the discrete gentility of Cheltenham, and it must be admitted that to the industrial archaeologist the main interest of the town lies in the ornamental details which have already been described. But a short tour around the back streets can be rewarding, as there are several items of note, including **Whitbreads Brewery** (SO947227), between Henrietta Street and St Margaret's Road (most of the buildings are late 19th century, but the brewery has been active since 1760); the startling red-brick **electricity substation** (*Plate 20*) on Clarence Street (SO947 225); and **Lansdown Station** (SO932220) built in 1840 for the Birmingham & Gloucester Railway and now part of the Birmingham to Bristol trunk route and still substantially intact with its cast-iron columns and decorative ironwork. There is a **railway level-crossing** at Swindon (SO939258), north-west of the town.

CHIPPING CAMPDEN

One of the most exquisite Cotswold towns, almost at the northern edge of Gloucestershire. The wide main street is lined with stone buildings which, despite variations in style, blend together in charming harmony. The **Market Hall** in the centre is a National Trust property (SP152391). Although the town owes its early prosperity to the wool trade, which accounts for its distinguished church and several other impressive buildings, there is little evidence of later industries and all modern development in the town has been tastefully performed. There is, however, one fine specimen for the industrial archaeologist in the shape of the **Silk Mill** on Sheep Street (SP149358). This is a substantial three-storey stone built slate-roofed structure. The front (away from the road) is regular, with 8 bays: the rear (seen from the road) is less regular. The water channel flows under the mill. It is now occupied by some of the fine craftsmen who have flourished in Chipping Campden in the 20th century, producing beautiful work in silver, iron, and other materials.

20 Cheltenham – Electricity Sub-station

CINDERFORD

The centre of some of the more important 20th century industries in the Forest of Dean, Cinderford has been too extensively re-developed to retain much of industrial archaeological interest. The surrounding area, however, deserves close study, **Guns Mill** (SO675159) is described by Hart (p. 70) as 'the best remaining furnace of the earliest phase of British blast furnace practice', and plans of it have been drawn by the Gloucestershire Industrial Archaeology Society. But it is difficult to recognize or approach because it stands amongst a collection of farm buildings, and has been converted to other functions with a half-timber superstructure built on top of the square stump of the furnace. The whole building, moreover, is shrouded with ivy. Nevertheless, the building is of considerable archaeological significance, and Hart is right to warn that 'if the structure is not to collapse soon it needs urgent attention' (p. 71).

CIRENCESTER

Cirencester seems to have over-reacted to the problem of urban traffic, having acquired in the last few years an elaborate system of bypass and relief roads. Although this has undoubtedly contributed to making the centre quieter and more free of traffic, it has meant the mutilation of the semi-open space to the south-west of the town which contained some of the most interesting industrial relics. The town itself presents a curious anomaly: as Corinium it was one of the major cities of Roman Britain, but the town seems to have turned its back on this Roman ancestry, virtually nothing of which remains on view except for the amphitheatre, now hemmed in and difficult of access because of a bypass road, and the relics gathered in the small town museum. To all intents and purposes, Cirencester is a late-medieval market town, associated with the woollen cloth industry which endowed its splendid church and left marks such as the Bishop Blaise amongst the public houses of the town. There was also significant development in the 18th and early 19th centuries, responsible for some fine houses: see, for example, the charming **Cecily Hill**, with its approach to the wide-ranging grounds of Cirencester Park, its **Tontine**

Houses, and its castellated **barracks**. The coming of the Industrial Revolution left its mark on Cirencester, without disrupting the essential character of a graceful rural market town. The main visible remains include: **the flour mill**, Lewis Lane (SP024017): **Cotswold Mills**, operated now by Henry & Co Ltd, but with the name Cotswold Association over the entrance in Watermoor Road (This is a large building, built for steam-powered milling, but has no great distinction today); **Cirencester Urban District Council Water Works** (SP024016) are the words inscribed in stone along the façade of this high one-storey building in Lewis Lane (It is now being used as a light engineering factory); **Cirencester Brewery Maltings** (Hugh Baird & Co Ltd) (SP023018) front onto Cricklade Street, the extensive premises including some characteristic malting ovens and other features now no longer fully in use. **The railway station** (SP020018), now used as a bus station, was once the terminus of the single-track railway linking the town with the main GWR line at Kemble (there was another station in Cirencester at Watermoor, on the north–south line from Cheltenham to Swindon, which has now disappeared). **Bowley's Almshouses** (SP024014), two pleasant ranges of cottages of different dates facing each other on Watermoor Street. **Canal Basin** (SP023013): only a very small fragment of masonry remains on the south side of the new bypass near Querns Road, showing where the basin and its warehouses stood. Nearby is the two-storey Regency façade of the **Watermoor Hospital**, now derelict but once the workhouse, with a lock-up and laundry room adjacent. The canal basin formed the terminus of a short branch from the main Thames & Severn Canal, with which it formed a **junction basin** (SU030996) at Siddington a mile south of Cirencester. There are the remains of a lock, and a canal bridge is still in use. Also at Siddington is a castellated **windmill tower** (SU041996).

CLEARWELL

An unusually compact village for the Forest of Dean. Clearwell's castle is largely 18th century, but its **iron mine** (SO578084) is genuine, although now converted into a museum and tourist attraction. The route opened up to the public demonstrates the cavern-like quality of the workings by which the miners pursued the mineral deposits. It was known as the Old Ham Mine and was active into the first half of the present century, although restricted to the exploitation of red ochre for the paint industry (open Sundays and Bank Holidays, from Easter to September). As so often in the Forest, coal was also mined in close proximity to the iron mine, in this case at **Ellwood Pit** (SO596076), where a fine wooden headstock survived until recently, but the site has now been cleared. There are two neat **toll houses** in the vicinity, at **Ellwood** (SO578070) and at **Orepool** (SO579076).

COALEY

A corn mill in this village became a fulling mill, and was converted in the late 18th century into an **iron mill** (SO760025) making 'Coaley shovels' and other tools. The main three-storey building has been reconstructed, incorporating used grindstones, by a small firm of turbine engineers.

COATES

A sleepy village, off the main roads, Coates is the closest community to the **East Portal of the Sapperton Tunnel** (SO965006) on the Thames and Severn Canal. The portal has recently been very handsomely renovated, and there are plans to clear the tunnel of the obstruction which has blocked it for many years and to make it available to pleasure traffic by raising the water level through it. Above the portal is the **Tunnel House Inn** (SO965006), used at the time of the construction of the canal for accommodating some of the workers, and since serving as a source of refreshment for people working the canal. The tunnel is just over two miles long, and as it provided no towing path it would have been necessary for the bargemen to 'leg' their way through while their horses were led over the top to Daneway, where another hostelry provided for their refreshment at the West Portal (see Sapperton). Part of the route over the hill has been interrupted by the railway which later cut across the tunnel before itself tunnelling through into the Golden Valley. The route of the canal tunnel is marked by the overgrown mounds of spoil excavated through the stone-lined circular shafts which

can be discovered at intervals along its length. One of the most accessible is near the point where the railway swings across the tunnel (SO961013). The canal emerges from the East Portal into a steep cutting, through which its course has been lined with cement in an attempt to deal with the serious leakage which was a perennial problem of this summit level of the canal. It passes under a neat **canal bridge** (SO968002), and shortly passes a **canal roundhouse** (SO970000), now sadly ruinous and overgrown. The roundhouse was close to a stop lock, now completely derelict as the whole length of the canal beyond the mouth of the tunnel has long been dry.

COLEFORD

A pleasant town in the Forest of Dean. Its chief industrial monument is the **Whitecliff Furnace** (SO568103), a coke blast-furnace on the southern edge of the town. The furnace is remarkably complete externally, although now very dilapidated and with a serious crack in the front arch. The bridge to the charging ramp behind the furnace is still intact, and there is a stone bearing the date 1804 on the front face. The lining is still intact but precarious, and as the furnace stands in a small-holding it should not be approached without permission. The remains of associated buildings can be seen on both sides of the road, although the plant appears to have been dismantled about 1816, having had a very short working life.

COOMBE HILL

This is a hamlet on the A38, where it runs along a low ridge between Gloucester and Tewkesbury. A **canal** 2½ miles long was constructed from the base of this ridge to the River Severn, and served a wharf dealing in coal and other commodities. The canal is now greatly overgrown with rushes, but survives, as do a few **wharf cottages** dating from the construction of the canal in 1796 (SO886273).

DRYBROOK

Drybrook is a village between Mitcheldean and Ruardean, on the northern edge of the Forest of Dean. Linked by a tramroad with Cinderford to the south, it had the usual range of Forest industries in the vicinity. On top of a hill to the south-east, much disturbed by extensive iron-mining and recent land-clearance, is **Fairplay Engine House** (SO659165). The walls of the engine house stand intact to about 20 ft, heavily guarded against intrusion presumably because of an exposed shaft inside, above which would have stood a Cornish 'Bull' engine (i.e. a steam engine on the Cornish cycle but without a beam, acting directly onto the pump rods). The building is now becoming hidden in a modern area of reafforestation.

DUDBRIDGE

Dudbridge is one of the industrial villages west of Stroud. The Midland branch railway from Stonehouse to Nailsworth passed through the village, with a **station** (SO834045) and a link with the Cheltenham–Paddington line in Stroud. **Dudbridge Mill** (SO836046) was an extensive cloth manu-factory owned by the Apperly family in the 19th century and there are substantial re-mains although converted to other uses and much modified. **Kemmin's Mill**, a five-storey building alongside the site of the railway station (SO834045), was a flour mill: the Nailsworth stream passes through a sluice at the end of the mill to its confluence with the Frome: there is a stone bearing the date 1849.

DURSLEY

Despite its market hall with a statue of Queen Anne on the front, and some comely old houses in the centre, Dursley has become in recent decades something of a company town. The company which has come to dominate it is the engineering firm of R.A. Listers, the major factory of which occupies the valley bottom between Dursley and Cam, while the offices and other premises of the firm have crept up into the town, taking over and refurbishing older buildings in some cases. In the process, some of the old cloth mills in the town have been absorbed into Listers and have little to show of their former function. But a walk around the back-streets which drop into the valley from the centre can still be interesting. At the bottom of Long Street is a group of buildings (ST758982) now

21 Dursley – Listers' Offices, Long Street

offices for Listers (*Plate 21*), partly adaptations but also with a rather distinguished purpose-built office. Near here, also, was the site of the **terminus** to the Dursley railway which ran down through Cam to the main line at Cam Junction. There is a **toll house** – Pike Cottage – beside the busy main road at the west end of the town (ST 753983).

EASTINGTON

At Eastington, four miles west of Stroud, the crowded Frome valley opens out into the Vale. The river supplied power for two mills in the village. **Eastington Mill** (SO 779061), also known as Meadow Mill, is a 19th-century cloth mill which has been adapted as a modern factory. **Millend Mill** (SO 782054) was a fulling mill but was converted to other functions. The Stroudwater Canal is north of the river, with a **lock-keeper's cottage** (SO 784061). The **workhouse** survives (SO 783063), a typical structure of this type, but is now derelict. There is a **fingerpost** in the centre of the village (SO 775054).

EBLEY

Ebley Mill (SO 829045) is one of the most

impressive of the Stroud valley cloth mills. The New Mill is a five-storey stone structure with a slate roof. Parts of the Old Mill still survive, and the outline of the reservoir, now drained, can still be seen. It is one of the few mills still in business manufacturing woollen cloth. The **Oil Mill** (SO 825045) derives its name from a linseed oil process installed in the 18th century. In the 19th century it became a cloth mill. It has three storeys and a lift and is of mixed stone and brick construction.

FAIRFORD

Although well down towards the Vale of Oxford, Fairford retains the distinctive qualities of a Cotswold town and is, indeed, one of the most charming specimens of this type. Its graceful parish church possesses some of the finest and most ancient stained glass in the country, and like many Cotswold towns its atmosphere is redolent with woollen industry associations, even though no active industry remains in it. The **mill house** (*Plate 22*) (SP 150013) has been pleasantly adapted for domestic purposes, as in so many cases of this sort, but the water courses still reveal clearly

22   Fairford – The Mill House

the original function of the building. Across the River Coln from the mill is the **Oxpen** (SP 148013), an interesting relic of rural industry dating from 1780 and nicely restored by the Ernest Cook Trust.

FORTHAMPTON

A secluded village on the River Severn opposite Tewkesbury. At **Lower Lode** (SO879317) there is an inn and slipway on the site of a small quay and ferry. Half a mile upstream is a weir and Severn Navigation **lock** with a **lock cottage** (SO881328).

FRAMILODE

The point where the **Stroudwater Canal** reached the Severn at Upper Framilode has now been filled in, but an attractive stretch of the canal survives 50 yds from the River wall, with a neat range of **lengthmen's cottages** (SO752103) and a **brick shed** in a field alongside what was the entrance basin and was probably a warehouse (SO751105).

FRAMPTON-ON-SEVERN

This spacious village with its long Green has two **swing bridges** with **lodges** over the Gloucester and Sharpness Canal (**Canal Bridge** SO746085; **Splatt Bridge** SO743067). **Fromesbridge Mill** (SO769073), used for fulling and for wire making, is now a corn mill: it is a brick building with slate roof, two storeys plus attic, with a chimney at the east end and a large detached metal breast wheel with rim-drive to the south of the building; there are a large number of copper-slag blocks in the walls of the site.

FRAMPTON MANSELL

A small village standing high above the Golden Valley, on the south side, close to the spot where the GWR main line from Swindon to Gloucester emerged into the valley from its tunnel. The railway is carried between the road and the derelict Thames & Severn Canal in the foot of the valley along a brick viaduct.

FROCESTER

Although close to Stroud, Frocester is firmly in the Vale. Its main feature of interest is a large **tithe barn** (SO788030). There is also a **turnpike house** (SO788028).

GLOUCESTER

Gloucester gives the impression of a town that has had the stuffing knocked out of it by modern development, with nothing of distinction to replace what has been destroyed. With a population of over 90,000 it is a substantial county town, but except for the Cathedral and a few elegant half-timbered buildings like the New Inn in Northgate, there is little of interest in the centre of the city. The Cathedral itself in an instructive structure, with a Norman nave developing into Decorated and Perpendicular styles, with what purports to be the largest window in Europe in its east window, and with very early fan vaulting in its cloisters, which also contain a stone trough for the ablutions of the monastic community when it was an abbey church. The gracefulness of the Cathedral Close has been marred by turning it into a car park. For the industrial archaeologist, by far the most important feature of Gloucester is its complex of **docks and warehouses**. The site of the city seems to have been attractive since Roman times on account of its possibilities as a port, at a point near the head of the tidal Severn, where it was convenient for trans-shipment between sea and river traffic, and where it was possible to build a bridge on the route into Wales. The Romans consequently established their city of Glevum here, although nothing remains of this except the basic street pattern. It became an important port, market town and administrative centre in the Middle Ages: it was at his court in Gloucester in December 1085 that William the Conqueror issued the instructions which led to the compilation of Domesday Book in the following year. But as a port Gloucester steadily lost ground to Bristol, which enjoyed a greater command of the Severn Channel and thus easier access to South Wales. The port of Gloucester also suffered from silting problems, but for several centuries reasonably satisfactory wharfage was provided along the street still known as **The Quay** (note the series of small bollards on the water front) and the **Old Custom House**, an 18th century building, survives from this period (SO827187).

A new deal began for the port of Gloucester with the passing of the Act for the **Gloucester and Berkeley Canal** in 1793. The 16 miles of this wide ship canal were not completed until 1827 when, on the advice of Thomas Telford, it terminated at Sharpness rather than Berkeley. The **new dock basin** (*Plate 23*) in Gloucester, however, was completed in 1810. The **inner basin**, or Victoria Dock, was added in 1848, and most of the large dock warehouses were constructed in the first half of the 19th century. Most of them are five- or six-storey brick buildings. The pleasing harmony of their style has been recognized by the DOE in giving a 'group listing' to the whole complex. Sadly, however, such legal protection does not prevent a building from falling down through ill-use or non-use, and the oldest of the Gloucester Dock buildings, the **North Warehouse**, is already in such a serious state of dilapidation that permission is being sought to demolish it. With little prospect of the trade of the docks reviving substantially, it is likely that the whole group of buildings will require attention before long.

The Gloucester Docks are, for the time being, still in business, so that it is not possible to wander at will around the wharfs and warehouses. However, there are several vantage points from which the main features can be clearly seen. From the Llanthony Road Bridge it is possible to see into the main dock basin, and also along the canal as it approaches the city with the Pillar Warehouse of 1836, one of two which could accommodate a train for loading under its balustrade, on the left. From the opposite end of the main dock a view can be gained alongside the lock linking the dock with the River Severn, and this point is close to the North Warehouse. The Victoria Basin can be seen from the docks entrance on Southgate Street, where the **weighbridge house** is also worth a glance. Other features in the dock complex include two dry docks, a Dock Office of about 1830; a custom house, various bollards, and the Priday or City Flour Mills,

23 Gloucester – The New Dock Basin

built in the mid 19th century and still in business. The Mariner's Chapel of 1849 also has a certain curiosity interest.

Gloucester has had a long industrial history apart from its port facilities. The city was traditionally an important centre for the iron industry, but most of the foundries have now disappeared. Pin making flourished until the 19th century, but declined rapidly in competition with the new mechanical techniques which were adopted in Birmingham and elsewhere. The bell-foundry owned by the Rudhall family was one of the most famous in the country between 1684 and its closure in 1830. The city also had long-standing links with the woollen cloth industry, being the home of many clothiers and mercers (traders in fine quality textiles) and their families. Little, however, remains to be seen of all these processes, although the **Folk Museum** in Bishop Hooper's Lodging on Westgate contains an interesting collection of tools, artefacts, and portraits, and was itself used in part as a pin factory during the height of the prosperity of that industry. Amongst surviving industries, the **Gloucester Carriage and Wagon Works** in Bristol Road have preserved a coach which they made for

the Metropolitan & District Railway 50 years ago (it can be glimpsed behind a wall alongside the main road). Industry tended to develop between the Bristol Road and the canal, and trade from the latter stimulated growth of saw mills and Morelands match factory. Just outside town, to the west, Telford's masonry masterpiece of **Over Bridge** (*Plate 24*), opened in 1831, and has been preserved although it has been isolated by the provision of a new bridge, from which its elegant chamfered arch can be admired (SO816196).

GREAT RISSINGTON

A neat Cotswold village standing above the wide valley of the River Windrush. The **Old Forge** (SP200175) is a very handsome adaptation into a dwelling house.

HARTPURY

A scattered village on the A417 between Gloucester and Staunton. The church is 1½ miles away with a monumental and now (Spring 1978) sadly ruinous **tithe barn**. Nearby, on a leat off the River Leadon, is a

24 Gloucester – Over Bridge

small brick **mill** with an external iron-frame undershot waterwheel, now derelict (SO778236) (also known as Highleadon Mill).

HEWELSFIELD

This tiny village is up on the west rim of the Forest of Dean, but its parish stretches down to the River Wye and includes **Brockweir,** where there is an undistinguished girder **bridge** on two sets of iron columns with a small masonry **wharf** just upstream (SO539011). There is also an old **malthouse,** a quaint sandstone cottage, now a pottery.

HORSLEY

Horsley is a mile south of Nailsworth, in the most southerly of the deep valleys which converge at that township. There are several cloth-mill sites on the stream between Horsley and Nailsworth. None is very distinguished, but they include: **Lock's Mill** (ST848994), **Millbottom Mill** (ST846990) – a two-storey building in stone with roof of corrugated iron – and **Lower Horsley Mill** (ST845986) – a two-storey building in stone with a 'weaver's window' in the attic, and associated buildings.

HUNTLEY

On the A40 from Gloucester to Ross-on-Wye, this village is on the east edge of the Forest of Dean. At the junction of the A4136 to Mitcheldean there is a well-preserved **toll house** (SO718194), of standard design but with some later additional building at the rear.

INGLESHAM

Strictly speaking, the small hamlet of Inglesham (although it does possess a church) is in Wiltshire, being on the south bank of the River Thames just before its confluence with the River Coln flowing down through Fairford. But on the north bank of the Thames, just before the two rivers join, is the point in Gloucestershire where the **Thames and Severn Canal** terminates with a lock into the River Thames (SU204988). It is marked by one of the distinctive **roundhouses** which are such a feature of this canal. Half a dozen survive, mostly ruinous, but this one at

Inglesham is incorporated into a private house and so is still lived in. The house is approached by a neat canal bridge over the entrance lock. The roundhouse is best seen from the footpath on the south bank of the Thames, which crosses the riverside meadows from Lechlade three-quarters of a mile away.

KEMBLE

The proprietors of the GWR had great difficulty and expense in appeasing the local landowner at Kemble House when they tried to bring their Cheltenham line through his property in the 1840s. They had to provide a **tunnel** (ST987970) to keep the railway out of sight of his house, and the nearest station was at **Thames Head** on the Tetbury road (ST981988), of which nothing remains. The present **Kemble Station** (ST985975) was built in 1882, a neat simple structure in Bath stone with cast-iron columns carrying a canopy on the two surviving platforms, an elegant water tower and a footbridge for passengers. Originally there were two additional platforms, for the branch lines which converged on the main line from Cirencester to the east and Tetbury to the west. These branches were closed in the 1960s, but their alignments are still clearly visible.

KING'S STANLEY

This is properly a village of the Vale, in the mouth of the Stroud valley of the River Frome, but it possesses in **Stanley Mill** (SO812043) one of the outstanding mill buildings in the country. The present mill was the result of a rebuilding in 1813, and the main five-storey block is unusual because it is built of brick rather than the traditional stone of the region. But it incorporates all the principles of fireproof mill construction, the interior showing elegant rows of cast-iron columns on each floor with traceried iron arches bearing the brick vaults of the floor above. It was designed to operate with five waterwheels, but steam power was introduced in the 1850s. The mill is approached through a court with ancillary buildings, also in brick, completing the mill complex. It is one of the few mills still manufacturing woollen cloth in the region.

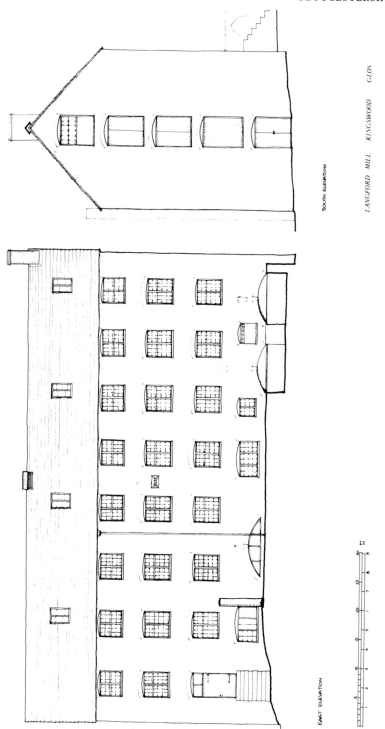

SOUTH ELEVATION

EAST ELEVATION

LANGFORD MILL   KINGSWOOD   GLOS

Figure 4   Gloucestershire: Kingswood. Langford Mill is fairly typical of the medium-sized Gloucestershire woollen cloth mills. It was built in 1822 and is now derelict. Drawn by Martin Watts.

KINGSWOOD

County reorganization in 1974 left Kingswood, a village on the Little River Avon 1½ miles south-west of Wotton-under-Edge, in a southerly salient of the County of Gloucestershire. This part of the county was once very active in the woollen cloth industry, and several significant mill sites remain. Working up-river, these include: **New Mills** (ST737930), a fine five-storey brick building with large mill pond and interesting ancillary buildings; **Langford Mill** (*Fig. 4*) (ST745923), also with five storeys, each having a loading door on the south side, and a date stone 1822; **Abbey Mill** (ST746922), rebuilt after a fire in 1889, undistinguished in stone and brick with a prominent Grecian water tank; **Walk Mill** (ST750919), a three-storey building now incorporated in a printing factory; and **Nind Mills** (ST754915), almost entirely demolished except for some small workshops. There is a quaint gothic **toll house** (ST741930) at the junction of the B4062 and B4050, now almost entirely covered in ivy.

LECHLADE

Almost the last of the Cotswold stone towns, Lechlade stands near the conjunction of the River Thames with the River Coln, and the point at which the Thames and Severn Canal joined the Thames Navigation at Inglesham (q.v., SU204988). The town turns its back on the river, with several small terraces running towards it from the main street, and the main road out of town to Swindon (A361) crosses the river on a narrow humped-back bridge, the **Halfpenny Bridge** (SU213993). This has a single wide stone arch across the river, with smaller arches for flood relief and a towpath. It dates from the 18th century, but the rather squat toll house at the north end was added later. There is a boat yard immediately to the west of the bridge. About a mile downstream, **St John's Bridge** carrying the A417 from Lechlade to Farringdon (SU223990), is much older in origin, dating from the 14th century at least. The 19th century rebuilding, however (Peter Cox, 1831 with subsequent modifications), is of no great interest, and the subsidiary arch over

25 Lechlade – Father Thames

the Thames Navigation lock has been inappropriately faced in blue engineering brick. Alongside this lock, incidentally (although strictly in Oxfordshire), is the statue of a reclining Father Thames carrying a spade (*Plate 25*) which until recently marked the source of the River Thames in a meadow near the village of Coates. It was moved to its present site so that it can be better looked after. **Lechlade Mill** (SU229997), some way out of town, is a substantial mill currently undergoing conversion into a house.

LECKHAMPTON

The large **quarries** (SO940180) are best approached from the B4070 road from Cheltenham to Birdlip: turn into the car park on Daisybank Road. They were active in the early 19th century, stimulated by the growth of Cheltenham, and continued in business until the 1920s, when some substantial limekilns were erected. But on the failure of this latter enterprise, the whole area was acquired as a public open space by Cheltenham Borough Council. The **Devil's Chimney** (SO947184) dates from 1800, and is a spectacular remnant of the earlier quarrying activity. The Gloucester & Cheltenham Railway was linked to the quarries by tramroads and inclined planes, flourishing from 1811 to 1861. The incline from Tramway Cottage can still be climbed with some stone sleepers in position.

LEONARD STANLEY

A mile downstream from Stanley Mill (see King's Stanley) is **Beard's Mill** (SO795049), the main part of which was demolished early in the present century, but a complex of lesser buildings, probably associated with the important dyeing processes carried out there, remain; they can best be viewed, however fleetingly, from trains on the main-line railway.

LITTLEDEAN

This village is named after the little 'dene' or valley which gave its name to the Norman earthwork, the Castle of Dene, and thence to the whole Forest of Dean. The eastern approach to the village from Westbury-on-Severn is dominated by the severe square stone building of the **prison** (SO674137), now a court house.

LOWER SLAUGHTER

The **watermill** (SP166207) is one of the best surviving in the county. Curiously, for such a typical Cotswold stone village, the mill itself is built of brick, and has a brick chimney attached. The wheel is of the high-breast variety, all metal construction, about 15 ft diameter. It is on a tributary stream of the River Dikler, and like the Windrush in Bourton-on-the-Water this runs through the village green, with small bridges over it.

LYDBROOK

The Lydbrook valley, running north towards the River Wye on the northern edge of the Forest of Dean, was the site of intense industrial activity in the 19th century, with heavy iron and tinplate works and a dramatic girder **viaduct** carrying the Forest of Dean tramroad across the mouth of the valley in Lower Lydbrook (SO596169). Only the abutments of the viaduct remain, and there are some indeterminant fragments of **wharf** on the River Wye (SO596170 and SO602169). Otherwise, the industrial sites have either been adapted to modern light engineering uses or have been cleared, so that the valley is rather disappointing to the industrial archaeologist.

LYDNEY

Lydney was an important outlet for the iron, coal, stone and timber traffic from the Forest of Dean. Its **harbour** is a canalization of the last mile of the river which flows down from Parkend to the River Severn, with a substantial tidal basin and entrance lock (SO650013). On the river-wall side above the tidal basin are the abutments of three staithes for loading coal from waggons into barges (or 'trows', as the sailing barges of the Severn estuary were called: the skeletons of several of these sturdy craft can be seen incorporated in the outer slopes of the river-wall at this point), and there were tramroads along both banks of the harbour. The harbour was continued up to Lydney as Pidcock's Canal. Apart from the harbour, there is not much to see in the town of Lydney, even though it was the southern terminus of the Roman road through the Forest of Dean, and has been developed as an important site by modern industrial units. Several small structures survive on the north side of the harbour, including Dock offices and limekilns. At **Cookson Terrace** (SO635018) there is a pleasant block of houses built by the Severn & Wye Railway in 1858 for its employees.

MAISEMORE

At an important bridge-point over the River Severn, even though the present **bridge** was completed as recently as 1956, being a single-arched concrete bridge with masonry facing (SO817210).

MORETON VALLANCE

Parkend Bridge (SO778108), one of the small swing-bridges over the Gloucester and Sharpness Canal, complete with its elegant lodge, is near this village.

MILKWALL

Typical of the scattered townships on the edge of the Forest of Dean, Milkwall is between Coleford and Bream. It contains the usual mixture of Forest industries – coal, iron and extensive quarries, the latter being particularly prominent in the steep valley down which the B4431 runs to Parkend (see, e.g. **Point Stone Quarry** at SO599084). The **Easter Iron Mine** site at Tufthorn (SO586093) is still in business as the British Colour & Mining Co with a medley of buildings including a small brick engine house. By far the most important industrial monument here, however, is the **Darkhill Iron Furnace** (*Plate 26*) (SO590088). It was here in 1819 that David Mushet, the pioneering metallurgist, established the business of making 'refined iron' which was carried on by him and his sons until 1847. The S&W railway, opened in 1875, obliterated the lower part of the site, but the rest, including the furnace itself, has been very impressively excavated, largely using job-creation labour. The site could well become a real industrial archaeological show-piece, possessing in addition to the remnant of the furnace, many ancillary buildings, an ore-crushing grindstone, and a tramroad with many sleeper-blocks *in situ*. Robert Mushet, the son of

26 Milkwall – Darkhill Iron Furnace

David, established a small experimental steel works, which became the *Titanic Iron & Steel Co*, on an adjacent site (SO588089). This closed in 1871, and the site was cleared in 1964 except for one small barn-like building with semi-circular gables.

MINCHINHAMPTON

A fine Cotswold village, almost a town, on the plateau between the Golden Valley and the Nailsworth valley, favoured by traditional clothiers and by latter-day commuters as a residential site. The industrial associations are mainly in the adjacent valleys, except for a certain amount of stone-mining carried on at **Balls Green Mines** (SO864955 and SO867995).

MITCHELDEAN

One of the townships on the northern edge of the Forest of Dean, this had the traditional industries of the Forest in its vicinity. **Wigpool Iron Mine** (SO652193) was a mile to the west, on Wigpool Common, an area intensively mined since Roman times, but little remains of interest. The engine house is now a dwelling.

MORETON-IN-MARSH

This extremely handsome Cotswold town, with its wide main street, has a quaint survival in its **curfew tower** (SP205324) in the north-east angle of the junction of the A44 from Oxford road with the Fosse Way. One and a half miles out of town on the Oxford road is another curious monument, the **Four Shire Stone** (SP231321), a rectangular plinth marking the conjunction of four counties (only three now that a detached part of Worcestershire has been assimilated by Gloucestershire, Warwickshire, and Oxfordshire).

NAILSWORTH

An important Cotswold township three miles south of Stroud where the main Nailsworth valley is joined by two tributary valleys of the Horsley and Newmarket brooks. Enclosed by steep hillsides, there was a concentration of mill sites in the narrow bottom of the valleys. Nailsworth was the **terminus** (SO848000) for the Midland Railway Dudbridge branch, and although the site has now been cleared a brick coal merchant's warehouse survives

27 Nailsworth – Dunkirk Mill

together with a Railway Hotel, and the alignment is clear enough. **Day's Mill** (ST850996) is in the centre of the town, with a shop front onto the main street, but is best approached from the coach station in the rear, from which the mill race can be seen. It is a compact three-storey building in Cotswold stone, with a brick extension. Although converted into a shop and showroom, there is stiil some hand-weaving done on the premises. Going down the main valley, **Egypt Mill** is on the northern edge of the town (SO848001). The mill pond has been drained so that the river now flows straight past the mill, but there are two openings on the impressive upstream face of this stone building for internal waterwheels, fragments of both wheels surviving. The main road is level with the upper floor of the mill, from which it can be entered at times when it is open to the public. There is a substantial clothier's house on the downstream side of the mill. **Dunkirk Mill** (*Plate 27*) (SO845005) is the next mill towards Stroud, and is one of the finest surviving specimens of a Cotswold cloth mill. Five storeys high, the long main block shows signs of having been extended and has a short wing at the south end. It is built in local stone with stone roofing throughout, and possesses an internal wheel pit (with fragments of a long mill pond stretching upstream almost as far as Nailsworth) and also an elegant chimney for the steam engine which was installed at a later stage. The mill is now fairly satisfactorily sub-let to various small industries. Going up the main valley from Nailsworth, there are mill sites at **Holcombe Mill** (ST859994), **Iron Mills** (ST863994) and **Longford's Mill** (ST867992). The latter is a particularly impressive complex of buildings, as the cloth mill is still in business and possesses a very large mill pond which enabled it to maintain its water supply for much longer during dry seasons than other mills in the district. This now forms a lake below the heavily wooded slopes of Gatcombe Park. In one of the tributary valleys there is a site at **Lot Mill** (ST841996). (See also entries under **Horsley**.) The town of Nailsworth itself is not of any great distinction, but it does have some interesting shop-fronts with cast-iron columns made in the local foundry of Daniels, and there are some curious shop-signs including a **padlock** for a hardware store and a **kettle** (ST851998) on a building which could have been a small forge.

NEWENT

A pleasant town, with brick and half-timbering predominating. Newent was the main settlement in the Vale of Leadon, and thus a market and transport centre. It had an iron industry in the 18th century, but this has disappeared. A modern bypass has interrupted the alignment of the Gloucester–Hereford railway, north of the town. This was opened in 1884, replacing the Herefordshire & Gloucestershire Canal, of which a good section complete with ruinous **lock, lock-keeper's cottage**, and **aqueduct** can still be seen at Oxenhall (SO712268). The canal was opened in 1796, and defunct by 1883.

NEWLAND

The fine parish church in this Forest of Dean village has been nicknamed The Cathedral of the Forest. It is worth a pilgrimage because, apart from its intrinsic elegance and charming setting, it possesses a unique monument – a small brass, only one foot long, depicting a **forest miner** holding a pick in one hand and a hod over his shoulder with the other, while a candlestick protrudes from his mouth. The figure is shown in relief, standing upon a helmet and with foliage around it. The neighbouring brasses are 15th-century, which suggests that we have here a contemporary pictorial representation of a medieval miner.

NEWNHAM

A pleasant town on a bluff overlooking the River Severn, Newnham stands astride the main A48 road from Gloucester to Chepstow. Mellow brick predominates in its buildings. There used to be a ferry, and fragments of **quay** survive (SO693115). There is a fine brick and timber **warehouse** (SO693118), dilapidated but incorporated into a house – the wall includes some black blocks which look like copper slag as found near brass works in the valley of the Bristol Avon. Newnham, however, does not appear to have had a brass industry, although glass was once manufactured in the village.

NIBLEY

Fragments of small mills can still be located in the narrow valleys of the Cotswold edge around Nibley. See, for instance, those at **Crowlbrook Mill** (ST745967).

NORTHLEACH

A typical Cotswold small town, standing just off the Fosse Way. The fine church reflects the prosperity of the wool and woollen cloth industries, and there is a house in the Market Place called the **Old Wool House** (SP113146). **The prison** (SP108149), now a police station, is a distinctive structure alongside the Fosse Way. It has a long stone frontage, incorporating a two-storey central block and two wing-buildings.

PAINSWICK

Painswick is an extremely well-groomed village of mellow stone buildings, many of them surviving from the days of its prosperity in the 17th and 18th centuries, when it was an important centre of the woollen cloth and

clothiers' industries. The growth of Stroud with the onset of rapid industrialization contributed to the relative stagnation of Painswick in the 19th century, and to its survival virtually intact into the present century. The picturesque church with its prominent spire, ornamental clockface, and avenues of clipped yew trees, still presides over the village, which is situated along a ridge separating two small but steep valleys – the Painswick Stream to the east and the Wash Brook to the west – which converge at its southern end, at King's Mill. The church dominates the northern end of the Painswick Valley which, funnelling out towards the south, allows glimpses of the spire to be seen from many places around Stroud. Amongst the many beautiful buildings of Painswick, few have specific industrial functions although many have associations with the woollen cloth industry and the packhorse routes which served it. There are thus several features of interest in the village itself, such as turnpike houses, roundhouses, and a brewery building, but by far the most significant industrial remains are those of the mills in the

28 Painswick – King's Mill

bottoms of the two valleys. **King's Mill** (*Plate 28*) (SO859089) is the most impressive of these sites. It drew its water supply from both the Painswick Stream and the Wash Brook, and parts of the water courses remain. There is a fine mill house with, at right angles to it, the remains of a mill building with long weavers' light windows. Following the Painswick Stream upstream from King's Mill, there are half a dozen distinct mill sites which may be readily identified: **Skinners Mill** on Stamages Lane (SO866091), now incorporated into a large farm building; **Painswick Mill** (SO868093), also known as Mason's Mill, on Knapp Lane, where the mill house survives as a listed building, and there is a mill pond with intact sluices, but no remaining mill; **Cap Mill** (SO869094), with a small mill incorporated into an elegant mill house; **Savory's Pin Mill** (SO871095) on Tibbiwell, also known as Brookhouse Mill, which has the distinction of being the only working mill remaining in Painswick, devoted now to manufacturing hairpins and

paper clips but once a cloth mill, with two low ranges of buildings and associated structures; and **Damsell's Mill**, a mile north of Painswick (SO877111), described by Dr Tann as 'one of the best small mills in Gloucestershire' but now converted into a house. On the Wash Brook, going upstream from King's Mill, there are mill sites at **Washbrook Mill** (SO857095) and **Little Mill** (SO858097), but the industrial remains at both are negligible.

PARKEND

The fine **blowing engine house** (*Plate 29*) (SO614082) in the middle of this village is externally complete, although it has been successfully adapted for other uses. Parkend occupies a clearing in the centre of the Forest of Dean, and was once the site of collieries, iron works, and a network of railways. Parts of the track of the latter survive being used by the **Dean Light Railway Society**. This had its headquarters at Parkend until moving them recently to Lydney.

29   Parkend – Blowing Engine House

PITCHCOMBE

Half way between Stroud and Painswick, Pitchcombe has two mill sites on the Painswick Brook: that of **Pitchcombe Mill** (SO852075), which has been demolished, and **Smalls Mill** (SO855083), where two storeys of the old mill remain, although in poor condition.

PURTON (EAST)

There is a **swing-bridge** with lodge (SO691042) over the Gloucester & Sharpness Canal here, giving access to the tow-path on the west bank of the canal and to the river wall consolidated with old Severn trows and other vessels which has led to Purton being called 'the graveyard of the trows'.

PURTON (WEST)

Near the north end of the Sharpness Railway Bridge, now disappeared, a section of masonry **quay** remains (SO671045), served by the Forest of Dean Tramroad, the alignment of which can still be traced down the valley, including a three-arch **masonry viaduct** (SO670049).

QUEDGELEY

This south-west suburb of Gloucester has three **swing-bridges** over the Gloucester & Sharpness Canal, all complete with graceful lodges (SO805150: SO798135: and SO790126). There is another (SO809155) without a lodge.

REDBROOK

There are two distinct sites here, in Lower and Upper Redbrook respectively, both having been associated with the 18th century development of the copper and brass industries. The **Lower Redbrook mill** (SO538097) has been re-used as a modern paper mill, so it is virtually impossible to explore the site. But the old mill house can be seen from the road, and copper slag blocks abound in neighbouring buildings. **Upper Redbrook** is a more rewarding site, as a road runs up it towards Coleford, passing under a steeply raked **bridge** (SO536103) by which a tramroad descended to a yard across the valley, and on to Lower Redbrook. The road climbs past a motley collection of buildings – including a mill, a malting and a brewery – as well as several ponds acting as reservoirs for the industries in the valley. The tramroad follows the line of the road, crossing a connecting road by a high stone and brick **arch bridge** (SO545108).

RODBOROUGH

On the north limb of Rodborough Hill, this village drops into Stroud. At **Butterow toll house** (*Plate 30*) (SO856040) it possesses one of the best preserved structures of this type in the county, and the only one with its toll-board intact.

RYEFORD

Adjacent to Stanley Mill (See King's Stanley), **Ryeford Mill** (SO815045) is much less impressive, but two sets of single-storey brick buildings remain alongside the Stroud-water Canal. The Dudbridge Branch of the Midland Railway had a **station** here (SO814046) and the alignment of the track can still be seen.

ST BRIAVELS

The 12th-century castle was the home of the constable who administered the Forest of Dean, the Free Miners of which were traditionally residents of the Hundred of St Briavels. The main industrial archaeological interest, however, is in the Wye Valley, where the **Bigsweir Bridge** (SO539051) carries the main A466 road across the river by an elegant single iron span. The bridge is a simple, unornamented design, with a toll booth, now derelict, on the Monmouthshire side.

SAPPERTON

This pleasant Cotswold village has given its name to the two-mile tunnel on the summit level of the Thames & Severn Canal, but its closest association with the tunnel is the **west portal** (SO943033), which is situated some little way below the village, in the bottom of the Golden Valley. The portal is more functional and gloomy than that at the east end (see Coates), but it is still impressive. There is a ruined cottage by the tow-path near the entrance. Follow the tow-path away

30   Rodborough – Butterow Toll house

from the tunnel, and you shortly arrive at the **Daneway Inn** (SO939035), a hostelry which provided refreshment for the bargees in the days when the canal carried traffic. (For other details of the canal tunnel see the entry for Coates.)

SAUL

Near Frampton-on-Severn, the main interest of this village to the industrial archaeologist is the **canal crossing** (SO758094), where the Stroudwater Canal and the Gloucester & Sharpness Canal intersect. A stretch of the former is still open for moorings east of the intersection, which is best approached on foot from the Whitminster House end. There is a **lock-keeper's cottage** at the junction and a drydock. To the south, on the ship canal, there is a **swing-bridge** (SO754090) with a small warehouse and modern grain storage facility.

SELSLEY

The village of Selsley straggles up both sides of the open-topped hill of Selsley Common. In the 19th century it was a mixture of a farming community and a home for workers at the mills in Dudbridge, Cainscross, and Ebley. The Marling family, owners of several of these mills, built themselves a mansion in the village, next door to the **parish church** (SO829038) which they had built on a Swiss style and embellished with Pre-Raphaelite stained glass. Selsley Common was quarried for lime, and the remains of a **limekiln** (SO832037) can be seen, having been converted to a cow-shed.

SHARPNESS

Sharpness Docks are still operating as a busy port for Gloucester and the Midlands. The **old entrance** to the Gloucester & Sharpness Canal (SO670030) gives access to the docks from the north, but the main **modern entrance** (SO668022) is at the south end of the main dock. The docks contain some substantial warehouses; the remains of several coal-drops of various vintages; road and railway bridges, both fixed and swinging; and some housing for dock workers. Just up the line of the canal to the north is the

abutment (SO678033) with the swinging section which is all that remains of the great **Severn Railway Bridge**, with its repetition of bow-girder sections.

SHERBORNE

One of the Windrush villages (although strictly on a tributory stream, the Sherborne Brook) Sherborne is a well-organized village with a large estate farm and several groups of **labourers' cottages** built in a uniform Cotswold style (SP175145 etc).

SIDDINGTON

This village, a mile south of Cirencester, has a prominent **windmill tower** (SU042996) converted into a residence with a castellated turret. It also marks the junction of the Thames & Severn Canal with the short branch which went northwards into Cirencester, with a **canal basin** (SU030996) at the junction and an overgrown derelict lock immediately east of the basin and a **canal bridge** still in use over it.

SLAD

In a rural valley three miles north-east of Stroud, there were several cloth mill sites on the river below Slad, the largest being **Lower Steanbridge Mill** (SO875077), of which the ponds remain, and **Steanbridge Mill** (SO879078), converted into a house. A mile lower down the valley, the site of **Vatch Mill** (SO872066) is still visible, although now occupied by a house.

SLIMBRIDGE

The graceful spire of Slimbridge Church can be seen from many points in the Vale. The road to the Wildfowl Trust Estate in the New Grounds alongside the River Severn crosses the Gloucester & Sharpness Canal by a **swing-bridge** at Shepherd's Patch (SO729042), and there is another **swing-bridge** with lodge at Ryall's Farm (SO738050).

SOUDLEY

Soudley is a double-village, with Upper and Lower parts in the steep valley between

Cinderford and Blakeney, separated by a bend in the river and a tributary stream filling a pond near Foundry Wood. There are several small industrial sites here, but the most interesting are those concerned with the alignments of the Forest of Dean Tramroad, opened in 1809 to give an outlet from Cinderford to Bullo Pill. It was constructed as a plateway, but relaid as a broad gauge railway in 1854 and again as a standard gauge railway in 1872. The line was closed in 1969, and the two **tunnels** (SO663104–SO665103 and SO666102–SO676099 – the Haie Tunnel) have been bricked up.

SOUTH CERNEY

A pretty village on the River Churn, three miles south of Cirencester. Now in danger of being overwhelmed by the huge gravel pits being worked in the vicinity, and exploited for recreational purposes. Fragments of the railway alignment from Swindon to Cirencester can still be seen. At **Cerney Wick**, 1½ miles south-east, there is a **roundhouse** (SU079960) alongside the derelict Thames & Severn Canal: it is well preserved and inhabited (like the Chalford roundhouse, it has a conical roof: the other three surviving

towers had a sunken roof to catch the rainwater), but it is just on the Wiltshire side of the river.

STAUNTON

The main historical interest of this village in the Vale of Leadon is its association with the Chartists in the 1840s, because it was chosen by Fergus O'Connor as the site of one of his experiments in utopian rural communities. About **30 cottages** (*Plate 31*) survive, in their separate small-holdings. Although many of them have been much modified in appearance the uniform basic design is apparent. The Chartist School, now the **Prince of Wales Inn**, is at Snig's End in the adjoining parish of Corse (SO792290).

STINCHCOMBE

Stinchcombe Hill juts out into the Vale from the Cotswold edge, and the small village of the same name is on the west shoulder of the hill. There is an **agricultural weighbridge** near the entrance to Stancombe Park (ST738974): the cast-iron platform bears the makers' name of Bartlett & Son Bristol.

31   Staunton – A typical cottage of the Chartist settlement

STONE

Woodford Mill (ST688956) is on the Little River Avon in the valley near the A38 road at Stone. It is a brick building, with its metal undershot wheel intact and also some equipment.

STONEHOUSE

Stonehouse is a large village at the entrance to the Stroud valley of the River Frome. The main railway (GWR and Midland) passes on its west side, with branches going off to Stroud and Paddington on the north side of the valley, and to Nailsworth (the Midland Railway Dudbridge branch) to the south. The latter has now been closed and the track lifted. The I.K. Brunel **station** (SO799053) on the main line has also been demolished. There are several significant mill sites in the village, including: **Bond's Mill** (SO793053), a cloth mill now converted to other uses; **Lower Mill** (SO801406), with a late 19th century three-storey brick building surviving of a larger complex; and **Upper Mill** (SO806047), a brick four-storey building with loft chimney, and ornate tower. The **clay pits** of the Imperial Brick & Tile Works (SO817049) are now disused, the chimney having been recently felled.

STOW-ON-THE-WOLD

A distinguished Cotswold town alongside the Fosse Way. It has the usual clutch of old forges and workshops, mostly converted into houses. Outside the town itself, two features deserve a mention. **Donnington Brewery** (SP173278) is a traditional country brewery with an elegant complex of stone buildings snuggled in a valley. It has waterwheels which are occasionally used. **Martin's Hill Mill** (SP212255) is the ruinous stone tower and adjacent buildings of a windmill.

STROUD

This town (population: 19,600) stands near the convergence of four of the most important rivers in the history of the Cotswold woollen cloth industry. These are, in order of importance, the River Frome, flowing down the Golden Valley (so-named on account of its industrial prosperity) from the east, the Nailsworth stream from the south, and the

Painswick and Slad streams from the north. None of these are large rivers, but they are strong and reliable and provided an excellent supply of water power for the many small and occasional medium-sized mills which proliferated at regular intervals along their banks. Although several of these mills served other purposes, most of them were involved at some stage of their existence with cloth making. Many of them have subsequently been converted to modern industrial uses in engineering, chemicals, furnishing etc (including piano making), while others have virtually disappeared even though the adjacent mill house has sometimes survived to become a desirable modern residence. After converging, the Stroud rivers flow westwards towards the Severn, and it is on the three-mile stretch below the town that the largest of the Stroud mills are to be found.

The effect of this concentration of industry along the rivers in steeply-sided valleys on the urban development of Stroud has been to give the built-up area a spider-like pattern of distribution, although the settlement has increasingly tended to climb the hillsides and the ridges between the valleys. Except for the occasional clothiers' houses, most of the urban building is fairly nondescript, but the prevalence of local Cotswold stone in construction gives even the drabbest architecture a pleasing quality. The town of Stroud itself has little character for the most part, but there is an urban core centred on the Subscription Rooms in George Street, with the adjacent Congregational Chapel in Bedford Street and the renovated Baptist Chapel on John Street nearby, which is worth more than a casual glance. The chapels signify the dominance of nonconformity in the industrial traditions of the town: an interesting variant on the more typical 'wool churches' of the Cotswold towns. The Parish Church is of no special distinction. This and the Town Hall are on Church Street. Below them, on Lansdown Street, is the intriguing 19th century building which now houses the Museum and Art School. It carries a fresco with the heads of Victorian Worthies (Faraday, Huxley, etc but no engineers) and drain-pipes bearing the date 1890. The Stroudwater Canal was completed to the town in 1779, and the **Wallbridge Wharf** (SO849050) is still identifiable, although a modern structure has been built along its

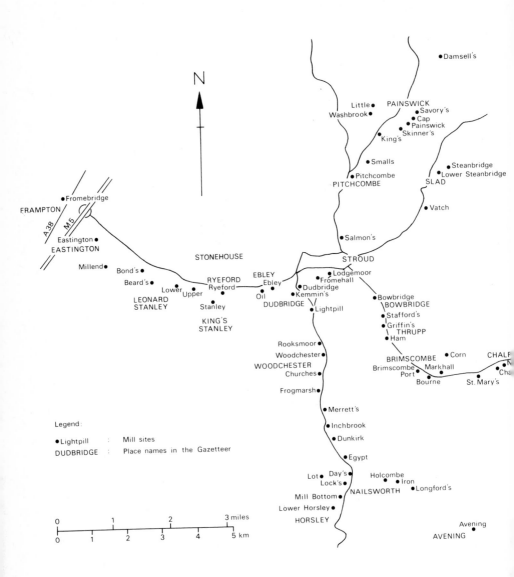

5   Gloucestershire: Stroud valley mills

northern edge and the lock below the wharf is derelict. To the east of the wharf, the Thames and Severn Canal commences, running up the Golden Valley through Brimscombe and Chalford to the tunnel at Sapperton. The railway came early to Stroud, as it is on the main GWR line from Swindon to Gloucester, completed in 1847. **Stroud Station**, however, is a very modest and undistinguished building. An engineering-brick viaduct carries the line away from the station over the valley of the Painswick stream. The Midland Railway brought a branch – the Dudbridge and Stonehouse – towards the town, but this turned away southwards to Nailsworth, and was linked to the GWR at Stroud only by a rather tortuous track which has now disappeared – as, indeed, has the line from Stonehouse to Nailsworth, even though much of the alignment can still be followed. Adjacent to the railway station in the centre of Stroud is a substantial square six-storey building which houses **Hill, Paul & Co Ltd**,

wholesale clothiers (SO849050). The firm is still in business, and the building is prominent, if not particularly graceful. Variously coloured brick has been used for decorative effect, and the main entrance has a stone portico around it. Below this factory, on the main road at Rowcroft and built into the southern wall of the railway embankment are the remains of a derelict **public weighbridge** (SO849051).

It is difficult to draw a line between the mills which fall in Stroud and those which belong to neighbouring villages for which we have separate entries. The principal Stroud site, however, is undoubtedly that of **Lodgemoor Mills** (SO845050), which is still in business under the name of Strachan & Co. Again, the use of brick for constructional and decorative purposes is well displayed in the new building of 1875 which resembles that of the Hill, Paul & Co factory. The older buildings of the Lodgemoor site are of Cotswold stone. The complex is quite

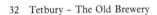

32 Tetbury – The Old Brewery

extensive and includes an office block, cottages, a dilapidated stone bridge over the River Frome and a swing-bridge (now fixed) over the Stroudwater Canal. There is a fine clothier's house and a mill pond between Lodgemoor and **Fromehall Mill** (SO842049) which is a four-storey, eight-bay stone building, now adapted as offices. The remains of **Stroud Gasworks** are nearby. At **Lightpill Mill** (SO839039) there is an elegant stone mill in the traditional style with a graceful chimney and a clock tower, incorporated in a modern chemical factory as part of BP Chemicals. **Godsell's Brewery** (SO848059) is an extensive brick building, including maltings, and incorporating the site of Salmon's Mill. (See also: Ebley, King's Stanley, Dudbridge, Woodchester, Nailsworth, Thrupp, Brimscombe, Slad, Painswick, Pitchcombe.)

TALLY HO

On the A436 road from Andoversford to Stow, at Foxhill Inn, is the overgrown quarry of Tally Ho (SP094232), which flourished in the early 19th century. It had a particular line in stone piping for water works, and pieces of piping have been incorporated in neighbouring walls.

TEDDINGTON

A remarkable and elegant fingerpost, **Teddington Hands** (SO963339), stands at the crossing of the A438 and A435 roads.

TETBURY

A pleasant Cotswold township. The market hall in the centre has associations with the woollen cloth industry. The principal industrial monument is the neat small **town brewery** (*Plate 32*) (ST887935) with engine house and chimney stack, now beginning to look rather dilapidated and used as a laundry. The words 'Tetbury Brewery. Established 1800' are carved in stone high on the wall. The only other industrial feature of any significance is the **engine shed** (ST893932)

33 Tewkesbury – Abbey Mill

in blue engineering brick which is all that remains of the terminus of the single track branch of the railway from Kemble junction. This branch was closed under the Beeching axe, but much of its alignment is still clear, where it runs close beside the Tetbury to Cirencester road (A429).

TEWKESBURY

A thriving market town on the northern edge of Gloucestershire, Tewkesbury was once an important inland port at the conjunction of the Stratford Avon with the River Severn. The town retains a strong historical character, with many half-timbered buildings dating from the 15th and 16th centuries, and an attractive maze of alleys and courts between the main roads and the River Avon on the west side and the Swillgate stream on the other. The Swillgate ran through the grounds of the once extensive Abbey, of which only the fine Norman Abbey Church remains. This contains memorials to some of the leading figures in the Wars of the Roses who were involved in the Battle of Tewkesbury in 1471. The church has little of direct industrial significance, but note the large Gurney Patent coal stoves installed by the London Heating and Ventilating Company, and the wrought-iron gates to the churchyard. The terrace of medieval town cottages adjacent to the church has been handsomely restored by the National Trust. The town was a prosperous centre of the hosiery trade, tanning, and several other industries, of which a few relics survive. The 18th-century cottages in St Mary's Lane, restored by the Civic Trust, were associated with the hosiery industry. The wide first-floor windows were designed to give the best possible light to the stocking-frame knitters. **Abbey Mill** (*Plate 33*) is close to the Abbey Church (SO889326), standing on the Mill Avon, the old course of the Avon which runs parallel to the High Street and Church Street. The two external undershot waterwheels survive, and there are races for the two other wheels. Externally, the mill has been nicely restored, but the interior has been converted into a restaurant. Like the Bell Inn nearby, the Abbey Mill features in the popular Victorian novel extolling the virtue of self-improvement, Mrs Craik's *John Halifax, Gentleman*, published in 1857. There is a monument to the authoress in the Abbey

Church. **Borough Mill** (SO892330) consists of two large brick buildings constructed in the second half of the 19th century (1850s and 1889 respectively), on the site of an older mill. It is still in business as a corn mill. It stands across the Mill Avon on the flat island called Severn Ham, being linked with the Old Quay by **Quay Bridge**. This cast-iron arch bridge has been spoilt by an extension on the south side, but is still intact. Opposite it on the Quay is the old brewery, still showing the name of Bizard and Colman who acquired the premises in 1864, and an interesting terracotta motif of a hand holding a sheaf of corn. This stretch of the east bank of the Mill Avon contains several old buildings, including a tannery and a malting, which have been converted to modern uses. Just north of Borough Mills, a lock connects the Mill Avon with the main river, linking the Severn with the Warwickshire Avon Navigation which, through the Stratford Canal, now gives access to Stratford. **King John's Bridge** (SO894332), a stone arched bridge, carries the A38 over the Old Avon and the Mill Avon. Parts of it date from 1205, but it has been substantially rebuilt. The Olde Bear Inn at the townward end of the bridge claims to be the oldest inn in the country. The black bear which it represents was the symbol of Warwick the medieval 'Kingmaker'. **The Mythe Bridge** (SO889337) is half a mile out of town, on the A438 where this crosses the River Severn. Designed by Telford and made out of cast-iron parts manufactured by Hazledine from Shropshire, it was built in 1827 and strengthened in 1923. It has a quaint gothic-style toll house at its eastern end.

THRUPP

Being in the Golden Valley between Stroud and Chalford, this village has a number of significant mill sites, including **Stafford's Mill** (SO859038) with some three-storey stone and brick buildings now engaged in the manufacture of paints; **Griffin's Mill** (SO859035), a three-storey brick building of the late 19th century with an iron bridge over the Thames & Severn Canal; and **Ham Mill** (SO861032), a stone building with a white-washed clothier's house nearby, now making carpets; there is a stone dated 1867 in the wall.

TINTERN

Although on the Monmouthshire side of the River Wye, Tintern was closely connected with the development of the copper and brass industries in the valley, and elsewhere in Gloucestershire and Avon. A **plaque** in the Abbey Car Park (SO533000) marks the site of an early brass works.

TIRLEY

On the west bank of the River Severn north of Gloucester, Tirley possessed a Severn Navigation **wharf** (SO845278), with adjacent inns. The present **Haw Bridge** which crosses the river at this point is an elegant modern structure.

TREDINGTON

On the main railway line north of Cheltenham, there is a **level crossing** with a two-storey brick keeper's lodge (SO926300).

TUTSHILL

Chepstow Bridge (*Plate 34*) (ST536943) over the River Wye between this Gloucestershire village and Chepstow, was opened in 1816. It was built by John Rastrick of Bridgnorth, on some preliminary advice from John Rennie. It is one of the most impressive surviving cast-iron bridges, with five spans totalling 320 ft, the largest being 112 ft wide. The bridge still carries its original lamp brackets.

ULEY

Uley is a tidy village strung out along the B4066 road from Dursley to Stroud. Little of industrial archaeological interest can be seen from the road, but this enclosed valley of the River Ewelme was the scene of intense industrial activity in the 17th and 18th centuries as the place where Uley blue cloth was manufactured, and if the valley is explored on foot several mill sites can still be identified. These include **Eyles Mill**

34 Tutshill – Chepstow Bridge over River Wye

(ST773980), a small two-storey building erected near his house, now Wresden Farm, by John Eyles, who introduced the distinctive 'Spanish cloth' to the district. The mill, reputed to be 'one of the oldest in Gloucestershire' (Tann p. 132), is fed by springs on the north side of the valley; **Rockstowes Mill** (ST777976), where two stone three-storey buildings survive, now houses; **Marsh Mill** (ST784977), which became a saw mill and is now largely ruinous and overgrown although the mill house has been pleasantly restored; **Dauncey's Mill** (ST787980), a small mill attractively converted into a house, with an internal 12 ft diameter breast wheel driving to a saw mill in the last phase of its operation. The mill probably began as a fulling mill, and the pond survives, with the ruins of a circular 'wool stove' on the north side; and **Sheppard's Mill** (ST794984), with a few buildings surviving from what was in the 1830s a large mill complex.

WINCHCOMBE

This attractive Cotswold town was once an important centre of the wool industry, with Hailes Abbey and Sudeley Castle nearby. For a short time in the 12th century it was a county town in its own right, before being merged into Gloucestershire. An ancient **saltway** – Salter's Lane climbs up Salter's Hill east of the town (SP048288). To the west, **Postlip Mill** (SP009271) is an old mill site, occupied now by a modern paper mill, but with fragments of old walls and gables surviving. There is a small **tannery** (SP027284) near one of the entrances to Sudeley Castle, with louvred sides to facilitate drying the skins. There were vineyards near the town in the Middle Ages, and in the 17th century the district became an important centre for growing tobacco until this was forcibly terminated by the opposition of tobacco-growing interests in the American colonies.

WOODCHESTER

Woodchester is in the valley running south from Stroud, half way between Stroud and Nailsworth. The village is on the west side of the valley, and possesses a famous **Roman villa site** (SO839031) in its churchyard. There is also a string of important mill sites along the bottom of the valley: **Rooksmoor Mill** (SO842031), little remains of the 19th-century flock mill, but furniture is now made here and there is an attractive sale room open to the public; **Woodchester Mill** (SO844028), an interesting complex of 19th-century buildings, now a piano factory; **Churches Mill** (SO843023), a two-storey building of brick and stone with two undershot wheels; **Frogmarsh Mill** (SO841018), a 19th-century three-storey stone building with, nearby, a distinctive circular tower variously described as a 'teazle tower' and a 'drying tower' (Tann p. 227 chooses the latter); **Merrett's Mill** (also 'Haycock's' and 'Grist's') (SO843014), the late 19th-century brick building having recently lost its graceful chimney, conceals older mill buildings not easily seen from the road; and **Inchbrook Mill** (SO844009), with a two-storey stone block now converted to houses.

WOTTON-UNDER-EDGE

Wotton is a pleasant old Cotswold town, on the west edge of the hills, and quite separate from the other cloth manufacturing centres of Stroud and Dursley. It has attractive shopping streets, with a **Jubilee clock** erected in 1897. At the lower end of the town are a series of small mill sites, most of them related to the water power available from the Tyles Bottom stream, but some of them probably having no inanimate source of power and being barely removed from the stage of domestic manufacture. **Waterloo Mill** (ST759932), probably built in 1815, had a steam engine but has now been converted into houses. **Old Town Mill** (ST757935) also depended mainly on steam power; it is a three-storey stone building with stone roof. There are other sites up the Tyley Bottom such as **Combe Mill** and dyehouse (ST770939).

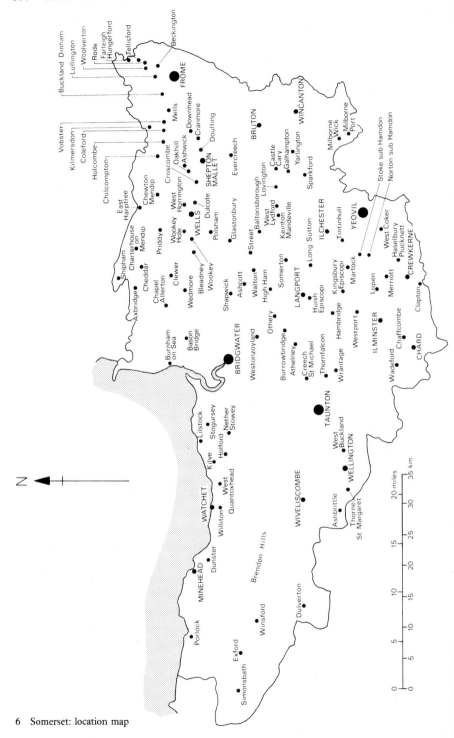

6 Somerset: location map

Somerset

Somerset is a county of contrasting scenery. To the north and north-west it is bounded by the Bristol Channel which has one of the highest tidal ranges in the world. This has always produced navigational problems for such ports as Watchet, Minehead and Bridgwater. It has also posed a permanent threat of flooding along the coast between the Parrett estuary and Brean Down when spring tides and westerly gales act in concert. The Romans built a protective wall against such an event but subsequent generations have struggled with the problem of draining the central plain of Somerset which stretches away to the east and south.

This vast area is drained naturally by the River Parrett and its tributaries, the River Brue and the River Axe. In each case the gradient is slight and they have all been substantially altered by drainage schemes developed since the Middle Ages. For part of their course they each run through beds of peat which function like sponges – soaking up the water in the wetter seasons and drying and shrinking in the rarer periods of drought. Although these peat moors are better drained today then ever before, winter flooding is still commonplace. The wholesale extraction of the peat for horticultural purposes is not helping the drainage function and planners are already anticipating that a Norfolk Broads-type environment will develop before the end of the century.

The low moors are split up by the Polden Hills and several lias 'islands' such as those of Wedmore and High Ham. The most famous of these must be Glastonbury Tor. These slightly elevated and dryer lands have provided the basic needs for cultivation and settlement for the majority of people who inhabit this part of the county.

To the north, the Mendips provide a sharp contrast in scenery. The carboniferous limestone, with its bleak but well drained upland, predominates, although the old red sandstone cap of Blackdown in the west and the igneous intrusions and adjacent coalfields to the east offer more variety. The whole Mendip region has witnessed intense industrial activity in the form of quarrying and mining. Although all mining activity has now ceased it is more than compensated for by the quarrying which is literally removing the Mendip hills. Most of the settlement in this region is to be found in the valleys, such as that which runs west–east from Nettlebridge, or on the lower slopes of the hills, where communities can benefit from the best that the high and low moors can offer.

To the east the low moors give way to the oolitic hills which form a geological link with the north west of Wiltshire and South Gloucestershire. A number of Iron Age forts top these hills – the most famous being South Cadbury – which suggests that the region once had some strategic significance. Today the area supports a mixture of arable and pasture farming. Apart from Frome, which forms part of the industrial area centred on Trowbridge, the area is thinly populated and the old settlements of Bruton, Castle Cary and Wincanton have not developed in recent years at the same rate as those in the central part of the county.

Somerset's borders with Dorset and Devon to the south are once more marked by the higher land of the oolitic limestone. Deep cuttings through this yellow stone are characteristic of the roads in the Yeovil and Sherborne area. In the south-west the Blackdown Hills mark the reappearance of the old red sandstone and form part of the boundary with Devon between Chard and Wellington. From this point the county boundary swings north and west across the wildest part of Exmoor to the coast. Again, human settlement has spurned the high moors and is concentrated in the narrow valleys. Dulverton is a prime example of this tendency and is beautifully sited on the banks of the Barle encircled by hills.

Exmoor and its extension to the east – the Brendon Hills – have produced several minerals of industrial significance, including copper and silver, but primarily iron. Building stone and slate have also been quarried in some quantity. Little has survived of the human settlements in these mining districts, and once again the population is relatively sparse.

Finally, the heart of Somerset is formed by the red clay vale of Taunton Dene which is bounded by the Parrett, the Blackdowns and Exmoor. It is divided by the Quantocks – a spectacular ridge which rises from the clay vale without the formality of foot hills. Taunton, the county town, guards the gap between the southern extremity of the Quantocks and the Blackdowns. It is a natural route centre, and although remote from the Eastern townships, the obvious administrative centre for the county.

Each of these areas, the coastline, the low moors, the Mendips, the eastern hills, the yellow settlements of the south, the enclosed plateau of the Blackdowns, the open expanse of Exmoor and the rich red lands of Taunton Dene offers to the industrial archaeologist not only scenic variations but a wide spectrum of industrial activities.

The new County of Somerset, which was created by the 1972 Local Government Act, has one of the smallest populations of all the counties in England and Wales. To some extent this is explained by the loss of the northern third of its ancient size to the new County of Avon. Equally important, however, has been the relative decline in the County's population since the middle of the eighteenth century. In 1700 only Norfolk, Devon, Lancashire, Middlesex and the West Riding of Yorkshire had larger populations than Somerset. The wealth which supported this relatively substantial population was derived from two principal sources, agriculture and the woollen cloth industry.

Although agriculture has continued to be a vital industry in the county's economy to the present day, the woollen industry has survived on only one site – at Wellington. Much of the earlier manufacturing associated with this industry was cottage based and little physical evidence of this stage of production has survived. In a sense, the most striking remains of this phase are the beautiful perpendicular church towers which reflect the great affluence of the county in the fifteenth and sixteenth centuries.

The decline of the industry became obvious to contemporaries in the middle of the eighteenth century. However, this decline was not cataclysmic and Somerset continued to produce woollen cloth in new premises which housed all of the major manufacturing processes and which were powered by waterwheels and, later, steam engines. The local firms could not compete in the mass production of the cheaper kinds of cloth and the industry contracted. Some premises and work people turned to the production of other textiles. The most common of these was silk. The manufacture of silk cloth was introduced to Somerset and the neighbouring parts of Dorset in the mid-eighteenth century. By 1800 it was well established in many towns and villages which had previously depended on the manufacture of woollen cloth – Taunton, Bridgwater, Bruton, Shepton Mallet and Milborne Port. The industry provided employment for women and children whose earnings supplemented those of the main breadwinner. The industry grew under the protective shield of a total ban on imported silks. Between 1823 and 1860 this protection was gradually dismantled and the industry declined. However, it survived in some centres into the present century and one firm in Taunton continues in production. The manufacture of shirts and collars is another mutation of this industry.

Other textiles were developed as a result of the long wars with France between 1793 and 1815. The defence of the country depended on the maintenance of a large and efficient navy. The loss of traditional supplies of flax and hemp prompted the government to subsidize the cultivation of these crops in Britain. The soils of southern and eastern Somerset were particularly suited and consequently there developed several establishments to process these raw materials. Rope-walks were commonplace in the county, as street names often remind us, but only two firms are producing twine and rope in the county today. Sailcloth production, which also used flax, has survived in more centres, although the raw materials are either imported or manufactured artificially. The weaving of horsehair has continued in Castle Cary, although the essential ingredient is now imported.

The lace and net industry also developed in the county during the nineteenth century. Traces of this and of the webbing industry can be found in the towns and villages of the south of the county.

The products of Somerset's agriculture have long been famous. Cheddar cheese has continued to be produced in farm and factory premises to the present day. Two developments fostered the expansion of Somerset's dairy industry – the reclamation of waste land, especially the Levels, and the establishment of a quick and efficient transport system, especially the railways. A whole series of enclosure acts were passed just before and after the end of the eighteenth century. As a result, the marshes of the Somerset Levels were drained and the higher moorlands of the Mendips and Exmoor were reclaimed. The creation of a railway network in the middle years of the last century enabled farmers to send their surplus milk to the urban markets of Bristol, London and the Midlands. They were helped by the construction of collecting depots, many of which have survived – in some cases retaining their original function long after the closure of the particular railway which brought them into being.

With agricultural pioneers such as John Billingsley and Thomas Dyke Acland residing within the county it is not surprising that several examples of nineteenth century model farms exist in Somerset. Nearly all the farmsteads of the central Mendip plateau were built after 1800, following the enclosure acts. Similarly, Exmoor had but one farmstead – Simonsbath – when John Knight bought the estate. John Knight (1765–1850) and his son Frederic (1812–97) began the process of reclaiming Exmoor about 1830. They established new farmsteads, built new roads and planned a canal and railway to service some of their mining enterprises. Consequently, many of these farms reflect the 'improving' concepts of the nineteenth century in their buildings and equipment. So much of the latter has now been lost that it is pleasing to record the establishment of a Museum of Rural Life in the Abbey Barn at Glastonbury.

Cider has been manufactured by dozens of small presses for many centuries. Farmhouse cider is still produced on a modest scale and cider presses are commonplace, but factory production has largely taken over in this industry. Although the manufacture of cider and perry is mainly dependent on imported raw materials, the trade appears to flourish. This is more than can be claimed for Somerset's brewing industry. Since 1945 every independent brewery has been closed. Malt is produced at Oakhill and Babycham at Shepton Mallet – but not a drop of beer. Many of the old breweries have been demolished but the malthouses have a far higher survival rate.

Somerset's leather industries originated in the availability of hides locally. Those firms which are still active in this industry depend to a large extent on imported skins. A number of tanneries and fell-mongering establishments continue to produce dressed skins for the local gloving and sheep-skin trades. The shoe industry now relies increasingly on man-made materials, although leather remains an important source material. Significant collections of machinery, tools and the products of these industries are housed in the museum at Yeovil and Clarks' Shoe Museum in Street.

Somerset has always had sufficient mineral deposits to encourage a variety of quarrying and mining activities. Quarries are most evident in the county today. Limestone and andesite are quarried on the Mendips for cement and roadstone on a massive scale. More modest workings in the past quarried stone for these purposes as well as for agricultural lime – which was burnt in hundreds of small kilns – and for building materials. The variety of the latter is evident to the most casual traveller through the county. The best Bath stone is common in the north alongside the yellower Cotswold stone. In the southern Mendip area the white stone from Doulting – which was used in the construction of Wells Cathedral and Glastonbury Abbey – and the rusty hue of the Draycott stone are much in evidence. In the centre of the county the towns and villages are built in the blue-grey lias. West of the Parrett the red sandstone dominates and the grey slate which was quarried from the old Devonian beds. Finally, in the south, reflecting the sun, are the buildings in the deep yellow ham stone. Although many of the older quarries have been filled it is possible to locate most and to wonder at the technology which enabled them to be exploited.

Where building stone was not available at a reasonable price other materials had to be used. Some of the mud or cob-walled buildings have survived. Much more permanent, however, are those structures built of brick. The clays of Somerset supported dozens of brick-making concerns in the nineteenth century. Today, most of these have disappeared. The brick works at Bridgwater, Glastonbury, Highbridge, Chard and Yeovil are closed and disappearing rapidly. One firm continues on an old site with modern equipment near Wellington. Urgent efforts are being made to preserve at least one of the old bottle kilns in Bridgwater, but elsewhere the battle has been lost. It is to the buildings built of Somerset brick and tiled with local tiles that we must look in order to appreciate the importance of this industry in the county in the past.

Somerset also witnessed a considerable variety of mining activities. Lead was mined and smelted on the Mendips from pre-Roman times until 1908. Calamine had a shorter life-span of exploitation but was mined intensively in the Shipham area between 1550 and 1850. Iron ore has been quarried and mined for a longer period even than lead. It was particularly important in the third quarter of the nineteenth century when hematite was at a premium in the steel industry. Copper was mined briefly in the northern Quantock area between 1780 and 1830. Coal was the mineral to be mined most recently. It was certainly worked in the north of the county in the Middle Ages, and possibly in Roman times. The last mine to be worked in the new Somerset closed in 1968.

The availability of this variety of minerals no doubt encouraged the development of foundries, forges, edge-tool works and engineering enterprises. These establishments serviced the needs of the local industries. They produced waterwheels and milling equipment, bridges, milestones, weighbridges, bicycles, ploughs, sickles and even motor cars. Their names occur on a wide variety of implements and structures – Phoenix Foundry, Murch, Culverwell, Sibley, Chidgey, Day, Dening, Cockey and many more.

Water power was widely used in Somerset throughout the nineteenth century for many purposes of which corn milling was the most common. With the introduction of water turbines the generation of electricity became practicable on a number of sites. Windpower was apparently only used for milling corn in Somerset. There is some inconclusive evidence that it may have been used to operate drainage pumps early in the eighteenth century. The efficient drainage of the Levels, however, had to wait for the introduction of steam pumps after 1830. Steam power was also used in the textile industries and in mining and quarrying from the early nineteenth century. Several towns introduced gas-producing plants after 1820 for street lighting. Unfortunately little effort has been made to preserve the early gas-retort houses, although a few have survived. The gas holders have a better record. Taunton introduced electric lights in 1880 and other towns began to develop this new form of power soon after. The early generating stations are even more elusive than their counterparts in the gas industry, but a few have survived the establishment of the national grid.

The remains of early forms of transport are one of the richest areas of industrial archaeology in Somerset. The extraction of peat from the Brue Valley has revealed the oldest man-made road system in Europe – the prehistoric wooden trackways. Rather later, the Romans left a network of roads across the county. After 1750 many miles of road were turnpiked and several toll houses and distinctive mileposts survived the passing of this age in the 1880s.

Water transport has a long history also. The Romans built a wharf at Ilchester and the abbots of Glastonbury Abbey traded by waterway across the valleys of the Brue and Axe to Uphill. Coastal traffic using the harbours in the Parrett estuary – Highbridge, Watchet and Minehead – was certainly significant by 1700. It was at this time that the first efforts were being made to improve the navigation of Somerset's rivers. Navigation companies were set up to improve the Axe, the Parrett, the Ivel and the Tone. These companies continued to operate into the so-called canal age and made a vital contribution to the developing economy of the county.

With the exception of the Dorset and Somerset Canal, which was started in the 1790s but never completed, the canals of Somerset were built at a relatively late date: the Bridgwater–Taunton Canal (1827); the Glastonbury Canal (1834); the Grand Western Canal – Somerset section (1838); the Westport Canal (1840); and the Chard Canal (1842). Although none of these was a great commercial success, they did contribute to the prosperity of the county. Because they were built so late, they incorporated some of the more advanced ideas in canal construction, such as cast-iron aqueducts and canal lifts instead of locks. The Bridgwater–Taunton Canal survives today in recognizable form and the Westport Canal is being restored. The remainder may be traced on the ground and many of their principal features are easily identified.

Even before the last Somerset canal was opened, the age of the railway had dawned in the county. By 1843 the Bristol and Exeter broad-gauge line extended across the county to Wellington. Spurs of the same gauge were built to Hendford in Yeovil (1853); Glastonbury and Wells (1859) and to Chard (1866). The GWR spawned another link from Thingley, via Westbury, Frome and Yeovil to Weymouth (1857). Connecting lines were built from Frome via Radstock (1873) to Bristol and from Castle Cary to Durston (1906).

In 1874 the Somerset and Dorset, which had already abandoned the broad gauge, connected with Bath and two years later it was amalgamated with the Midland Railway which could now challenge the GWR's monopoly of the county's rail network. An earlier challenger was the London and South Western Railway, built on the standard gauge, from Salisbury to Exeter (1860). This line came within two miles of Yeovil, Milborne Port and Crewkerne and a short link was built from Chard Junction to Chard Town.

Another east–west link was established with the construction of the East Somerset line from Witham Friary to Wells (1862) and the Cheddar Valley line from Wells to Yatton (1870). This made Wells a town with three railway stations, although only one is barely recognizable today. The west of the county was served by two extensions of the GWR – the Taunton to Minehead line (1874), and the North Devon line to Barnstaple (1873).

Although the original main lines of this network are still in use for goods and passenger traffic, most of the spurs and links have been abandoned. Efforts have been made to revive the Taunton–Minehead line but the destruction of the remainder has been even more ruthless than that of the county's canals. Not only have the public been deprived of – in some circumstances – their only means of public transport, but the railway enthusiast will be faced with a frustrating task in trying to trace the very routes which some of these railways followed.

Today, Somerset is a mixture of modest-sized towns and expanding villages. The distinction between town and country is less obvious than in other parts of the country. There always was industry in rural areas and the flourishing revival of craft industries in recent years is a reversion to an older order of society. The towns are still heavily dependent on the prosperity of the surrounding countryside. The needs of the farmer and the processing of his products are still reflected in the range of urban industries. The long process of interaction between town and country has produced the unusual variety of industrial remains in Somerset today.

ASHBRITTLE

Tracebridge Slate Quarry (*Plate 35*) (ST067212) is the principal feature of this small industrial hamlet on the Somerset-Devon border. The quarry is impressive although it is partly filled. It ceased to produce slate in 1939 following a tragedy involving the proprietor's son. The original **slate mill** (ST067211) on the river bank below was linked to the quarry by an adit which is now blocked. This mill was water-powered and the remains of the building and the wheel pit have survived. A later mill which was worked by a petrol engine is recognizable in the field opposite the entrance to the quarry. West of the quarry is a **saw mill** (ST066212) built in the local grey slate. An overshot wheel, four feet wide with rim gearing survives. The premises were last utilized for the manufacture of wooden skittles.

ASHCOTT

On the peat moors north of the village is **Ashcott Station** (ST449397). Now a private

residence, it is one of the few to survive the closure of the Somerset and Dorset Railway in 1965. One of the level crossing gates is *in situ*. To the east, the Glastonbury Canal was carried across the South Drain by an aqueduct, the stone abutments of which are still visible (ST451396). The canal bed is submerged beneath the line of the railway to the east, but is visible again on the north side. At **Sharpham Crossing** (ST472392) the railway cottage is inhabited.

ASHWICK

Moorewood Colliery (ST643495) is set in a pleasant wooded valley. It was originally sunk in the 1860s and closed in 1932. A limestone engine house survives but the substantial brick chimney has been demolished recently. The colliery was linked to the Somerset and Dorset line at Old Down (ST629509) by a 2 ft gauge tramway parts of which can be traced, although the incline down to the mine has been obliterated.

ATHELNEY

Withies are grown in and around this small

35 Ashbrittle – The slate quarry at Tracebridge, (F Hawtin)

village on the banks of the River Tone, made famous by King Alfred's misadventure with the cakes. In the winter months the stripped willows are stacked alongside the road to bleach in the sun. In order to produce darker withies, for use in the local basket trade, the branches are boiled with their barks in long vats with short, red brick chimneys. Several of these are to be seen in this area. The banks of the River Tone are entirely artificial. Originally, this river joined the Parrett further north. **Curry Moor Pumping Station** (ST344288) has preserved an Easton Amos & Son steam engine of 1864 together with its original centrifugal pump. The mechanism can now be turned by electricity for demonstration purposes.

AXBRIDGE

This is a quaint medieval town with a small museum housed in the happily restored King John's Hunting Lodge. On the Mendip slope which dominates the town are the remains of an **ochre mine** (ST432551). The ochre was transported down an incline and sections of the 15 in gauge track survive together with a horizontal wheel cast by Dening & Co of Chard. Below this site, but still above the town, are the **station and goods shed** of the Cheddar Valley Railway. They stand by the side of the bypass which was built over the track of the old railway (ST433546). The buildings are both occupied. They are built in local stone and the station has retained the decorative tiles and chimney pots which were a distinguishing feature of the line. The woodwork of the gable ends and the cast-iron gutters with lion head decorations are also worthy of note.

BALTONSBOROUGH

There were two watermills in this low-lying village. They were served by a leat which stretches for a mile up-stream to a weir on the River Brue. **Upper Mill** (ST538347) was a paper mill when A. Baily bought it in 1866 for his fell-mongering business. Today, the premises are used for the processing of waste paper. **Lower Mill** (ST537347) which was a corn mill has been converted into a domestic residence and the mill pond has become a tennis court.

BASON BRIDGE

A large **milk depot** (ST347458) is still operational although the reason for its original siting, the Somerset & Dorset Railway has now been removed. The large brick building is alongside another redundant transport system: the Glastonbury Canal joined the River Blue at **Cripp's Corner** (ST361452) and incorporated this navigable section of the river in its link with Highbridge. To the east are the abutments of the viaduct which carried the railway across the river. In the nearby hamlet of Watchfield is one of the best surviving **windmills** in Somerset (ST348469). It is built of lias stone and rises to a modest height of 26ft. It was last worked in 1918 and has recently been renovated although all the internal gearing has been removed.

BECKINGTON

The substantial houses of this village testify to the prosperity of the woollen industry in the neighbourhood in the 17th and 18th centuries. **Eden Vale Mill** (ST797522) is also known as Carpenter's Mill. In the 18th century it was used for grinding corn as well as for making cloth. The building has recently been converted to a dwelling. **Clifford's Mill** (ST797526) is on the site of an earlier fulling mill. Very little of the mill, rebuilt after a fire in 1802, has survived.

BLEADNEY

The River Axe, which flows alongside the road through this straggling village, powered at least two mills. No buildings survive of the **paper mill** which stood near the Piccadilly Inn, but a tastefully converted **grist mill** (ST484454) stands at the west end of the village. The iron overshot wheel is *in situ*, although it has been made superfluous by a water turbine which is used to generate electricity.

BRENDON HILLS

These hills – in the main – have been incorporated in the Exmoor National Park. The narrow ridge, rising to almost 1400 ft above sea level contains much of interest. The most dramatic remains are associated with the mining of hematite in the third quarter of the 19th century. For as long as the steel industry of South Wales needed an iron ore which did not contain phosphorous, mining in this area prospered. It is possible to locate many of the mine shafts, e.g. **Gupworthy Mine** (SS966351) and **Raleigh's Cross Mine** (ST025342). Almost all the surface buildings have now disappeared but both of these mines have drainage adits which still function. The destruction of the **Kennisham Hill Engine House** (SS963361) in 1978 has left only one surviving example, the **Burrow Farm Engine House** (*Plate 36*) (ST004343). This was built in the local stone and it incorporates a round chimney, with its upper courses of brick on the Cornish pattern. Alongside, is a single-storey stone building which provided drying facilities for the miners.

The mining area was served by a railway which provided transport to and from Watchet Harbour. The most spectacular section of this West Somerset Mineral Railway is the **incline** which extends for three-quarters of a mile at a gradient of one in four from Roadwater to the summit ridge west of Raleigh's Cross Inn (ST023345). Originally, haulage up this incline depended on a counter-balancing system which necessitated two railway tracks and a large winding drum which was housed below the track on the summit level. The remains of this arrangement can still be seen, although the walls and iron-framed windows were installed at a much later date. The railway line can be traced for most of its length along the top of the Brendons. **Brendon Hill Station** (ST023344) survives as a private dwelling. The **terminus buildings** at Goosemoor (SS963356) are also intact. **Limekilns** (ST022342) were built alongside the track. Although most of the mining activity in this area had ceased by 1880 and the railway barely survived into the present century, a

36   Brendon Hills – the Burrow Farm Engine House, (F Hawtin)

number of dwelling houses associated with the industry have survived. **Sea View House** (ST025345) was the residence of the mines captain. **Brendon Hills Farm** (ST023345) was the local shop. The ruins of cottages can be seen alongside the road to the east towards the now restored **Beulah Chapel** (ST028342).

Slate was quarried on the Brendon Hills at **Treborough** (ST015368). Although the quarry is now being filled in the most insensitive manner, it is possible to appreciate its size from the mountains of spoil which have been deposited below. The adit which ran beneath the road into the workings and the wheel pit of the **slate mill** (ST014368) are still visible. Limestone was also burnt in the kilns which survive on the road side.

BRIDGWATER

This thriving commercial and industrial town is situated at the lowest bridging point over the River Parrett. Until the arrival of the Bristol and Exeter Railway in 1841, the town's commercial life centred on the river. The quays below the town bridge have recently been restored. **Iron bollards**, cast by the local foundry of Culverwell, and a **crane** have been included in this restoration (ST300372). Several interesting buildings survive on the waterfront including the large red brick **warehouse** of Peace Ltd. A **'floating harbour'** was constructed in 1841 (ST298375) which provided a safer anchorage than the river quays and their formidable tidal changes. The harbour is divided by the road to Chilton Trinity, which crossed over the central lock gates by means of a bascule bridge. Unhappily, this is in a state of collapse at the present time and will need extensive repairs to restore it to full working condition. The outer harbour was scoured by a system of sluices, the control mechanisms of which stand on the harbour wall. Although now sealed by concrete, the two locks into the river, one for narrow boats and the other for ocean-going vessels, are clearly visible. Alongside the inner dock, and facing the mound of earth which was excavated to form the dock, stands a four-storey warehouse in red brick with stone dressings.

Two commercial sites have survived the closure of the harbour to water-borne transport. The **coalyard** of Messrs Bryant is

visible behind the red brick buildings which are topped by the 'ton of coal' – a solid lump of that mineral at chimney level (ST299375). A **steam mill** (ST296375) used to grind corn and animal-feed stands at the north-west corner of the inner harbour. Although damaged by fire, much of the original building survives including the chimney. In front of the mill is the site of the first lock of the Bridgwater–Taunton Canal, which is currently being restored. When first constructed this canal joined the Parrett at Huntworth where the site of the original lock can be identified (ST309354). **Crossway Bridge** just south of this point is the only surviving bridge on the canal which has retained its swing mechanism. The section of the canal which circles north from this bridge to the harbour was opened in 1841, and the lock at Huntworth was abandoned. Unfortunately, the prize exhibit of the Bridgwater harbour has been removed to the Maritime Museum at Exeter. This is a steam-powered dredger which was identical to that designed by I.K. Brunel to dredge the Cumberland Basin in Bristol.

In 1871 the Bristol and Exeter Railway was extended across the Parrett to the coal yard and the harbour by means of a **telescopic bridge** (ST300374). This was designed to allow sailing vessels to continue up the river to the town bridge. The central portion could be rolled back on to the east side of the river. Motive power was provided by a steam engine located in a small brick building at the eastern end. Unfortunately, it was this side of the bridge which suffered from one of the worst cases of 'official' vandalism seen in this town in the recent past. The bridge still stands, but it is highly improbable that it will ever function again. The remains of the line can still be seen on the western side of the river. At the level crossing gates (ST298374) railway enthusiasts will recognize the **Barlow Rails** used as uprights. Just south of this crossing are the remains of the **glass and pottery cone** (*Plate 37*). This was built early in the 18th century by the Duke of Chandos, who also financed the building of nearby Castle Street. The glass cone was demolished in 1943 and provided hard core for Westonzoyland Aerodrome. The foundations of the cone were recently excavated by SIAS and are now scheduled for preservation.

Two good **toll houses** have survived in

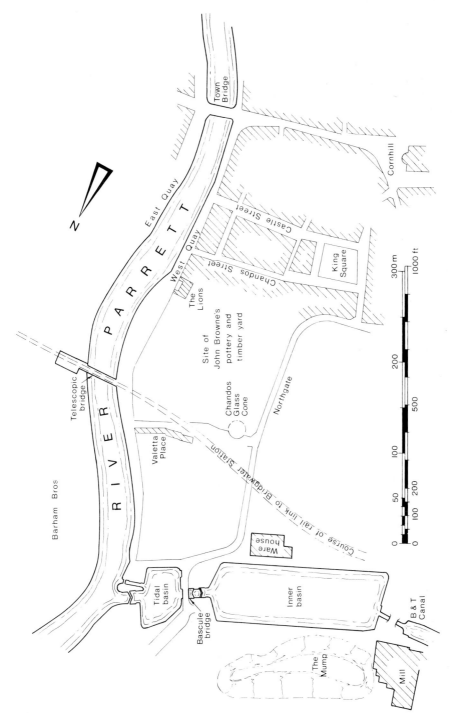

7 Somerset: Bridgwater docks

Bridgwater, one on the Taunton Road (ST302362) and the other at the junction of the Bath and Bristol roads (ST304374). Until the Broadway was constructed, all road traffic had to cross the river by the town bridge. The original stone bridge was replaced by one cast at Coalbrookdale and erected in 1797. The present structure replaced this iron bridge in 1883 but it is possible to see the grooves in the stone abutments from which the iron arches of the earlier bridge were sprung. Another survivor of this old iron bridge is the plaque of the town's coat of arms which adorns the entrance to the **Royal Clarence Hotel** (ST298371). The Royal Clarence is, in itself, an interesting survivor of the turnpike age because it is probably the most famous of Bridgwater's coaching houses.

Many industrial sites in Bridgwater have been the victims of 'improvements' in recent years. Starkey's Brewery at Northgate and the retort house of the gas company have almost completely disappeared. However, the original building of the **Electric Supply and Traction Co Ltd** (ST296371), opened in 1904, stands in Mount Street. On the Chilton Trinity road is a two-storey building in red sandstone with a red tiled roof. It is now a carpet store but was originally a **tide mill** owned by Spillers (ST298377).

One of the town's major industries in the past was the manufacture of bricks and tiles. The physical remains of this industry are now fast disappearing. The best site today is north of the telescopic bridge where Barham Bros had their works. At least one **pinnacle (or updraught) kiln** survives (*Plate 38*). It was converted to operate on the down draught principle and should be preserved as a reminder of this important local industry. The site at Barham's also produced Bath Bricks which were made out of the silt deposited by the Parrett in specially constructed slime batches (SIAS Journal No. 1, p. 19). At Chilton Trinity there are remains of the clay pits which were worked for the adjacent **brickworks** – a large three-storey brick building (ST299392). There are some remains of the **brick and tile industry** at Dunwear (ST318354) and Huntworth (ST318344). Perhaps the best evidence for this abandoned industry is to be found in the buildings and roof tops of the district. A rich variety of roof tiles, chimney pots and terra cotta ware survives.

Bridgwater had two railway stations. The main-line station, which was built to the design of the GWR is still in use – a modest, one-storey structure (ST308369). The second station was the terminus for the branch line which joined the Somerset and Dorset line at

37 Bridgwater – The excavated base of Lord Chandos' Glass Cone, (F Hawtin)

Edington Burtle. The line closed in 1952 but some of the **station buildings** can be identified (ST304375).

BRUSHFORD

Exebridge (SS930245) crosses the county boundary. It has a span of 34yds over three arches and dates from the 18th century. **Exebridge Mill** (SS932247) was powered by a low breast wheel. The line of the Devon and Somerset Railway and the railway bridge over the Exe are still visible. Brushford **Station** is well preserved (SS926255). It is a substantial two-storey building of stone. A stone goods shed has also survived to the east.

BRUTON

The elegant parish church and Sexey's Almshouses testify to the prosperity of the woollen industry in this town before 1700. As the industry declined workers sought employment in silk throwing and weaving, horsehair weaving, brewing, tanning and the preparation of timber. In some cases several of these industries were practised consecutively. **Gant's Mill** (ST675342) is built on the

site of an early grist mill. In the Middle Ages it became a fulling mill, but late in the 18th century it was adapted for silk throwing. By 1866 this industry had become extinct in Bruton and Gant's Mill reverted to the status of a grist mill. The building is three storeys high with an attic floor. It is built of stone and has a red tiled roof. The floors are now supported by cast-iron pillars – presumably a 19th-century addition. Originally powered by an overshot wheel, the pit for which survives, the mill now has a turbine which was installed in 1870. The building is used for storage and the grinding of animal feed.

Another **mill** in Quaperlake Street (ST686349) had a similarly complicated history. Originally a fulling mill it became a silk mill in 1798 and subsequently was used for the preparation of horsehair seating. More recently it served as a bacon factory and is now occupied by a transport company. Not all of the mill buildings have survived and there have been some recent additions.

There are two **toll houses** in the town; a two-storey cottage in West End (ST679347) and a more substantial building with three pretty gable ends – the Burrowfield toll house (ST687352) at the junction of the Frome and

38 Bridgwater – Barham's Brickworks

Maiden Bradley roads. **Bow Bridge** (ST684347) is a beautiful stone, single-span bridge which may have been designed for packhorse traffic. A wider bridge stands a short distance upstream. This is **Church Bridge**, a medieval structure which was widened for vehicular traffic in the 19th century.

In 1856 the Wilts, Somerset & Weymouth Railway reached the town. A plan was later devised to link this line with the Somerset and Dorset and although the plan was never implemented, much of the ground was prepared and a building erected to serve as a **signal box** (ST663341).

BUCKLAND DINHAM

A square stone **lock up** with a stone tiled roof and a ball finial stands outside the Parish Church (ST755512). At the bottom of the hill leading to Frome is a small packhorse bridge. Alongside is a round, stone building, about 20ft high, which is believed to have been a stove for drying woollen cloth after scouring (ST756509). The building has one doorway and an opening on the side of the river for a flue. The whole building is draped in ivy. The adjacent cottage may have been part of a fulling mill. At a **colliery site** (ST745508) a chimney, slag heap and brick kiln are still visible. **Murtry Aqueduct** (ST762498) is a low stone structure of three arches which was built to carry the Dorset and Somerset Canal across the river which flows from the Nettlebridge valley.

BURNHAM-ON-SEA

This seaside resort is situated north of the estuary of the River Brue and facing Stert Island, across the main navigable channel into the mouth of the Parrett. The effect of the tides and currents has been to create a mixture of sand and mud banks which are pleasing to the eye but less so to the feet. When shipping in and out of Bridgwater was more plentiful, the shoals off Burnham posed serious problems to navigators. Two of the most striking industrial monuments of the town are a product of these difficulties. The two **lighthouses**, one on the high ground, rising in a conventional tower to 91ft above sea level (ST304505), and the other on the tidal flats, built principally of timber and rising to 36ft (ST299504), were built as a result of a survey carried out in 1832 by Trinity House.

Jutting into the sands is a stone **pier** which was created in 1857–8 to serve the needs of the Somerset Central's line (ST302488). In 1860 the Burnham Tidal Harbour and Railway Company was formed to provide a steamer service from Burnham to Cardiff. The pier was designed to allow railway coaches to be driven alongside the waiting steamers. The railway lines can be seen in the surface of the pier, in spite of determined efforts to obliterate them. The pier was abandoned by the railway company in 1905 and the berth for the steamers is completely silted up. The rail link with Highbridge was closed to passengers in 1951, although occasional excursion trains continued to use it until 1962. Goods transported by the Severn trows used to be unloaded on the beach near the lower lighthouse and were then transported on a horse-drawn tramway into the town. No remains of this tramway have survived. To the north on Berrow Flats, the hull of the barque **Nornen** is still visible at low tide.

An attempt was made to establish a fashionable spa at Burnham in the 1830s when the Rev. Davies found a mineral spring there. The more elegant buildings on the front date from this enterprise, but the town's growth owed more to the railway. Very little has survived of the brick works and the brewery which were important until 1939. Administratively, the town is now linked with its neighbour, Highbridge.

BURROWBRIDGE

This hamlet has grown up at an important crossing point on the River Parrett. The **bridge** (ST357304) has a single span, with a flood relief channel let into its western side. It is built in lias stone and has an iron hand-rail on the downstream side and a stone parapet on the upstream. It was built in 1826 by John Stone of Yarcombe. Until 1939 tolls were charged at the bridge; the toll-collector's cottage was abolished at the same time as the tolls.

The **Museum of the Wessex Water Authority** is on the east bank of the river, below the bridge (ST357306). The centre piece of this display is the Easton Amos and Anderson steam engine and pump which were installed in 1869. A replacement boiler, installed in 1924, has also been preserved but the chimney of the boiler house has been removed. The museum also includes a small collection of pumps and smaller items associated with land drainage. Permission to view the contents of the museum must be obtained from the WWA.

The cultivation of withies for basket ware is common in this area and several examples of withy boilers are to be seen – (ST357303; 358301; 360300; 356297).

CASTLE CARY

This quiet town may disappoint those in search of the feudal remains implied in its name, but it contains plenty to interest the industrial archaeologist. The Market Hall was built in 1855 and now houses a small **museum** with many useful exhibits. To the rear of this building is the delightful stone **lock up** (ST640323) which dates from 1779 and is capped by a roof which is reminiscent of a constable's helmet. To the east is the iron frame of the **weighbridge**, inscribed 'COCKEY FROME 1843'.

In 1840 the pond in the centre of the town provided water for five mills, three of which were spinning flax. The remains of one of these mills is still in use today – the **Torbay** or **Higher Flax Mills** (ST635323). Although the mill pond has been filled, an engine house and the stone base to a chimney survive. A three-storey block with an iron crane hoist is dated 1870. The original rope-walk has been covered by a modern, one-storey building, now used for storage. The main part of the factory is used for the manufacture of webbing. A terrace of workers' cottages, **Bridgewater Buildings** (ST637323), stands to the east of the factory site.

The **weaving of horsehair** was first introduced to the town in the 1830s by John Boyd. His original premises are identified by his name, carved into the stone archway which is set in a mellowed brick façade at the east end of the High Street (ST644325). Behind this frontage there is a three-storey block in yellow sandstone set on lias foundations. The building has a slate roof and stone bellcote. To the north is a single-storey

block of weaving sheds. The manufacture of woven horsehair was transferred to the Torbay site where it is still continued on a small scale. Boyd's premises are now occupied by Strode Components Ltd.

Florida Works (ST640325) were built in the 1860s on a site which had housed an earlier silk mill. The existing buildings were used for the manufacture of girth webbing and hair seating. They are two storeys high and built in stone with a slate roof. Little has survived of the original premises at the **gas works** (ST638324) except the foundations of the storage cylinder erected in 1905. Clanville **toll house** (ST622328), a two-storey building which is in a derelict condition, stands near the east end of the Langport, Somerton and Castle Cary Trust road. The **railway station** at Ansford (ST636335) is still used. It is north of the junction between the Wilts., Somerset and Weymouth line and the main line to Durston and the West, opened in 1906. Adjacent to the station is a red brick building with a chimney; it was originally a milk collecting depot. To the north is a **toll house** (ST634338) at the southern end of the Shepton Mallet Trust road, a pretty two-storey building with gothic windows.

CHAFFCOMBE

The Chard Reservoir was originally built to supply water to the canal. Under the road which runs along the embankment are a number of brick culverts designed to cope with flood water. Below the road is a red brick building which has served as both a **butter factory** and a **cider factory** (ST339103). The factory was powered by an overshot wheel which is still *in situ*. An interesting feature above the wheel is a governor which regulated the flow of water and the speed of the wheel. North of the factory, across the track of the abandoned GWR line, is the last **inclined plane** on the Chard Canal (ST339105). This raised boats 86ft on a single railway truck by means of water power. The incline is badly overgrown and there is no trace of the mill which provided the power for haulage.

CHAPEL ALLERTON

Ashton Windmill (*Fig 5*) (ST414503) is one of the best surviving examples of a tower mill

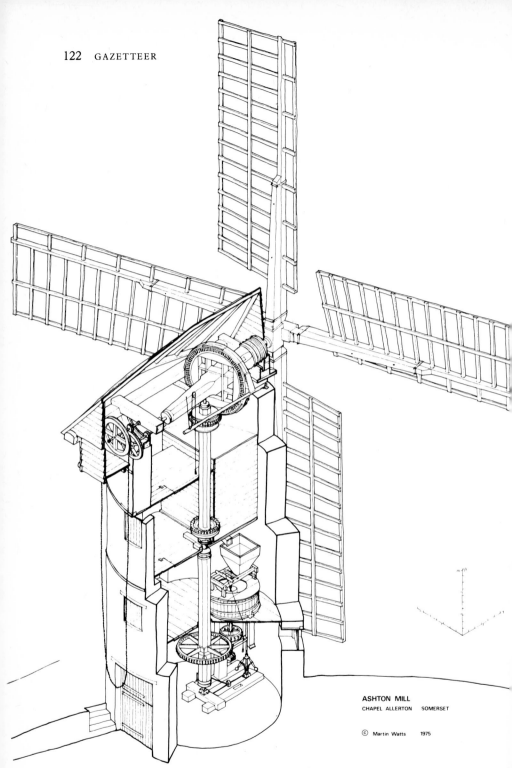

ASHTON MILL
CHAPEL ALLERTON   SOMERSET

© Martin Watts   1975

Figure 5   Somerset: Chapel Allerton. Ashton Mill is the only complete windmill surviving in the county. This isometric/cut-away drawing shows clearly the gearing and internal arrangements of this typical small windmill. Drawn by Martin Watts.

in Somerset. It was probably built in the late 18th century and continued in use until 1927. It was thoroughly restored in the 1950s and presented to the City Museum in Bristol in 1966. It is built in the local lias stone with three iron bands to prevent distortion. The cap is now cedar-boarded but was originally thatched. Internally, the mill is complete, having been refitted with machinery from Moorlynch windmill in 1900. The sails have recently been removed for repair and a considerable amount of maintenance work needs to be carried out if this important monument is to be preserved for another generation. At **Stone Allerton** (ST 406515) the tower of a similar windmill has been incorporated in the adjacent miller's cottage to form a domestic residence.

CHARD

This is a distinctive Somerset town in which manufacturing industry has always been important. After 1820 the lace or plain net trade became established by manufacturers who fled from the Luddite resistance they had faced in the Midlands. **Gifford Fox's Works** (ST 323085) dominate the skyline. They consist of a red brick building, five storeys high with a wooden locum at the north gable. Only the lower part of the chimney survives. To the west, fronting on Holyrood Street, is the later **Model Mill** – a single-storey red brick building of seven bays with yellow brick and tile decorations. **Boden's Works** (*Plate 39*) (ST 234085) has a main building of four storeys with an attic range. Also built of brick, these works have windows with rounded heads and more of the chimney has survived than at Gifford Fox's. A handsome red brick gate house is dated 1901. To the west on Boden Street is the elegant brick **Boden Institute**, built for Henry and Walter Boden in 1892, which now houses the County Library Service. Both of these large mills have ceased to operate as lace-producing units and the textile industry in the town is only recognizable in Sussman's **Shirt and Collar Factory** (ST 317085). A small museum in the High Street contains some machinery and tools associated with the town's industries. Of particular note is the large **cider press** worked by a horse gin.

The needs of the local textile industry and agriculture were met by the engineering works which developed in the 19th century. The buildings of **Dening's Iron and Brass Foundry** survive at Crimchard (ST 318092). They consist of a three-storey range with a gatehouse and a stone bell cote. The manager's house, with a frontage of local flint stone, stands next door. At the town end of Combe Street are the **Phoenix Engineering Works** which are still in production (ST 321087). **Hockey's Engineering Works** were sited in Station Road; the red brick gatehouse and bell cote survive. Like Gifford Fox's and Boden's, these works utilized water power, but all the ponds have now been filled.

Tom's Brewery and Malthouse were sited behind the Victoria Inn, but only a part of the exterior wall survives (ST 329088). **Mitchell's Brewery** amalgamated with Toms before it was taken over by Charringtons. Only some out-buildings and the manager's house survive off the High Street (ST 319085). Next to the brewery was a cider factory, most of the buildings of which have survived. An interesting link with Mitchell's, who originally operated a distillery in the town, are the **bonded warehouses** in Silver Street (ST 324086).

One of the more famous names associated with Chard is that of John Stringfellow. Born in Attercliffe, near Sheffield, he developed the first model aeroplane to make a flight powered by steam in his Chard workshop in 1848. The workshop building survives at the top of the High Street, identified by a commemorative plaque (ST 318085) and a replica of his engine can be seen in the Castle Museum, Taunton. Although much of Chard is built of brick, very little of this industry has survived. Several of the older buildings are built from the flints which were quarried on Snowdon Hill. The remains of these quarries can still be identified (ST 313088). One of the most attractive of the flint buildings is the single-storeyed **toll house** on Snowdon Hill which is capped with a thatched roof (ST 313087). Another **toll house** has survived next to the old borough boundary post at Crimchard (ST 318094).

Very little remains of the **Chard Canal Basin** except the perimeter wall and parts of the original canal warehouse which have been incorporated within the present industrial premises (ST 328093). To the east of the canal basin is the well-preserved **Chard Joint Station**, which was the terminus of the

39   Chard – Boden's Lace Factory

broad-gauge line opened in 1866 (ST329093). It is a single-storey building of red brick with ham stone dressing and some pretty pieces of iron work. The line which linked this station with **Chard Town** (or 'Tin') **Station** which served the London and South Western line from Chard Junction on the main line, has been completely filled and landscaped. Nothing remains on the site of the Town Station.

CHARLTON HORETHORN

Horethorn **toll house** at South Cheriton (ST693248) is the only one in Somerset which has retained its board of toll charges. The building is two storeys high with a semi-hexagonal front and built of stone with a red-tiled roof and porch. **Waterloo Crescent** (ST665223) was reputedly built to house labourers at the end of the Napoleonic Wars in 1815. The curved terrace is two storeys high, built of stone with a red tiled roof. The **Crescent** at Compton Pauncefoot (ST645258) is similar in design to Waterloo

Crescent, except that it is three storeys high and was only designed for five cottages. It is dated 1808. There were originally communicating doors on the second floor. The Crescent has recently been tastefully restored.

CHARTERHOUSE ON MENDIP

This exposed hamlet contains evidence of the mining and refining of lead from Roman times to the 20th century. Although little is apparent on the surface of Roman settlement, aerial photographs and archaeological excavations have proved the existence of a substantial lead-working community on both sides of the B3134 road. To the south-east, close to the ruins of Bleak House, there is an area of intensive mining activity, characterized by deep grooves. Within this area (ST506555) it is possible to locate shafts, some with dry stone linings.

The Blackmoor valley runs between the mining area and Charterhouse. It was in the bed of this shallow valley that most of the

40   Charterhouse on Mendip – Remains of lead condensing flues, (F Hawtin)

substantial remains of the 19th-century lead industry are to be found. There are several examples of round **buddles** (ST504555). These vary in diameter from about 26ft to 20ft and are about 2ft deep. They were used to refine crushed slag by centrifugal force. Normally the buddles are located in batteries of six or more, which suggests that the process was repeated several times before sufficiently concentrated deposits of lead were accumulated. The round buddles were introduced to the area by Cornish prospectors who worked the old slags in the second half of the last century. A range of **condensing flues** (*Plate 40*) has survived in the small nature reserve at the east end of the valley (ST507560). These are about 5½ft high and were built in the local limestone. The chimney has been demolished, as has the furnace. However, large quantities of the black lead slag are evident, and it is possible to distinguish the reservoir which stored the water used lower down the valley in the buddles. In Velvet Bottom there are less well preserved remains of buddles (ST502554) and

a flue system (ST496552). The base of the chimney and a section of the flue which served the **Pattinson Silver** plant can be identified (ST505556). The remains of the silver works were used to repair the embankment of the service road from Charterhouse which was swept away in the floods of 1968. Adjacent to the site of the silver works is the base of a stable which was uncovered by children who were being taught the principles of archaeology at Somerset County Council's Field Centre in the old village school (ST502558).

CHEDDAR

Although justly renowned for its cheese, strawberries and Gorge, this town has retained some sites of industrial interest. In the 18th century there were seven watermills working, four for grinding corn and three for making paper. At the bottom of the Gorge there are three distinct mill sites but very little of the original buildings have survived the impact of modern tourism. However, the

41 Cheddar – Railway Station

establishment of a **Museum of Motor Transport** (ST462537) proves that the interests of tourism and industrial archaeology are not incompatible. The water from the Gorge has been appropriated by the Bristol Water Works Co, who built a large red brick pumping station to the south of the town (ST452533).

One of the original **paper mill** sites at the bottom of Redcliffe Street (ST462532) is occupied by a concrete works. The water course and sluices can be seen; the single-storey wing of stone buildings bears the date 1890. Upstream another mill site is identified by the converted mill house. At the **tannery** (ST462531) a large, toothed wheel of Draycott stone, used for the dressing of leather has been discovered. Below the tannery the river runs into a water course known as the River Yeo. This provided a means of transport and possibly explains the siting of the **gas works** on its east bank (ST459528). The retort house, a single-storey building, and the manager's house have survived, together with an original gas light above the gate. Downstream, at Hythe was the original **wharf** for Cheddar on the Axe Navigation (ST448522). A stone cottage stands on the site.

In 1869 the Cheddar Valley Railway reached the town and stimulated fruit-growing as a local industry. The **Railway Station** (*Plate 41*) (ST454532) has lost its overall roof but appears to be otherwise intact. Built of stone, it has retained its splendid tiled roof, decorative chimney pots and ironwork. A large goods shed to the west has survived and the coalyard to the north is still occupied.

The all-pervading industry of Cheddar today is quarrying, on a scale which is a cause for some concern. There are several examples of disused quarries in the area, some with abandoned plant *in situ*, e.g. east of the road up Callow Hill (ST449559).

CHEWTON MENDIP

This parish contains considerable evidence of the mining and processing of lead. Chewton Warren and Stock Hill were intensively mined in the 16th and 17th centuries, but the sites of these workings have now been obliterated by the Forestry Commission's plantation. West of the old road from Wells to Bristol are the remains of a **reservoir** (ST547515) which was built in the mid-19th century to conserve water for the refining processes. Rivalry between the Waldegrave Works at the north end of this shallow valley and St Cuthbert's in Priddy Parish, ended in the law courts. It is possible to identify a number of small reservoirs on the side of the valley, which were designed to catch as much water as possible. There are the remains of two **lines of buddles** which were associated with the Waldegrave Works (ST544509 and 547513). Unlike those at Charterhouse, these buddles formed a straight line, with two large buddles at the top followed by ten smaller. Presumably, the crushed slag was worked from top to bottom of these lines. Although nothing remains of the furnace area, two sets of condensing flues have survived in part. One flue ran up the side of the valley towards Priddy Nine Barrows, the other ran at right-angles, down the valley above the track which once carried a tramway. Near the focal point of these **flues** (ST547512) are heaps of the characteristic black slag.

CHILCOMPTON

There are a number of coal mining sites in this area. **New Rock Colliery** (ST647505) was the last coal mine to be worked in the new Somerset. It closed in 1968 but much of the slag heap and surface buildings survive. From 1957 this colliery was linked to **Mendip Colliery** (ST648496) on the site of abandoned Strap Colliery. All the coal mined at New Rock was wound to the surface at Mendip, which closed at the same time as the former. Although both the shafts have been filled, there are still some mining buildings surviving at Mendip as at New Rock. A square, stone **toll house** of the Wells Turnpike Trust survives (ST629513) although the original gothic windows have been replaced. The **Old Down Inn** (ST625513) is an old Mendip coaching house at the junction of the Wells and Shepton Trust roads. The original alignment of the roads can still be seen in front of the Inn.

CLAPTON

On the B3165 south of Crewkerne, just before the old bridge over the River Axe, is **Clapton Mill** (ST414064). The mill still grinds corn by water power which is generated by an overshot wheel fed from an iron conduit carried on brick piers. The mill is three storeys high, built of stone, with a wooden locum over the road side.

CLEWER

A small, single-storey, hexagonal fronted **toll house** built by the Wedmore Trust (ST441510) stands on the side of the B3151 road.

COLEFORD

As the name of this parish suggests, coal mining has been an important local occupation. Although many of the early workings were shallow, and even the more recent slag heaps are overgrown with grass and trees, it is still possible to identify the sites of several collieries. **Mackintosh Colliery** (ST692496) – the spoil heap and line of the narrow-gauge tramway can be seen. **Newbury Colliery** (ST696497) – the site is now occupied by a firm manufacturing stone, but several of the original buildings are in use. Two terraces of **miners' cottages** (ST693497) are occupied between these two collieries.

There are two watermills in the bottom of the valley – **Hippey's Mill** (ST689487) and **Sargent's Mill** (ST686486). The latter has been restored to working order and contains a breast shot wheel. To the south of this mill is a **packhorse bridge** (ST687485) known as Packsaddle Bridge. The Dorset and Somerset Canal can be traced through the village but is best seen opposite the chapel (ST688488) and at the **aqueduct** (ST685487) a stone structure of two arches which is heavily overgrown.

CRANMORE

The line of a railway which ran from the now abandoned and water-filled **Waterlip Quarry** (ST661445) to **Cranmore Station** (ST665430) can be traced to the south end of the cutting under the A361. The station has been most tastefully restored by the Cranmore Railway Company which has bought a section of the East Somerset line from British Rail. The Company has built a new engine shed to house its collection of steam locomotives which includes **Black Prince**. These engines are used to give the

public short rides under steam power. The attendant buildings include a signal box and a beautifully restored iron urinal. **Long Cross Toll House** (ST659451) belonged to the Shepton Trust. It is a two-storey building dated 1790. **Cranmore Toll House** (ST679441) also belonged to the Shepton Trust. It is a two-storey building, built in stone with gothic windows.

CREECH ST MICHAEL

The principal landmark in this village is the red brick chimney of the **paper factory** (ST269254). Although recently truncated, this bears the date 1875. The factory is still in production. The **Bridgwater–Taunton Canal** passes under the main road which is carried by a typical, red brick, single-arched canal bridge (ST273255). To the east, on the south bank of the canal are the remains of the **Charlton Pumping House** (ST287261). This three-storeyed, red brick building housed a steam engine which pumped water from the River Tone into the Canal. The engine has been removed and the buildings are derelict. To the west of the road bridge it is possible to distinguish the point at which the Chard Canal joined the Bridgwater-Taunton Canal. The lock-keeper's cottage was demolished recently, but the stone retaining wall of the **Chard Canal** can still be seen (ST270256). The Bristol and Exeter Railway had to pass under the Chard Canal by means of an invert, although this was filled in soon after the closure of the canal. A splendid **aqueduct**, built of stone, carried the Chard Canal south across the River Tone (ST271254). To the west is the stone **viaduct** which carried the Bristol and Exeter's branch line to Chard (ST269253). Recent alterations in the course of the River Tone have left the three-storey brick **mill** without a source of water power. A hoist survives on the north side of the buildings (ST273254). The main road through the village is carried over the River Tone by a fine cast iron **bridge** (ST274253). Although widened, the bridge still bears the inscription 'Murch 1848'. Further downstream there is **Ham Mills** (ST279253). Before the Tone was made navigable to Taunton this marked the head of navigation on the river. There is a corn mill on this site which later used steam power. The red brick chimney is standing.

CREWKERNE

The principal industry in this town over the last 100 years has been the manufacture of canvas and webbing from flax and, more recently, from artificial fibres. **Viney Mills** (ST449091) date from about 1800. The older premises were built in stone with round headed windows. A blackened chimney stands towards the south of the complex which is still used for the production of sailcloth. Another webbing factory complex survives to the north of South Street (ST444095). As at Viney Mills there are two or three blocks of stone buildings which rise to three storeys, and a square brick chimney. These premises, which housed Robert Bird & Co, Linen and Woollen Manufacturers, are now occupied by a number of other concerns. South Terrace (ST446094) is a good example of **workers' cottages**; they are dated 1864. Just west of North Street (A356) is a four-storey **factory** (ST441100) which originally housed a company manufacturing shirts. The lower storeys are of stone and the fourth storey of brick appears to have been added later. In the river valley, the weaving sheds of a **sail cloth works** (ST440102) are now occupied by a number of modern businesses and the mill pond is cultivated as allotments. In Abbey Street a series of buildings, progressing from a stone block behind the market to a three-storey red brick block, are occupied by a shirt factory (ST441098). The stone building in the centre of this range may have been the owner's house.

At the junction of North Street and Brickyard Lane is a **tannery** (ST441101) – a stone building with timber louvred windows and a squat red brick chimney. Nothing survives of the **brick, tile and pipe works** at the top of the lane (ST445103) except for a partly filled clay pit. More survives at the Maiden Beech **Brick Works**, south of the railway (ST437083) – two single-storey drying sheds and a two-storey private house built of bricks of contrasting colours. Although the Crewkerne United Brewery has been demolished, the large red brick **malthouse** (ST442104) is preserved as a cash-and-carry store. An unusual feature of the building is that the drying kilns were situated in the middle and not at one end. An antique shop in South Street still carries the monogram of the Crewkerne Gas & Coke Company, but only one line of two-storey buildings survive behind, and one **gasholder** (ST445094). **Crewkerne Station** is situated at the east end of the town (ST453085). It is in use today and the original stone building, dated 1859, has been preserved. The centre block is three storeys high.

CROSCOMBE

This is a pretty village whose industrial remains relate principally to the water course which sweeps from one side of the main road to the other. A red brick **chimney** (ST591443) opposite the market cross stands on a carved stone base. It is detached but probably relates to the three-storey stone building immediately behind which also has a mill leat. A short distance upstream is a stone **corn mill** (ST593443), three storeys high with a wooden locum on the north gable. There is a stepped weir beneath the sluice gates which are set in a wooden frame. The overflow passes beneath a **packhorse bridge** with two round arches, one of which is built on the skew. The bridge has a cutwater on the upstream side.

DOULTING

St. Andrew's Quarry (ST647435) supplied the building stone used in many local churches, including Wells Cathedral and Glastonbury Abbey. Although most of the original quarry has now been filled, the stone is worked today on the east side of the road to Chelynch on a small scale (ST649435). Traces of **edge-tool works** survive at the head of the valley running down to Shepton Mallet (ST645432). These include the remains of millponds and one waterwheel. An excellent **tithe barn**, built in the local stone, stands south of the church (ST647430). A cement rendered **toll house** stands in Chelynch, although it now bears little outward sign of its original function (ST649439).

DOWNHEAD

Downhead Quarry (ST684461) began to produce andesite for the Somerset Basalt Quarry Co in 1905. Initially, the stone was crushed at the roadside in Downhead where masonry associated with the crushing plant survives (ST690460). A 2ft gauge railway on which the stone was transported can still be traced, and sections of the track are *in situ*. About 1907 this line was extended west to Waterlip Quarry and from there to Cranmore Station. A new crushing plant was erected next to the original quarry. Some masonry survives, but the quarry is abandoned and water-filled. In 1945 a new quarry was opened to the east (ST688461) but this has also been abandoned recently. The crushing plant still stands. A stone **mill** has been partly demolished but the wheel pit is recognizable (ST689459).

DULCOTE

The **paper mill** (ST565449) dates from the mid-18th century. Late in the following century it produced leather board before it was burnt down in 1904. A brick chimney stack and stone containers have survived amidst the masonry ruins. The red brick Georgian mill house is occupied. Across the road to the west **Farm Mill** (ST564449) has retained its small iron breast wheel with rim

gear, which was used to power agricultural machinery. A number of millstones adorn the adjacent garden. **Dulcote Quarry** (ST568442), to the north of the East Somerset Railway line, is still worked for road metal.

DULVERTON

This is a distinctive town, set in the narrow valley of the River Barle and built in the local red stone. **Marsh Bridge** (SS907289) consists of a fascinating mixture of building materials. The cast-iron work, dated 1866, was produced by Hennet & Spink of Bridgwater. **Barle Bridge**, at the west end of the town (SS912278) has five pointed arches with double arch rings. It was widened by John Stone in 1819 – a fact recorded on a stone which also refers to repairs carried out in 1684. **Hele Bridge** (SS933278) over the River Exe, has three pointed arches and massive cutwaters on the upstream side. Water power has always been plentiful in Dulverton. **Higher Mill** (SS913279) and **Lower Mill** (SS913277) both survive. The

42   Dunster – The overshot waterwheels

latter, now a laundry, was a wool and then a crêpe mill. There was an **edge-tool works** at Town Marsh (SS915281). About a mile downstream from Barle Bridge Armfield turbines were installed about 1890 to generate electricity. The weir and the building which housed the turbines survive (SS919269) although they stopped producing electricity on a regular basis in 1938. The relative isolation of the town may explain why the **Union Workhouse** was erected in 1855, 20 years after the introduction of the New Poor Law into Somerset. The building (SS912279) now houses the Tourist Information Office.

DUNSTER

Dominated by its medieval castle, this little town epitomizes Somerset to thousands of visitors. In the centre, is the covered **yarn market** (SS992438), a reminder of the importance of the woollen trade. South of the castle is a three-storey, stone corn **mill** which has two wooden **overshot waterwheels** (*Plate 42*) *in situ* (SS991434). The axles of the wheels and the launder which fed them with water are also made of wood. North-west of the Church is the famous Priory **Dovecote** (SS990437) which has retained its wooden revolving ladder which turns easily on its 400-year-old bearing. **Gallox Bridge** (SS989432) is a two-arched packhorse bridge with an unusual protective wall 24 yds long. It is three ft wide between the parapets. West of the bridge, on the Timberscombe Road is a **toll house** (SS988434). It is a pink washed building of two storeys but its only distinguishing feature is its name.

EAST COKER

Drake's **Webbing and Twine Factory** (ST537129) appears near derelict. It is built mainly of stone with a slate roof. The round brick chimney appears fairly modern, and there are a three-storey block and several weaving sheds. The factory was originally water-powered. A **corn mill** (ST536129) built of stone stands on the west side of the village. It is a three-storeyed stone building of six bays which contained an overshot wheel beneath the stone archway.

EAST HARPTREE

Smitham Hill lies on the new county boundary which cuts the parish in two. On this site (ST556547) stands the only surviving **chimney** associated with the Mendip lead industry. Although it lost a few courses of bricks in the process, the chimney was recently made secure by the efforts of the Mendip Society. The structure is built in local stone and brick on the Cornish pattern. It was erected by the East Harptree Lead Works Co Ltd to re-process the slags, abundant dumps of which survive to the east of the chimney. The remains of the reservoir, buddles and condensing flues can be traced in the surrounding forest area.

EVERCREECH

Several industries have left their mark on this growing town. In Queens Road there is a building which was a **silk factory** in the first half of the 19th century (ST649389). It is a two-storeyed stone building with two short wings projecting towards the road. More recently it housed a mineral-water factory. To the north, on the opposite side of the road, is another stone building, three storeys high with stone-framed windows. Originally this formed part of the silk factory but is now incorporated in the adjacent **creamery** (ST648390) which Unigate took over from C. & G. Prideaux in 1959. The **brick works** of the Somerset Brick and Tile Co (ST638369) are now occupied by a firm of builders' merchants and only the former offices of the brick company survive. Three large **lime kilns** are standing to the west of the old railway line (ST644388). They are about 30ft high with a ramp running north to the site of the original quarry, now abandoned.

Pecking Mill (ST640378) is a handsome two-storey stone building of Georgian design. The millpond to the north is completely overgrown. The **toll-board** which stood at the now demolished toll house on the Shepton Road, has recently been rediscovered. Evercreech **Town Station** (ST645387) has been demolished but Evercreech **Junction Station** (ST639365) survives. It is a single-storey stone building with a stone goods shed to the north. The public house standing next to this once important railway junction has unfortunately abandoned its apposite name, The Silent Whistle.

At **Elbow Corner** (ST630383) one crossing gate over the abandoned railway line survives together with the keeper's house.

EXFORD

This is probably the most important community and route centre on Exmoor. Iron ore has been mined in the area and several sites of **mines** have survived, e.g. in the **Exe Valley** (SS809401). **Water mill** buildings have survived at Westermill (SS824398), Edgcott (SS849387) and **Lower Mill** (SS843890) but an overshot wheel has also survived at the latter. **Newland Quarry** (SS824385) was worked for limestone. Two water-filled pits mark the site of the quarry but several associated buildings have survived including two sets of **lime kilns** and a **T Bob House**. An incline and a drainage adit which linked the quarry with Pennycombe Water also survive. Last worked in 1914, these quarries supplied lime to the Knights and other improving farmers on Exmoor.

FARLEIGH HUNGERFORD

There was an important woollen factory between the River Frome and the mill leat, but little survives except the **watercourse** (ST803576). A **toll house** stands on the hill above the Castle entrance (ST800574) – a two-storey rectangular building with colour-washed stone walls. A splendid round **water tower** built of stone with a conical roof stands above a cast-iron stand pipe with a lion's head (ST801573).

FROME

This is the most interesting urban centre in Somerset. The old town is built on the steeply sloping hillsides in the mellow stone of the locality. As a result of pressure from the Frome Society and other interested bodies, at least part of the area of **industrial housing** off Trinity Street (ST772482) which was built between 1675 and 1725, will be preserved. In the middle of this period Defoe expressed the opinion that Frome could become 'one of the greatest and wealthiest inland towns in England.' The prosperity which Defoe witnessed and which stimulated the development of weavers' houses in the Trinity area was the result of the expanding woollen industry, especially the growth of the trade in Spanish medleys. Towards the end of the 18th century water power was applied to more and more processes in the manufacture of woollen cloth and several mill buildings have survived in the town.

At Adderwell an 18th-century **factory**, originally water-powered, has two storeys and a mansard roof (ST781472). To the south and east two large stone buildings comprise **Providence Mills** and are now occupied by a chemical works. They are both stone built and are served by an octagonal section chimney. **Wallbridge Mills** (ST787478) were the last to produce woollen cloth in the town, ceasing production in 1965. The premises are now occupied by a carpet manufacturing company. To the north of the road and alongside the river there are two stone buildings, both of three storeys with brick decorated windows. To the south is a large red brick building which was a dye house with ventilated walls and roof. It is dated 1887. Another **woollen mill** stands to the north of South Parade (ST774479). It is a stone building of four storeys with stone-framed, segment headed windows. It was rebuilt in 1821 after a fire. **Leonard's Mill** (ST772493) is a stone building alongside the River Frome. Further downstream **Jeffreys Mill** has retained two blocks (ST773498), one of which is three storeys high and has a tiled locum. The adjoining wing has been restored as a dwelling. **Iron Mill** (ST781502) is a three-storeyed stone building with two light windows. Reference has already been made to a dye house at Wallbridge. At one time there were many similar establishments on the banks of the Frome. The town was famous for its blue dyes which were derived from locally grown and imported woad. One round, stone-built **drying stove** stands in Justice Lane (ST777483) and another may be seen north of Willow Vale (ST779481). The latter is behind a stone building with ventilated walls which stands on the road side. On the town side of this **dyehouse**, and also in Willow Vale is a **woollen factory** building of three storeys with a tiled mansard roof which has also served as a piano factory.

The **silk factory** in Merchant's Barton (ST778478) has some of the characteristics of the early woollen mills. It is a stone building of four storeys with seven bays and stone segment-headed windows. When it produced silk it was owned by the Le Gros family. Another building which looks like a woollen factory is on the site of the **Selwood Iron Works** in The Butts (ST776476). It is a stone building of three storeys with segment-headed windows. Singer's **foundry** (ST776482), in which the famous statue of Queen Boadicea which graces the Thames Embankment was cast, is still in production. Another **iron works**, once occupied by the bell-founding firm of Cockey can be identified at Garston (ST782479). The **railway station** (ST785476) is one of the few GWR stations to retain its overall roof. In view of its historical interest the site is disappointing. The famous roof of rusting corrugated iron with central ventilation louvres is standing above wooden clad walls which are badly in need of a coat of paint. The goods shed of stone and timber to the south is surrounded by litter. Decay and dereliction pervade the site. Alongside the station site to the west, one wall, one storey high, survives of the **maltings**. One or two of the windows have retained the iron frames which look identical in design to those in the **maltings** of Lambs Brewery (ST776477) which are dated 1897. Another **malthouse** has survived at Locks Hill (ST781474). Industrial premises which are also close to the railway are the red brick buildings of the Express Dairy Company, dated 1934 (ST784477). East of the Station is Frome's only surviving **corn mill** (ST787476) although the building at Rodden (ST792475) is probably the original **grist mill**.

The **gas works** (ST776486) have survived at Welshmill. The large stone-built retort house and several out-buildings are occupied by a manufacturing concern. The splendid 19th century premises of Butler & Tanner's **Selwood Printing Works** dominate Trinity Street (ST773482). The line of the **Dorset & Somerset Canal** can be traced from Spring Gardens towards the town. The most impressive feature is the great masonry embankment which constitutes what is known locally as **Roman Wall** (ST771495). **Toll houses** survive at the foot of Gibbet Hill (ST759473) – a square stone building of two storeys with a tiled roof – and at Cottles Oak (ST769481) which is of similar design and is dated 1861. **Boundary stones** from the turnpike era survive in Bridge Street (ST777482) and Christchurch Street East (ST778477). Several

of the roads in Frome pre-date the turnpike age. St Catherine's Hill, with its **raised pavement** (ST775480); the **cobbled paving** of Gentle Street (ST776478) and what might have been a 17th century shopping precinct, complete with central **water course**, Cheap Street (*Plate 43*) (ST777480), are the best examples. The **Town Bridge** (ST777481) is the only bridge in the county to retain its shops, although only on its north-west side.

GALHAMPTON

A pretty two-storey **toll house** (ST636302), built in the local yellow stone stands at the junction of the A359 and B3152 into Castle Cary. The road from Castle Cary to Sparkford was turnpiked by the Langport, Somerton and Castle Cary Trust and there are several excellent cast iron **mile posts** inscribed 'Wightman – Founder', e.g. (ST632294).

GLASTONBURY

Chaingate Mill (ST499387), which stands to the west of the perimeter wall of the famous Abbey, is in a state of total dereliction behind its crumbling façade. It was a three-storeyed grist mill, built in blue lias stone with a square brick chimney. It contained at least two pairs of stones and had a wooden locum on the east gable wall. Originally it was powered by water, but all trace of the wheel has gone. More recently, steam power was used. A large reservoir – now empty – stands to the south of the site and several millstones have been used for decorative purposes in what was once the garden. In spite of its medieval yearnings, modern Glastonbury is a brick town. Very little survives of the **brick works** which operated on both sides of the Wells Road beneath Windmill Hill. Some of the drying sheds are now occupied by a timber merchant (ST507402) and the remains of the clay pits can be identified in the hillside behind. A row of brick cottages on the A39 have the name **Pottery Cottages** (ST505402) and **Merrick Terrace** (ST495388), dated 1903–13, is a reminder of Frederick Merrick proprietor of the Avalon Brick and Tile Works in Wells Road. The town has been associated with tanning and the manufacture of leather and sheepskin goods for at least 100 years. The **tannery** at Northover (ST487379) was taken

43   Frome – Cheap Street

over by Morlands in 1870. The water needed in the tanning process was extracted from the much older millstream which powered the medieval **fulling mill**, the two-storeyed stone building which now forms part of the factory complex. Another **tannery** is also sited on this millstream at Beckery (ST488384). It belongs to Bailys and the premises stand above the site of an older **corn mill**, of which only a few foundations and the water courses survive. The oldest part of the tannery is situated between the road and the millstream. One timber-sided building actually straddles the stream and the hooks from which sheepskins were suspended in the water are *in situ*. There are two three-storeyed buildings of blue lias, one on each side of the road. The firm's offices are housed in the original Baily family house. Some employees were housed in the red brick terrace to the east, opposite a now derelict building with gothic windows which was built for the company secretary. The millstream supplied water for the upper pound of the **Glastonbury Canal**. It is not possible to distinguish the site of the original canal basin at the end of Dyehouse Lane (ST492391) but the line of the canal can be traced from this point to the **aqueduct** across the River Brue (ST480392). This was a cast-iron structure, but the canal was blocked by two masonry walls after its closure. What was the Canal Company's cottage for the lock-keeper stands at the roadside. It was subsequently used by the keeper of the railway level-crossing. The **iron bridge** which carried the Somerset Central railway across the Brue, just to the south of the aqueduct site is also standing. The **railway station** at Glastonbury survives in a ruinous condition (ST491389) having been incorporated in a coal and timber yard since the closure of the line. To the south the red brick building which was built as The Abbey Arms and Railway Hotel in 1861, but later served as the offices of the Somerset & Dorset Railway, has also survived. The line of the railway can be traced through the outskirts of the town to **Tin Bridge** (ST511405) which is a notorious traffic hazard on the A39. To the north of this bridge a stone commemorates the site of the **Hartlake Toll Gate** (ST512409) and to the north again is the medieval earthwork known as **Fountains Wall** which may have been a wharf to serve the town (ST511412), but more probably

formed part of the early defences against flood water. The **gas works** in Northload Street (ST498392) have been demolished and the surviving gas holder is an object of complaint by local councillors. The **tithe barn** of Glastonbury Abbey has been tastefully restored to house an excellent collection of agricultural machinery and rural crafts (ST504385). This Museum of Rural Life is very necessary in a county such as Somerset where agriculture has always been a vital industry, and its present site has ensured the preservation of a splendid building which is an exhibit in its own right.

HAMBRIDGE

A pretty **brewery** building (*Plate 44*) stands on the B3168 where it crosses the River Isle (ST397224). It is a stone building with a timber clad upper storey which overhangs the ground floor. It is four storeys high and has a stone bell cote. The main brewery premises which stood to the west have been pulled down. The waterwheel and grindstones of an associated **corn mill** have been preserved behind a modern extension. The wheel was a broad, iron breast shot manufactured at the Parrett Ironworks by Sibley & Sons. The junction of the Westport Canal with the River Isle is marked by a **half lock** at Middlemoor Bridge (ST405224). This has been blocked by a stone wall and sluice mechanism, but the siting of the single lock gates can be identified. They were probably designed to prevent back-flooding of the canal when the river flooded. At Midelney the masonry of a more substantial double-gated **pound lock** survives at the junction of the Isle and the Parrett (ST417235).

HASELBURY PLUCKNETT

Haselbury Bridge (ST459109) which carries the old road from Crewkerne to Yeovil over the River Parrett has been described as 'the most perfect medieval bridge in this part of the country'. It has two pointed arches with centre piers and a sill at the foundations. It has a span of 24ft (7·35m) and is 12ft (3·27m) wide between the parapets. **Easthams Tollhouse** (ST457107) is a two-storeyed building with gothic windows. It is built in ham stone with a slate roof. In the centre of the village is a fine milestone inscribed 'YEOVIL VII' (ST472107). **Hasel-bury Mill** (ST459112) is a handsome stone building of three storeys and three bays. It was powered by an overshot wheel, but the leat is now overgrown and dried up. It was a corn mill.

HIGH HAM

Stembridge Windmill (*Plate 45*) (ST433508) is unique in that it is the only windmill in Britain which has retained its thatched cap. The tower has recently been restored by the National Trust. It is built in blue lias stone and dates from 1822. It continued in use until 1898 when the cap jammed. The sails are recent additions. The mill originally drove two pairs of stones and the drive shaft and gear wheels are in working order. The whole structure stands on a raised, wall-lined mound. The mechanism for turning the cap is housed in the tail. A number of millstones have been used for decorative purposes in the garden of the adjacent mill house.

HOLCOMBE

Holcombe Maltings (ST673498) is a substantial stone building of three storeys which is now used by a transport firm. **Edford Colliery** (ST673489) still retains some of its original buildings although the site is occupied by a concrete block factory. To the west is a pretty **packhorse bridge** (ST668488) which carried an old road over the Dorset and Somerset Canal. It is a single arched structure with stone parapets. **Ham Mill** (ST676486) was a grist mill built in 1845. In 1925 the site was used for a brickworks but quite recently has been converted into a private residence. It is a three-storeyed stone building with an attic.

HOLFORD

The ruins of a **dye house** stand on the site of a silk factory (ST155411) although the vat has been destroyed. In 1803 the factory employed over 100 workers, mainly women and children. The large iron overshot waterwheel

44   Hambridge – Brewery

45   High Ham – Stembridge Windmill, (F Hawtin)

of the **tannery** stands alongside the hotel in Holford Combe (ST151406). There are the remains of other dams and water courses higher up the combe.

HUISH EPISCOPI

The site of a **corn mill** (ST429266) can be distinguished although the mill pond has been almost obliterated. The mill changed over to steam power and the square brick chimney dated 1867 is the most imposing survival on the site. Nearby, at Pisbury, the mound on which a **windmill** stood until it was demolished in 1921 can be identified (ST442266).

ILCHESTER

Hainbury Mill (ST527234) was operated by the Ilchester Flax Co in 1822. The premises are now derelict and one building has been reduced to one storey. The mill leat survives but the machinery has been removed. It probably housed an undershot or low breast wheel. Ilchester was a port in Roman times and the wharves on the side of the River Ivel have been excavated. The river was also used by the Ivel Navigation Company in the early 19th century. A fine **pack horse bridge** carries the old road from Ilchester to Long Sutton over the river (ST500234). Known as Pill Bridge it has three round arches and two piers on both sides. It is built of lias stone and is 4ft (1·2m) between the parapets. Recently a bypass has been built round the town. Before this, it was an important route centre. A stone **milestone** (ST522226) records the mileage to London (127½ miles).

ILMINSTER

On the north side of the pleasant market place is the imposing façade of the **shirt and collar factory** (ST362145). It is a three-storeyed building of ham stone. On the south side of the market place, at the end of the road from Chard, is a single-storey block of red brick weaving sheds which now house an antique shop. At Dowlish Ford the premises of a rope, twine and sailcloth **factory** are occupied by C. & J. Clark Ltd (ST359135). Originally powered by water, the mill pond and sluices have been retained for decorative purposes. **Rose Mill** (ST344150) was occupied by the Chard Lace Company. The weir

and sluice gates have survived although the mill pond has been filled in. The main factory block is stone built and three storeys high. To the west a partly demolished building houses two Armfield turbines. Two cast-iron staircases are on the north side of the factory and to the east is a single-storey roundhouse, built of stone, which appears to have served as a drying stove. A small **rope walk**, a single-storey building on the A3037 is still in production (ST349130). On the Chard Road out of the town are the remains of the **gas works** (ST361141). The base of the gas holder and the brick retort house have survived. A terrace of cottages to the north appear to have been associated with the works. A two-storey **toll house** stands at Hazel Well (ST347152) and another at Old Gate (ST365173). The Chard Canal was raised 82ft (24·9m) by an **incline plane** before it plunged into a short, double-width red brick **tunnel** (ST357139). Although the incline is clearly visible the tunnel has been almost completely filled by systematic tipping. The line of the canal is visible again to the south where it crossed the Chard Road at Dowlish Ford. A line of cottages stand on what must have once been the bank of the canal at this point (ST359134). The town has retained one or two coaching houses, including **The George Hotel** (ST362145) which accommodated the future Queen Victoria in 1819.

KEINTON MANDEVILLE

At the end of the 18th century this village was renowned for its quarries which produced slabs of lias stone two or three inches thick. This was used extensively in Somerset for paving slabs both inside and outside buildings. Little remains of this industry except the name of a public house and an occasional abandoned quarry (ST546306).

KILMERSDON

The two-storeyed stone **toll house** (ST695524) belonged to the Buckland Dinham Trust. It originally stood at the top of the hill to the west but was moved to its present site about 1830. A good example of the cast-iron **milestones** of this trust can be seen on the hill previously mentioned (ST691524). To the east of the village is a **bridge** on the skew which carried the Bristol & North Somerset

Railway (ST705523). The bridge is decorated with a coat of arms.

KILVE

A **corn mill** which was powered by an overshot waterwheel has retained most of its working parts (ST150431). By the side of the track to Kilve Beach there are the remains of an **oil processing plant** (ST145444). This dates from the 1920s when an attempt was made to extract oil from the shales which occur locally. To the north again is a large **limekiln** (ST145445) which used culm brought up the beach in shallow draught boats from South Wales to burn the local limestone.

KINGSBURY EPISCOPI

Thorney Mills (ST428227) is a three-storey building of blue lias on the west bank of the River Parrett. Until 1968 it was owned by a trading company. They ground corn in the mill which is powered by an iron higher breast shot wheel, made by Coombs of Beaminster in 1866. The gearing and iron sluice gates were made by Sibley at the Parrett Iron Works. Three of the original four sets of grindstones have survived and the present owner is preserving the mill machinery in working order. Coal was brought to the site by river transport after the establishment of the Parrett Navigation Company. This company built a lock at the opposite end of the weir to the mill and the masonry is clearly visible. Withies are also processed close to this site and withy boilers can be seen to the north and south of the mill.

The Durston–Hendford branch of the Bristol & Exeter Railway helped to make river transport uneconomic but led to the establishment of a milk collecting depot at **Thorney** (ST428231) which is still operational although the railway line has been abandoned and the milk is now collected and distributed by road tanker. The **toll house** (ST435213) is a pretty one-storey brick building which mirrors the now derelict house at Muchelney. Both were built in the 1820s for the Langport, Somerton and Castle Cary Trust. On the Green, in the middle of the village, is an octagonal **lock up** (ST434211) built of ham stone with a ball finial.

LANGPORT

This ancient town developed at a natural crossing point of the River Parrett. The latter was for long the principal means of transporting bulky commodities to and from the south of the county. The Stuckey family grew rich on the trade in corn, salt, coal and timber which flowed through the town. Although mainly remembered for their banking expertise, this family helped to improve the river transport system. In 1839 the Parrett Navigation Company replaced the medieval **bow bridge** with that which stands today at the west end of the town (ST415265). At the same time the company built a **lock** north of the bridge (ST415269), the masonry of which and the lock-keeper's cottage have survived. Alongside the river there are red brick **warehouses** and the original **quay** can also be seen on the east bank north of the bridge. South of the bridge a brick, three-storeyed warehouse stands. Another building at the north-west end of the bridge appears to have been a public house, but it is distinguished by a metal **swing-bridge** which links the road at bridge level with the first floor. West of the bridge it is possible to distinguish the line of the Hendford–Durston railway but the **West Station** (ST414264) has been demolished together with an interesting weighbridge house clad with tiles. Langport still has the Castle Cary and Paddington line but the **East Station** (ST424272), although standing, is no longer used. On this line, the **viaduct** which carries the railway across the flood plain of the Parrett is the only significant monument (ST416274). The **Town Hall** (ST419267) – a well-proportioned building of brick over stone arches – is alongside a slight hump in the road which marks the site of the Little Bow Bridge over a canal which was cut to bypass the larger bridge to the west. This waterway has now been culverted. Almost opposite the Town Hall is the National Westminster Bank which originally housed the bank of Stuckey and Bagehot.

LILSTOCK

The deserted harbour at Lilstock (ST173454) once provided employment for local lime burners. There is a long shallow harbour now blocked by the shingle beach. When the tide is well out, the foundations of a substantial

breakwater are revealed. On the quayside, which has an iron ring *in situ*, are the remains of a limekiln, a coal store and two rooms which have been cut out of the rock. It is claimed that an inn was once housed here. A line of steps up the hillside behind the limekiln lead to the cliff top and the site of another **limekiln** (ST174453).

LONG SUTTON

The **bridge** over the Ivel at Long Load (ST467238) is basically medieval. It retains four pointed arches but the central rounded arch is post 1660. In the 19th century boats unloaded coal and other goods on the river bank, from whence it was carried to the coalyard a short distance to the south. Lime burning was extensively practised in this area, a fact which is commemorated by the name of a public house on the A372 (ST481257). A large **limekiln** stands on the main road opposite the turning into the village (ST469258) and another to the west (ST454265).

Knole Mill (ST483251) has a higher breast wheel of iron which was manufactured by the Somerset Wheel and Waggon Co, Martock. The wheel, which has a rim drive mechanism, powered one set of millstones and various farm machines. The water is carried to the wheel by an iron launder set on stone piers. A short distance upstream is the site of an earlier mill which has also been used as a sheep dip.

LOPEN

Very little has survived of the flax, sailcloth and twine **factory** (ST430142) except for a long wall on the boundary of the site and the stone and brick cottage with mullion windows dated 1795. The adjacent modern premises of a linen factory are built in red brick and now house a different industry.

LOVINGTON

West Lovington Mill (ST593322) is a stone building of two storeys with an attic and red tiled roof. The mill extends over the leat and the wheel appears to be in place. This and the mill house form a private residence.

LULLINGTON

Staplemead Mill (ST787508) was originally used for carding, spinning and finishing woollen cloth. Only minor buildings of this industry survive on the site which is occupied by the Edenvale Dairy. **Lullington Mill** (ST787516) is a short distance downstream. It was originally a fulling mill but more recently served as a saw mill. The mill building is now one storey high and five bays long. It is built of stone with segment headed windows. The weir and sluice gates survive as does the two-storeyed factory house alongside. A **limekiln** (ST774529), in a ruinous state, stands on the side of the road to Laverton. The quarries which provided the raw material have been mainly in-filled. **Henham Bridge** (ST784529) is on the line of a Roman road in a very isolated position. It consists of a single round arch with two large keystones which protrude above the level of the track. The bridge has no parapets and a span of about 6ft (1·85m).

MARTOCK

This very attractive town, built mainly of ham stone, is still associated with two industries which have been important in the locality for at least 150 years – the manufacture of sailcloth and of gloves. Yeo Bros Paull & Co established their sailcloth business in 1864 and the original stone frontage has been preserved in the High Street (ST463196). The premises have now extended considerably behind this frontage. Glove making is organized on both a domestic and a factory basis. There are small factories in the town, one behind the **Market Hall** (ST463193) and the other in **Water Street** (ST458189).

Very little survives to indicate that Martock once stood on a railway line. The **Station Hotel** and offices of the **coal yard** (ST462201) are two clues; most of the adjacent **gas works** have been demolished. **Hurstbow Bridge** (ST458189) in Water Street has been restored and strengthened but the original iron span cast by Murch in 1848 has been retained. The **sawmills** to the south were established in 1860. At Bower Hinton the **Somerset Wheel and Waggon Company** of W. Sparrow & Sons (ST457178) has been on its present site for more than a century. The outstanding industrial monument in this parish – and arguably in the county – is the **Parrett Works** (*Plate 46*)

(ST446187) on the road to South Petherton. This industrial site stands on the east bank of the River Parrett and includes the **manager's house** and a terrace of **workers' cottages**. The works were originally dependent on water power and the **weir** and iron sluices together with a one-storeyed **keeper's cottage** have survived. The premises have housed several industrial processes and at one time included an iron foundry and engineering works together with rope and canvas works. The main building is a handsome stone structure, four storeys high excluding the attics. Every effort was made to render the building fireproof. The floors are of stone and they are supported on cast-iron pillars. The slate roof rests on an elegant network of cast iron. The circular iron staircase is supported by a vertical column which also serves as a fire hydrant. Considerable damage has been caused by the persistent leaking of the water tank and consequently the iron breast shot **waterwheel** which was manufactured on the site is now covered in debris. The wheel not only drove the mill machinery but also pumped water into the water tank. Behind this block is a splendid square chimney built of ham stone in a style analogous to those on Brunel's atmospheric railway. A second **waterwheel** powered another range of buildings south of the chimney. These housed a rope-walk. Another **rope-walk** now serves as cattle stalls on the south perimeter of the site. The engineering works were housed in a single-storey building to the east. Its roof is supported by beautiful cast-iron trusses. Altogether this site is most interesting and deserves preservation and even restoration.

MELLS

This quiet stone-built village in the lower Nettlebridge Valley has retained its square stone **lock-up** (ST726489). The principal interest for the industrial archaeologist is the site of the **iron works** established by the Fussell family. The river supplied power for a number of forges. An ivy-clad **chimney** and some masonry indicate one site (ST735488)

46 Martock – The Parrett Works, (F Hawtin)

but the main works were situated about 500 yds (457m) to the east. James Fussell obtained a lease for this site in 1744 and his family continued to produce iron and steel implements on the premises until the close of the 19th century (ST738488). The derelict and overgrown site has been methodically excavated by BIAS under the direction of John Cornwell since 1974. From their work it is clear that the river provided the principal source of power until 1860 when steam was introduced. The substantial weir and sluices survive and the sites of several waterwheels have been uncovered, including one iron-rimmed overshot wheel which is still *in situ*. Three wheels which were under large masonry arches worked the forge hammers. The base of a **gasometer** and retort house have been uncovered and a row of hand forges alongside the river have been cleared. A range of stone buildings which provided storage and stabling space have survived in good order. The premises are privately owned and permission should be sought for those wishing to gain entry. A James Fussell was also involved in the construction of the ill-fated Dorset & Somerset Canal. In 1798 he patented a 'Machine or Balance Lock' which worked on a counter-balancing principle. Preparations were made to build a staircase of six such locks on the side of Barrow Hill (ST748500) but the company collapsed before the project could be completed. The earthworks associated with this scheme have survived as well as the site of the original **trial lock** (ST735505). The enterprise of the Fussells is the inspiration behind the stone angels which stand at the four corners of **Chantry Church** (ST719470). Each one holds a symbol of the local iron industry – sickles, keys and chains.

MERRIOTT

Tail Mill (ST449124) was built for the manufacture of sailcloth. The mill was originally water powered and consists of a central three-storeyed stone building with curved brick lintels. There are three bays on each side of a central gable which originally sheltered a hoist at roof level. To the north of this building are extensive single-storey weaving sheds. On the west side of the lane which serves the mill is a stone engine house and a single-storey brick rope-walk.

MILBORNE PORT

The large **tannery** of J. Clark & Sons (ST675190) stands on the west side of the stream which flows through the town. To the east are two buildings of four storeys which appear to have formed part of a textile works. In North Street a **glove factory** (ST676188) extends east behind a handsome stone façade of three storeys. A separate three-storey brick building with a hoist was the **dye house**. Newtown is a suburb of the town which was built during the Napoleonic Wars. It consists of a large square of whitewashed two-storeyed cottages which originally had thatched roofs. The centre of the square has been devoted to gardens and allotments. The original water reservoir and **pump house** has unfortunately been destroyed (ST668188). In the centre of the town is a two-storeyed **market hall** built of ham stone. Between this and the Church is a **ball court** (ST676186) built by Sir W.C. Medlycott in 1847 in the earnest hope 'that this court which is meant for the health and amusement of the Town will be protected from injury'.

MILBORNE WICK

An undershot **waterwheel** (*Plate 47*) with iron paddles stands alongside the road (ST668207). The sluice gate and pond have also survived. A three-storeyed stone mill building is in the process of renovation. The wheel pit which housed an overshot **waterwheel** is in the centre of the building (ST667206).

MINEHEAD

The **harbour** (SS972471) is of medieval origin and Defoe described it as 'the best port, and safest harbour, in all these counties, at least on this side: No ship is so big, but it may come in, and no weather so bad, but the ships are safe when they are in. . .' The trade associated with seaborne traffic rapidly dwindled in the 19th century but a row of **limekilns** (now topped by a car park) and the **gas holder** bear witness to its earlier importance. Tourism is the principal industry of the town today. The holiday camp is built on the site of the **brickworks** at Warren Point and nothing has survived of Marley's Victoria Brick & Tile Works at Alcombe

(SS973453). Tourism has stimulated the revival of the West Somerset Railway which operates from its terminus at **Minehead Station** (SS975463). The station is a single-storey, stone building with elegant two-light round headed windows. During the summer months coaches hauled by steam locomotives make the return journey to Williton several times each week. British Rail relinquished passenger traffic on the line in 1970.

NETHER STOWEY

Samuel Coleridge's **cottage** (ST191398) is an interesting example of a modest dwelling of the late 18th century. Coleridge's patron, Thomas Poole owned the **tannery** (ST190398) which has recently been converted to a dwelling. The profusion of oak trees on the nearby slopes of the Quantocks bear witness to the importance of this industry in the locality. At the end of the 18th century copper was mined in the West Quantock region, especially near Dodding-ton. The **Beech Wood Engine House** south

of the manor house is now in a highly dangerous state (ST174405) but the **Glebe Field Engine House** (ST177401) is in good repair and clearly visible from the A39 road. The exit of a small drainage adit survives in the lane between the two engine houses (ST177405) and two buildings which were originally associated with the mining industry stand on the A39. These are the Castle of Comfort, once an inn, and the **Counting House**, where the miners were paid, at the bottom of the lane leading to Walford's Gibbet (ST174399).

A two-storeyed **toll house**, built of rough stone and with pointed brick arches over the windows and door, stands in St Mary Street (ST193397). A short distance to the east is a small lias stone slab bearing the inscription, 'Here Ends Bridgewater Road' which marks the terminus of the Bridgwater Trust's road.

NORTON SUB HAMDON

Little Norton Mill is situated beneath the ramparts of Ham Hill (ST479157). It is a

47 Milborne Wick – Undershot waterwheel

stone building with an overshot waterwheel. The latter has an iron frame with wooden buckets.

OAKHILL

Oakhill Brewery (ST634473) has retained only the west façade of its buildings. **Courage's Maltings**, a short distance to the west (ST632473), are still in production. Although the plant has been substantially modernized, the original stone building stands at the side of the road. Little survives of the narrow-gauge railway which linked the Oakhill Brewery with the Somerset & Dorset railway at Binegar.

OTHERY

Othery Mill (ST384315) is a three-storeyed building with a tapering square-section chimney. The chimney and the upper two storeys are built of brick, the ground floor of blue lias. Attached at the west end is a single-storey brick engine house. The portable steam engine which supplied the power for the mill has been removed and the small reservoir which supplied water for the boiler has become overgrown. There were two sets of stones on the first floor but only one set is now complete. On the second floor a hoist wheel with a cogged drive has survived together with the trap doors through which the sacks were lifted. The mill stopped working in 1944. The stones and mill equipment had originally belonged to the village windmill but nothing has survived on that site.

POLSHAM

The only station between Glastonbury and Wells on the Somerset Central Railway was opened in 1861 at Polsham. The **station** has survived and is occupied as a domestic residence (ST517428). Various pieces of railway impedimenta adorn the site.

PORLOCK

This village nestles at the foot of the notorious hill which still provides a trial for the internal combustion engine. A toll road with an easier gradient lies to the north. Porlock is well placed to utilize water power and a **water-**wheel is *in situ* beside the High Street (SS886468). **Hawkcombe Mill** (SS885462) was one of the first in the country to generate hydroelectric power, which was also generated at **Bossington Mill** (SS901476).

The hamlet of Porlock Weir developed as a port in the early 19th century (SS863480). A **harbour** with lock gates was constructed complete with a **warehouse** and a **limekiln** – all of which survive, although the harbour never developed significantly. This is partly the result of the failure of Frederic Knight's railway scheme, of which some of the earthworks can be identified on the hill above the harbour.

PRIDDY

This is a pretty upland village with the hurdles for the sheep fair stacked under a neat thatched shelter on the green (ST527512). **St Cuthbert's Works** (ST544505) were the last to smelt lead on the Mendips. They finally closed in 1908. The works were similar to those at Charterhouse, Chewton Mendip and East Harptree, and resulted from the application of Cornish technology to slags left by earlier lead smelters. The site is ruinous but retains two systems of condensing flues, one of which is almost entirely subterranean. The buddles which are shown on early maps of the site have been completely obliterated but the masonry wall of the **condenser** survives behind the site of the **furnaces**. The condenser reduced the reliance on the flue system and dates from the last period in the operation of the works when lead slag was fed directly into the furnace. This was made necessary by the injunction which followed the pollution of the River Axe by the buddles.

RODE

Significant remains of the woollen industry have survived in this village. **Rode Bridge Mill** (ST802543) is a three-storeyed stone building with segment headed windows. In the millstream which runs underneath the mill there are parts of the undershot waterwheel. The building is now very dilapidated. About 1850 it was converted into a corn mill. Scuttsbridge **woollen mill** (ST789538) was demolished in 1975; the weir, mill leat and a heap of rubble mark the site. **Rockabella Factory** (ST801539) was ruinous in 1858; the site and mill leat can be traced only with difficulty. At the west end of the village is a three-storeyed stone building which served as a **woollen factory** (ST803547). Today the village is dominated by the red brick building of Sidney Fussell's **brewery** behind the Cross Keys (ST804587). The main block is five storeys high and it is served by two square brick chimneys. The premises are used as a brewery store.

Scuttsbridge (ST799539) is a packhorse bridge about 3ft (0·90m) wide between the parapets. It has three round arches and two large cutwaters on the upstream side. **Rode Bridge** (ST802543) has two rounded arches with a cutwater on the upstream side. It is linked to the mill by a causeway which keeps the road across the Frome and the millstream at the same level. In the middle of the bridge is a boundary stone separating ROAD (*sic*) from NORTH BRADLEY. At one time this also marked the county boundary.

SHAPWICK

A tower **windmill** stood on the Polden ridge above the village (ST425374) but only the mound and a few feet of stone wall have survived. An older **post mill** stood to the west between the A39 and the road leading down to the village. A later **mill** powered by steam or petrol engine stands three storeys high (ST417377). On the peat moors of the Brue Valley it is possible to trace the line of the Glastonbury Canal to the south of the disused railway. The only **lock** on this canal can be seen on Shapwick Heath (ST412418) – it consists of two substantial stone walls and a few pieces of ironwork.

SHEPTON MALLET

Until the mid-18th century this was an important woollen cloth manufacturing town. Little remains of this industry although some of the woollen factories were undoubtedly used for other trades. **Jardine's Factory** (ST627436) in Kilver Street was used for manufacturing lace. It is a handsome stone building of three storeys with a bell cote and is now occupied by the offices of Showerings Ltd. The mill pond has been retained for decorative purposes. The **silk mill** at Darshill (ST607439) has recently been destroyed but the site of the mill, the pond and the surrounding industrial hamlet are worthy of a visit. To the west alongside the road to Wells is a building with a ventilated brick wall which may have been used for **drying teasles** (ST605439). There are two beautiful **clothiers' houses** at Bowlish (ST613440) which reflect the great prosperity of the area at the end of the 17th century. When the textile trades declined the town became dominated by brewing interests. The **Anglo Bavarian Brewery** (*Plate 48*) (ST616437) is the best piece of architecture in the town – with the possible exception of the Parish Church. The brewery building is four storeys high and built of stone. The top floor has wooden louvred windows. There is a splendid chimney built in red and yellow brick, a three-storeyed maltings and a single-storey weighbridge at the entrance. The brewery was built in 1872 to manufacture Indian Pale Ale. Gartons – a Southampton family – bought the premises and produced lager there until the end of World War I. **Charlton Brewery** (ST631433) was established by Berryman in what had been a woollen mill. He drew his water from the mill pond which is still visible on the east side of the Fosse Way. By the side of the pond are very substantial maltings which are still in excellent order. The brewery ceased production in 1961. **Kilver Street Brewery** (ST627436) can be identified by the name painted over a stone archway. It marks the humble origin of the Showerings empire. It has been almost engulfed by the more recent buildings which dominate both sides of the A37 in Kilver Street.

Little remains of the **Charlton Lias Lime Works** (ST629431) except the quarry and a square stone chimney. The site has been developed as a trading estate. Across the road there is a pretty single-storeyed **toll house** (ST631431). Another relic of the days of coach travel is the **milestone** fixed to the market cross in the centre of the town (ST619437). It lists the distance in miles to 12 other towns including London and Bristol. Shepton had two railway stations – one on the Somerset & Dorset line (ST629431) and the other serving the East Somerset line (ST617432). Only the latter has survived; it is a single-storeyed stone building. The spectacular railway **viaduct** which forms an impressive backcloth to the business premises of Showerings was built for the Somerset & Dorset railway (ST628436).

48 Shepton Mallet – The Anglo-Bavarian Brewery

The town has earned some notoriety because of the presence of a prison for the last 3½ centuries. The House of Correction was first erected in the 1620s and although the treadmill was removed before World War I the premises are still in use.

SHIPHAM

There is little evidence in this village of the depravity and wretchedness attributed to it by Hannah More, but several remains of the calamine industry survive. This mineral was mined extensively in the village and the surrounding area. It was calcined before being transported to Keynsham, Bristol and the Wye Valley where it was used in the manufacture of brass. There are examples of calamine **mines**, some with stone 'ginging' near the surface (ST 445574 and 441582). A reputed calcining **stove** stands opposite the church (ST 444574). A **toll house** which belonged to the Wedmore Trust stands at the top of Broad Way (ST 444578). It is a single-storeyed building with white walls and a tiled roof.

SIMONSBATH

Simonsbath House was the only habitation on Exmoor Forest when John Knight bought the estate in 1820. The surrounding landscape with its walls, pastures, farmsteads and windbreaks, is an enormous monument to the improving agriculture which he and his son brought to the area. Note, e.g., the farmsteads at **Emmett's Grange** (SS 752368) and **Wintershead** (SS 772367). The Knights also revolutionized the transport system of the Forest. The ancient **trackways**, e.g. at Great Vintcombe (SS 725395), were replaced by the present road system. **Pinkery Pond** (SS 723423) was probably constructed as a reservoir although for what purpose is not known. The remains of an artificial watercourse leading from the pond are visible. Frederic Knight certainly attempted to link the Simonsbath area with Porlock Weir by means of a **railway**. Although never completed, substantial diggings were made and sections of the line can be detected, e.g. (SS 815414). The railway was intended to facilitate the development of the iron deposits on Exmoor. These have been worked since Roman times and some of the early workings are visible at Burcombe (SS 752382). As with the Brendons, a systematic attempt to exploit

these deposits was made in the third quarter of the last century. At **Cornham Ford** (SS 749387) there are the remains of several adits and a spoil heap on the downstream side of the footbridge. One of the most spectacular sites is at **Wheal Eliza** (SS 784381) where an adit and shaft survive. The mine was pumped dry by a waterwheel which was erected on the opposite bank of the River Barle. Only the wheel pit and mill leat are now obvious. A large spoil heap stands above the mine entrance, but the cottage which graced the hillside above has almost disappeared. The mine is reputedly haunted by the victim of a family tragedy which occurred in 1858.

SOMERTON

A two-storeyed stone **mill** (ST 498285) was originally powered by a waterwheel. The leat and sluices are visible. The short, square chimney dates from the subsequently installed steam engine. A linen collar **factory** stands in Broad Street opposite the end of New Street (ST 491286). Although it ceased production before 1939 the three-storeyed grey stone building is still occupied. The remains of a **gas retort house** stands near B3151 at the bottom of what used to be called Gas House Lane. The building has been extensively altered to serve as a milk depot, but the gable ends and adjoining cottages are original. Alabaster was quarried in the hill north of Hurcot (ST 507298). The five-arched **viaduct** (ST 492292) carries the main Exeter –London railway. It was completed in 1906. The town's **railway station** (ST 488284) is no longer used but a signal box and red brick goods shed stand.

The **Red Lion**, in the Market Square (ST 491285), is a fine example of a coaching inn. Until recently the inner archway of the courtyard bore the inscription 'Licensed to let post horses' and the post office occupied the rooms to the north of the main arch, illustrating the close connection that once existed between the Royal Mail service and coaching houses such as this.

SPARKFORD

A **milk depot** (ST 605263) which once belonged to the Sparkford Vale Co-operative Dairy Society Ltd, now houses a firm of publishers. It is strategically placed alongside the old Wilts. Somerset & Weymouth Railway – now reduced to a single track. An old **mill** and adjoining house stands (ST609256) behind the church. A **roundhouse** (ST608263) which is actually octagonal has been recently restored. It was not a toll house but it might have been a drying stove as used in the woollen industry.

STOGURSEY

On the footpath to the Castle is a **mill** (ST204426) with an iron overshot wheel which was manufactured by J. Culverwell of Bridgwater.

STOKE SUB HAMDON

This yellow stone village lies at the foot of the hill which has been quarried since Roman times for its distinctive building material. **Ham Hill Quarries** (ST479168) are still worked and the grossly disturbed surface of the hill top gives some indication of the importance of the stone which was used as far away as Exeter. For some time, the principal industry of the village has been gloving. The buildings which housed **glove factories** stand on the side of the main road (ST473173) and down the lane directly opposite (ST472175). The former is a three-storeyed building of eight bays with a loading hatch on the second floor. The latter is still used as a glove factory. It is a complex of stone buildings with a square brick chimney. A splendid thatched **tithe barn** (ST473174) stands immediately behind the Priory building.

STREET

This blue lias town has been dominated by the activities of the firm of C. & J. Clark for over 150 years. The original **factory** now houses a **Museum of Shoemaking** (ST485368) which includes early machinery and a full range of shoe styles. A **tannery** building is used as a shoe store at the junction of Leigh Road and Middle Leigh (ST484360). It consists of a two-storeyed brick building and several one-storey buildings of local stone. The **Avalon Leatherboard Factory** (ST489372) is a handsome building erected in the 1880s to manufacture leatherboard from waste materials. Because water is used in

large quantities in the manufacturing process the factory is built over a drainage rhine. It is a three-storeyed building of 12 bays with a red tiled roof and a pretty tiled locum.

A white painted **toll house** (ST486372) stands near the roundabout at the east end of the bypass. It was built by the Wells Turnpike Trust and the **gate** which is believed to have been used at this place can be seen at the north end of Brutasche Terrace (ST484371). This Terrace is one of many distinctive groups of artisans' houses built by Clarks for their employees. Wilfred Road, opposite the High Street entrance to the factory is perhaps the best example. In the centre of the town there are a number of late 19th century civic buildings, including the Crispin Hall and Vestry Room (ST484366).

TAUNTON

This busy county town stands on the River Tone which originally powered a number of mills. A **millstone** commemorates the old town mill which stood between the castle and the river (ST225246). An elegant **steam engine** is on view in the Castle Museum (ST224246). This operated in the silk factory of James Pearsall and was manufactured by Bury, Curtis & Kennedy who also supplied a similar engine for the **tannery** of E. & W.C. French in Tancred Street (ST232246) where it is today. Once a centre for the woollen industry, Taunton has little to show for its association with this and other textile trades. The silk manufacturing company mentioned above is still in production in modern premises and the **shirt factory** of Van Heusen is also on a site which was developed in 1961. Only the premises occupied by the Somerset Manufacturing Co in South Street have the characteristics of a 19th century factory (ST235244). The oldest wing is three storeys high, built of brick with 11 bays. It stands at right-angles to a more modern wing which is end on to South Street.

A number of buildings associated with brewing have survived. In Canon Street a large **malthouse**, three storeys high and built in red brick (ST229248) belonged to Starkeys but is now used as a store by Hall and Woodhouse. A nightclub occupies part of the premises which served **Jacob's Brewery** in Mary Street (ST228242). The antique shop on the road side used to be the brewery pub, known as the Bird in Hand. S.W. Arnold & Sons' **brewery** stands on the Kingston Road at Rowbarton (ST226261). Formerly a manure works, the premises were bought by Arnold in 1876 and continued to produce beer until 1955. It now serves as a store for Watneys. The central two-storey building with the water tower on top is built of red brick, but most of the other buildings are of stone. The brewery house is dated 1854. A manager's house is all that survives of the **West Somerset Brewery** below the Town Bridge, but the name has been perpetuated in the new Brewhouse Theatre which stands on the site (ST228248). A stone **cider mill** and trough have been preserved in the gardens next to the Public Library (ST225245). Other industries which prospered in the town were gloving – a **factory** was housed in the building above Millets dated 1886 (ST225249) – and brick-making. The brickworks in Wellington Road have disappeared but another site in Silver Street has recently been excavated (ST233242).

Transport facilities have always been important to the town and the river was made navigable to the Town Bridge (cast in the local Phoenix Foundry) by a company established by statute in 1699. The importance of this route is demonstrated by the location of the **gas works** at Tangier (ST224245) which depended on water-carried coal. In 1827 the Bridgwater & Taunton **Canal** was completed to Firepool (ST232253) where the top lock can be seen at the north end of the weir. Two large **limekilns**, now surmounted by the railway water tank, stand on the north bank of the canal below the lock. In 1831 work began on the Grand Western Canal which was to link Taunton with the Tiverton Canal. North of the cattle market and below the perimeter wall of the station goods yard it is possible to see the masonry of the first **canal lift** (ST228253). As a result of litigation it was decided to make a direct link from the Tone below **French Weir** (ST222247) to the Grand Western Canal at Freize Hill (ST217254). This so-called **Parliamentary Cut** was completed in 1834 and involved a lock at its east end. It is possible to trace the line of this cut, although it has been substantially filled in. The Grand Western Canal predated the opening of the Bristol & Exeter Railway to Taunton in 1842 by only four years. Brunel's original **station** was on the

down side (ST227253). Very little has survived of this and a double track was installed in the 1930s. A few of the standards which carried the cables for the Taunton & West Somerset Railways & Tramways Co Ltd can be found, e.g. in Greenway Crescent (ST222260). The tramway ran from Rowbarton to East Reach where the original **tram shed** stands (ST237247). The company closed their service in 1921. **Toll houses**, belonging to an earlier transport system, have survived in Silver Street (ST232244) and in Shuttern (ST223242).

TELLISFORD

A **fulling mill** stood on the west bank of the River Frome in the 16th century (ST806557). In 1874 it was converted to a flock mill. The surviving buildings are roofless and a turbine appears to have been installed. To the east is a fine **packhorse bridge** (ST806556) with three round arches. It has one cutwater on the upstream side. It was built without a parapet but wooden handrails have now been fitted.

THORNE ST MARGARET

The **inclined plane** at Wellisford (ST102217) – the only one on the Grand Western Canal – was designed to raise tug boats 80ft over a gradient of about 1 in 5½ft. The incline carried two sets of railway lines. The original design was to provide motive power by using the weight of large buckets of water which could be raised or lowered in two vertical shafts, to counterbalance the weight of the caissons carrying the boats. The shafts are now covered but the horizontal adits which allowed surplus water to flow into the lower pound of the canal can be seen. The system failed to work efficiently and a 12 hp steam engine was installed in time for the opening of the canal in 1838. The building which housed the engine stands next to the cottages at the top of the incline. The line of the canal can be traced to the Devon border beyond Greenham where the last of the **lifts** was installed to raise the boats 42½ft vertically (ST078198). This site has been almost completely obliterated although the keeper's house is occupied.

THORNFALCON

At the bottom of the drive to Canal Farm it is

possible to see the partly in-filled bed of the **Chard Canal** (ST281242). To the east of the farm is the first of the four **inclined planes** on which boats were raised 28ft. The **tunnel** at Lillesdon is not easy of access (ST295235); although the north portal has survived, the south end has become hopelessly overgrown and silted.

TINTINHULL

A three-storeyed, stone **factory** with red tiled roof is still used as a glove works (ST497193). A square brick chimney stands at the rear. A stone **milestone** gives the mileage to Yeovil on the road to Montacute Station (ST497191).

VOBSTER

Mells Colliery (ST712501) was closed in 1943. Many of the original buildings are now occupied by a concrete-block factory. Vobster **Breach Colliery** (ST698489) was closed before 1900. The slag heap which is covered by substantial trees is obvious, but the ivy-clad square stone chimney is well camouflaged. The ruins of an office building have survived but most significant of all are the two lines of **beehive coke ovens**. Vobster **quarry** (ST705497) is now filled with water. To the south the Dorset & Somerset Canal can be seen as it turns north to the Vobster-Mells road (ST708494). Nearby, the railway which linked Newbury Colliery with the Frome-Radstock line can be seen (ST708496). It was built as a broad-gauge line about 1860 by the Westbury Iron Company. At first trains were hauled by horses but later locomotives were introduced. The line later served Mells Colliery and Vobster Quarry.

WADEFORD

The tributary of the River Isle which runs east from this village powered several mills. **Court Mill** (ST312106) was a corn mill. The **lace mill** at Pudleigh (ST317108) has been demolished but the back wall and the leat can be seen above the modern trout farm. To the east, is a terrace of red brick cottages which housed some of the mill workers. At Nimmer a **brush factory** (ST322108) is still in operation. It is powered by a waterwheel driven directly from the leat. It is a three-

storeyed building with a small bell cote (minus the bell). **Hornsbury Mill** (ST333108) has been developed commercially as a museum. It was a corn mill but now contains a fascinating range of exhibits. The overshot wheel is *in situ* together with the gearing which was made by W. Sparrow of Martock. Should all this fail to tempt the reader, the cream teas just might!

WALTON

Walton Windmill (ST462352) is a major landmark on the Polden ridge. Although much altered since its conversion into a dwelling in the 1920s, the mill was operational until about 1910. It then had a thatched cap similar to that at High Ham. Nothing of the machinery has survived but three French Burr stones are set in the ground outside. To the north across the road is the old bakehouse where the flour was made into bread. On the A39 a **toll house** survives. It is a two-storeyed building at the end of Asney Lane (ST466364) but has retained none of the usual characteristics of these structures.

WATCHET

The **harbour**, which is still frequented by ocean-going vessels has been rebuilt several times as a result of storm damage. It was linked by rail to the West Somerset Railway of which the town **station** and a stone **goods shed** survive (ST072433). The West Quay of the harbour was the terminus for the West Somerset Mineral Railway. Quite recently the rails in the surface of the quay were covered by a 'protective' layer of concrete. South of the quay, the original **engine shed** stands (ST069435) and a little way towards the town, the **passenger station**, of which the platform has been enclosed to form a skittle alley. To the west, on the hill above the town, are the old **limekilns** (ST066435) which are now used for burning local refuse. The alabaster which was quarried from the cliffs between Watchet and Blue Anchor has been used in the local paper industry for over 200 years. An old **chimney** of the St Decuman's **paper mill** stands (ST065429) although most of the existing buildings are modern. The façade of the **foundry** of Messrs Gliddon & Son can be seen on the west side of Swain Street (ST072434). The

foundry and engineering works of Messrs J. Chidgey at Mount Pleasant (ST073432) contain many interesting implements and patterns associated with their production of waterwheels and turbines. Most of these items were donated by Mr Norman, the grand-nephew of the original proprietor, to the Museum of Rural Life in Glastonbury.

WEDMORE

A pretty red brick **gas works**, dated 1870, stands next to the original manager's house on the east side of the borough (ST437479). The retorts have been removed and the gas holder has been demolished but a gas light stands outside the house and a small square chimney with decorative brickwork appears to be in good order. An **electricity generating station** was established in 1907 in a wooden shed off Billings Hill (ST435477). The single-storey timber-clad building has survived. Heath House **windmill** (ST421469) was demolished in 1962; only the miller's house and a couple of millstones have survived on the site.

WELLINGTON

At Poole to the east of the town are the **brickworks** of W. Thomas & Co Ltd (ST149218). Unfortunately the two Hoffman kilns which graced the premises until recently have been demolished and little of significance relating to the last generation of brick manufacturing has survived except the clay pit. The modern plant made a vast complex of buildings obsolete and the products of those earlier works have become collectors' items. The firm's bricks, no doubt, help to explain the predominance of red brick buildings in the town. Wellington contains the only **woollen factory** in the county which has had a continuous history of production on the same site for over 200 years. At **Tone Mills** (ST126219), alongside the River Tone, the buildings which housed the original fulling and dyeing works may be seen. They form part of the present works of Fox Brothers & Co Ltd, and date in part to 1754. The processes have changed since that time, but the settling tanks for the dye house effluent can be seen to the east of Tone Bridge. About 1800, Thomas Fox purchased the flour mill at Tonedale which he

transformed into a water-powered **woollen mill** (ST128215). The present red brick premises were started in 1821, following a fire which destroyed the original buildings. They were constructed on the fire-proof principle, with cast-iron pillars and stone floors. In the 1840s steam engines were introduced to replace the waterwheels.

At Westford, the same stream which powered the waterwheels at the Tonedale works also powered a number of other woollen mills. There are a number of interesting **mill** buildings in this industrial hamlet. A three-storeyed stone building (ST120203) is now occupied by an antiques firm. The three-storeyed stone building to the west is occupied by a haulage firm and Unigate Dairies have occupied a third mill site. West of these buildings, the mill leat and mill pond have survived. **Prowse's Mill** (ST114199), originally another woollen mill, but latterly a butter factory, is a three-storey building of eight bays with a square brick chimney. The elegant **chimney** in the centre of Westford stands next to a single-storeyed red brick building which houses the pumps which were used to lift water into the **water towers** (*Plate 49*) at Rockwell Green (ST126200). The original ram pumps which were worked by steam have been retained inside this pumping station.

The Grand Western Canal passed through the northern outskirts of Wellington and it is possible to follow its course with little difficulty. To the east, near to the Poole Brickworks, there is a pretty stone **aqueduct** (ST147223) which has retained its original cast-iron trough. To the west **Wharf Cottage** (ST145220) stands on the bank of the canal bed, although little has survived of its earlier commercial activity. Across the road to the west is Nynehead **canal lift** (ST144218) undoubtedly the most complete of those which were built on the canal. It was designed by James Green to lift tug boats 24ft vertically. Another **aqueduct** (*Plate 50*) neatly housed in an elegant greensand bridge which carried the canal across the main drive to Nynehead Court, stands to the west of the top of the lift. Basically, this aqueduct is another cast-iron trough, although the base has been curved to match the shape of the top of the bridge arch. To the west again, at Winsbeer is the site of another lift (ST122215) which had a rise of 18ft. Although the lift is

49 Wellington – The water towers, Rockwell Green, (F Hawtin)

barely recognizable, this section of the canal's course is one of its most dramatic, giving the walker views down into the Tone Valley below the tow path. The Bristol and Exeter Railway reached Wellington in 1843. The town **station**, a modest red brick structure, has survived (ST130212). To the west the **Whiteball Tunnel** (ST095182) carries the line over the watershed into Devon. It is over 1,000 yds long and 14 vertical shafts were sunk during its construction.

WELLS

Sheldon's Mill on St Andrew's Stream (ST545453) was originally water powered. Only the wheel pit survives behind the green door which opens on to the pavement. Some of the original gearing and milling equipment have survived but the millstones have gone. **Keward Mill** (ST539449) is a large three-storeyed building of Draycott stone. The high breast shot waterwheel is in working order but the millstones were replaced by modern milling machinery in 1934. There is a French Burr stone outside the building; the weir and sluice mechanism are intact.

Three **toll houses** which belonged to the Wells Turnpike Trust stand on the outskirts of the city. At Keward (ST542450) there is an elegant two-storeyed building of three bays with an ashlar stone frontage. Stoberry Toll House (ST551466) is a more modest structure, also two-storeyed, of colour-washed stone. A two-storeyed house on Tor Hill (ST559455) completes the trilogy. A handsome cast-iron **milestone**, now unique on the Wells Trust roads, stands on the A39 west of the city, one mile from the centre (ST538447). At one time Wells had as many Railway Stations as she now boasts toll houses but unfortunately their survival rate has not been so impressive. The **level crossing** (ST546452) on the A39 is recognizable and to the west one platform of the Somerset & Dorset's station can be seen and a stone goods shed. The Station of the East Somerset Railway has been demolished; it stood to the east of the crossing. More recently the GWRs Tucker Street station has also been demolished but a **goods shed** (ST543455) and a terrace of railway cottages are standing. The red brick **Unigate Dairy** was originally linked to the railway system (ST544450).

50 Wellington – The Nynehead Aqueduct on the Grand Western Canal, (F Hawtin)

The Wells Cathedral **clock** is of interest to horologists and it is claimed that **Vicars Close** to the north (ST552459) is the oldest complete street in Europe. The **museum** on the Cathedral Green contains several items of interest to the industrial archaeologist. Priory Road Hospital (ST544452) was built in 1837 as the **workhouse** for the Wells Poor Law Union.

WEST BUCKLAND

A small **brewery** site, including the malthouse has survived at Ham (ST156217). Cutsey House (ST188205) was built as a model **farm** in the mid-19th century. The site can be seen from the M5 at the Taunton Dean service station. The farm is built on sloping ground so that livestock could be fed gravitationally. A steam engine supplied power for farm machinery; the boiler and chimney have survived. The stalls are served by a tramway to facilitate the collection and disposal of manure. A hydraulic ram from the farm is on display at the Schools Museum Service premises at Weir Lodge, Taunton (ST221251).

WEST COKER

Job Gould & Sons manufacture twine in a complex of single-storey brick buildings which have been used since the 19th century (ST521134). The **rope-walk**, which stretches to the south is completely covered, with timber walls. An octagonal section brick chimney is dated 1898. The steam engine which it served has been replaced by a diesel engine. The **rope-walk** at Millbrook Works (ST514136) is standing although the works have been closed for 10 years. **Holywell Mill** (ST528133) is a three storeyed stone building of three bays. The overshot wheel has been removed but some of the gearing and millstones (there were two pairs) have survived.

WEST HORRINGTON

The **Buddle House** (ST571481) stands by the side of the stream in Biddlecombe, at the bottom of a valley which bears the marks of lead mining. Although the roof has fallen in, the circular stone walls survive. Some galena was found when the floor was excavated some

years ago. If the building was used for buddling – and there is still some doubt about this claim – it is quite unique on Mendip. Just above the school, a short section of the old **turnpike road** has been bypassed by the modern road (ST575474–581477).

WEST LYDFORD

The **bridge** near the church (ST565318) has unusual semi-circular openings in the parapets to allow flood waters to escape. It is probably a 17th-century structure. Opposite the entrance to Lydford Park on the Fosse Way is a **stone** which marks the boundary between the Shepton and Ilchester Trust roads (ST581332). It replaced the original Red Post mentioned in the Ilchester Trust Act of 1753. A good example of that Trust's **milestones** stands at Lydford Cross (ST567309). It is a cast-iron plate on a stone pillar. To the south a building which was once a **creamery** stands in the angle between the Fosse Way and the railway (ST564304).

WESTONZOYLAND

The **pumping engine house** (*Plate 51*) on north bank of the River Parrett houses an Easton & Amos Steam Engine which was installed in 1861 (ST340328). This replaced an earlier engine which like its predecessor was used to pump water from the drainage rhines on Weston Level into the river. The engine has been restored to working condition by the Westonzoyland Engine Group in co-operation with the owners, Wessex Water Authority. The two-storeyed red brick building which houses the engine also contains an Appold Pump and a Lancashire boiler. The square red brick chimney is a good landmark on the levels. The whole complex was rendered obsolete in the 1950s by a modest diesel engine housed in an adjacent building.

WESTPORT

This hamlet developed at the terminus of the **Westport Canal** (ST385198). The canal basin and a number of warehouse buildings have survived. On the side of the B3168 is a two-storeyed warehouse, the ground floor of which is built of lias stone. The upper storey is brick built with tall arches which appear to have been filled at a later time. Alongside the canal basin is another warehouse which is a three-storeyed stone building. These premises have been partly converted into a private residence, but the loading bay and wooden crane have survived on the third floor, overlooking the basin. A fine stone **bridge** (ST385199) carries a drove road across the canal just to the north. The canal was opened in 1840 and is currently being cleared and restored.

WEST QUANTOXHEAD

Home Farm (ST105429) was developed by the Acland-Hood family as a model farming unit about 1850. The buildings are thoughtfully laid out and machinery was originally water powered. The wheel has been removed but the wheel pit can be seen. A **dovecote** of the same period has a revolving iron ladder and a number of iron staddle stones have survived. To the west is the prettiest **gas house** in the West Country (ST104428). The cylinder and retorts have been removed but

the stone building which housed the latter serves as a barn. It is a one-storey building with a superb gothic round air vent, a ventilator in the roof and a square, brick chimney.

WILLITON

Sutton's Mill (ST073406) stands on the Orchard Wyndham estate. This corn mill has retained all its machinery in working order, although the mill leat is in some disrepair. The overshot waterwheel was manufactured by J. Chidgey of Watchet. At **Bridge Farm** (ST076407), to the east of the church, is an iron undershot wheel used to turn farm machinery. There are two **toll houses** in Williton. One stands on the Taunton road (A358) at (ST079407) the other on the Bridgwater road (A39) at (ST082414). Just east of the latter is Townsend House which was built in 1838 as the **workhouse** for the Williton Union. It was designed by the famous architect, Gilbert Scott.

51 Westonzoyland – The pumping engine house, (F Hawtin)

WINCANTON

This is a disappointing town for the industrial archaeologist. The Somerset and Dorset railway line and station have largely disappeared. The Union Workhouse was demolished recently and a splendid **town mill** (ST711286) which had iron-framed windows, was pulled down for no very apparent reason. The most interesting survivals relate to road transport. Several interesting **coaching inns** survive. The Bear Hotel, with its wrought-iron sign is amongst the best of these (ST713287). A **toll house** stands on the south side of the road to the east. (ST717286) and several good **milestones** survive, e.g. (ST698285). There are a number of pleasing **civic buildings**, the red brick town **clock** (ST212286); the **court house** (ST212287) with its iron-framed windows and the stone building of the Somerset Constabulary (ST212288).

WINSFORD

This pretty village, the unlikely birth place of Ernest Bevin, has a **packhorse bridge** (SS907348) and is near to the most famous clapper-bridge in the country – **Tarr Steps** (SS868321). The total length of this bridge is 180ft (54·86m). It is about 5ft wide with an interval of approximately 15ft between the stone piers. The present structure is the result of many rebuildings because the bridge has been frequently damaged by flood water. **Eisen Hill** contains a number of **iron mines** which were sunk in the third quarter of the 19th century, e.g. (SS909371).

WIVELISCOMBE

The town is dominated by the fortress-like structure of Arnold & Hancock's **brewery** (ST083278). The original buildings are stone built, but late additions have been made in red brick. An interesting liquor tank of local slate is situated above the gateway. The brewery ceased production in 1956 and the premises were taken over by a frozen food firm. Today the buildings are empty and derelict, and demolition cannot be long delayed. Outside the main entrance is a short terrace of workers cottages. There is a **malthouse** building at Ford (ST094289). The yard and outbuildings of the town's **gas**

works can be seen in Style Road (ST083282). The **town mill** (ST085275) is a stone building which has retained the base of a chimney. A **toll house** stands at the junction of the A361 and B3188 (ST085277). The single-storey railway **station** and adjacent goods shed are all that have survived of the Devon and Somerset line (ST085276).

The quarrying of slate was important in this area in the last century. **Oakhampton Quarry** (ST085301) is a spectacular excavation which is now partly filled with water. The remains of an incline and engine house can be traced, together with the foundations of an aerial haulage system. When the quarry closed in the 1880s the hole was 300 ft deep. There is no trace of the adit which was cut to drain the workings. Other slate quarries occur in Combe Wood (ST082302).

WOOKEY HOLE

The 'quick streams and clear water' which emerge from the cave have been utilized for the manufacture of paper in this hamlet for over 200 years. The top **mill** (*Fig 6*) (ST522478), which was owned by the Hodgkinson family until 1951, has recently been purchased by Madame Tussauds who have established a working museum of hand paper-making in the old workshop. The premises consist of a large three-storeyed building which stands over the River Axe. Two conduits – to east and west – bring water to power the turbines, which are still *in situ*, and for the paper-making processes. Immediately down stream is a single-storey building, alongside the river, which is thought to have housed an early paper manufactory. St Cuthbert's **paper works** (ST531466) is the only site on the River Axe which still produces paper. The two mills at Wookey, **Henley Mill** (ST527459), which is being restored, and **Burcott Mill** (ST521456) which is in full working order, have not been recently associated with the paper industry. The latter was a grist mill and it has retained an iron overshot wheel and one set of grind-stones. **Underwood Quarries** (ST540467) are now worked for roadstone, but in the past they provided stone which was burnt in two **limekilns** at the bottom of Round Wood Quarry (ST539471).

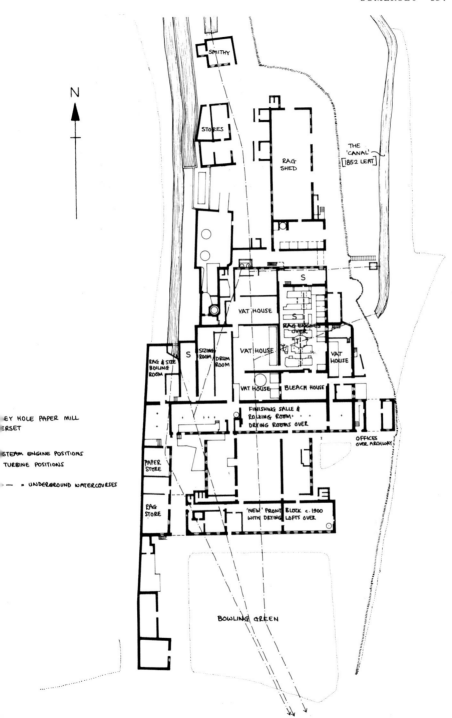

N

SMITHY

STORES

RAG
SHED

THE
'CANAL'
[1852 LEAT]

S

VAT HOUSE

S

RAG ENGINES
OVER

VAT HOUSE

SIZING
ROOM

DRUM
ROOM

S

VAT
HOUSE

RAG & SIZE
BOILING
ROOM

VAT HOUSE

BLEACH HOUSE

EY HOLE PAPER MILL
ERSET

FINISHING SALLE &
ROLLING ROOM·
DRYING ROOMS OVER

OFFICES
OVER ARCHWAY

STEAM ENGINE POSITIONS
TURBINE POSITIONS

PAPER
STORE

UNDERGROUND WATERCOURSES

RAG
STORE

'NEW' FRONT BLOCK c. 1900
WITH DRYING LOFTS OVER

BOWLING GREEN

Figure 6   Somerset: Wookey. This ground plan of the paper mill at Wookey Hole shows the lay-out of the principal buildings and watercourses. Drawn by Martin Watts and reproduced by permission of John Mosse, Architect, and Wookey Hole Caves Ltd.

WOOLVERTON

Shawford Mill (ST793534) is a two-storeyed stone building with segment headed windows. It has two channels which today power a turbine which provides electricity. The buildings were originally used for dyeing and more recently as a laundry. Now they serve as a concert hall. The **toll house** (ST793535) was erected by the Warminster and Frome Turnpike Trust, better known as the Black Dog Trust. It is a two-storeyed building with a stone tiled roof and a rounded frontage. Another **toll house** stands at the junction of the A36 and the B3110 (ST791542)

WRANTAGE

The remains of the **aqueduct** which carried the Chard Canal across the A378 near the Canal Inn are quite clear (ST308224). By following the old road to the south-east it is possible to distinguish the **inclined plane** which raised the tug boats 31ft. The keeper's house at the top is no more than a heap of rubble, but to the south is the entrance to the

Crimson Hill Tunnel (ST312221). This was originally 2,000yds (1828·80m) long. The stonework at this north end is reasonably well preserved, but the south end at Beercrocombe has been obliterated. There was no tow-path through the tunnel and the horses had to take the track to the west over the hill.

YARLINGTON

A well preserved **toll house** stands in Green Lane (ST667295). It is a two-storeyed building with a semi-hexagonal frontage.

YEOVIL

In the last ten years, several sites of considerable significance have been destroyed in the interests of 'progress'. The **brewery** is mainly submerged under the inner relief road; Yeovil Town **station** – one of the few secular buildings deemed worthy of comment in Professor Pevsner's admirable survey – has been demolished to provide a car park. The **gas works** and several buildings associated

52   Yeovil – Perrin's Leather Dressing Works, (B Murless)

with tanning and gloving have met similar ends. One gain from this wholesale extermination of industrial sites has been the creation of a longitudinal park along the old railway track from Pen Mill to Hendford which has opened up some new perspectives of the old town. Until the advent of Westlands, the principal industry of Yeovil was undoubtedly the dressing of leather and the manufacture of leather goods, especially gloves. The best building of this industry to survive is occupied by Perrin Leather Co Ltd (*Plate 52*) in **Eastland Road** (ST561162). An internal wall carries a date stone marked 1853. There are two parallel, four-storeyed buildings. The east range has double gables. Both are stone built with wooden louvred walls on the top floors. At the north end of the wing which follows the line of Eastland Road there is a brick extension with perforated walls and wooden louvres. This was the original drying room for the factory. Also to the north is a detached engine house with a small square brick chimney. The original steam engine has been replaced by an oil-fired engine. The premises are still used for tanning. There is an associated **glove factory** in Goldcroft (ST559163). This is a three-storeyed, double-gabled brick building of 18 bays. Another building, to the rear, has wooden louvres on the third floor and there is a detached brick chimney. These buildings are dated 1888.

Opposite the Post Office in Middle Street, a DIY shop occupies the buildings which originally housed the **works** of Pittards in 1848 (ST561161). Most of the remaining leather factories are sited along the stream which runs between Penn Hill and Summer House Hill. At Hendford, the Lambskin Shop (ST553154) occupies a **tannery building** of three storeys with a wooden-louvred top floor. Another substantial complex stands to the east, down the valley (ST558156). It consists of three-storeyed red brick buildings with a square chimney. The premises of Messrs Ricketts, Leather Dressers and Glove Manufacturers appear to be more modern (ST558157). To the east, at the bottom of the car park, there is another complex of brick

buildings which run parallel with the river. In Mill Street there is an attractive three-storeyed brick **factory** (ST561158). It has seven bays with stone lintels and a slate roof surmounted by a decorative ventilator and a weather vane.

At the east end of the town is **Pen Mill**, a corn mill built of stone (ST571161). It was powered by an overshot wheel and five iron sluice gates have survived. Petter's **Nautilus Works** in Reckleford (ST559162) is now occupied by the Western National Omnibus Co. The office block on the main road is built in the municipal gothic style, in brick and stone. Another Yeovil firm which had a nationwide reputation was the dairy business of Aplin & Barrett. Founded in 1888 they established their **creamery** in Newton Road in 1897. Their trade name, St Ivel (adopted in 1901), soon became a household word. The business was acquired in 1960 by Unigate. The three-storeyed brick building, which was extended in 1932, still presents a handsome façade.

Three toll houses survive in Yeovil. The **Penstile House** was re-erected opposite Aplin & Barrett's, at the corner of South Western Terrace (ST562159). It is a single-storey building of stone with a bay window and lattice window frames. **Yeovil Bridge House**, on the Sherborne Road (ST574160), is a two-storeyed building with an unusual triangular abutment which juts out into the road. This has windows on each face at both ground and first-floor levels. **Mudford Road House** (ST557177) is a two-storeyed stone building with a dormer window. It is roofed with a variety of red tiles in similar decorative patterns to those on the Yeovil Bridge House. At Hendford there is considerable evidence of the earlier presence of the railway. There is a large Goods Shed, the offices of Bradfords and the **Railway Hotel** (ST552153). At the other end of the town, **Pen Mill Station** (ST570163) is still in use. It is a modest single-storey building on what used to be the Wilts Somerset and Weymouth Railway. The old Southern Railway Station is at Yeovil Junction (ST571141) which is just across the border in Dorset.

8 Wiltshire: location map

Wiltshire

Wiltshire is the largest of the four counties in this study and its population is second only to that of Avon County. Geographically, the county's most distinctive feature is its total lack of a coastline. One could even claim that its frontiers demonstrate a total disregard for such simple geographical concepts. So diffuse is its terrain that it has proved necessary to provide two administrative centres – Trowbridge and Salisbury – whilst its largest town, Swindon, is at the opposite pole to the cathedral city.

The centre of the county is dominated by the great chalk plateau which stretches from Cranborne Chase in the south to the Marlborough Downs in the north. Although intersected by the Vale of Pewsey and the valleys of the rivers Ebble, Nadder, Wylye, Avon and Bourne, the chalk upland with its wide open vistas is the most striking feature of the area. Generally inhospitable, this upland has been abandoned as an area of settlement. The towns and villages are located in the broad river valleys, alongside the clear waters which drove the mills, flooded the meadows and fed the beds of cress.

The rivers which flow off the chalk converge on Salisbury. This medieval 'New Town' is built at a natural route centre. The various transport systems which replaced the older ridgeways, have developed in the river valleys. South of Salisbury the valley of the Avon led to the coast at Christchurch and the parallel valley of the Test to Southampton was easily accessible.

North and west of the chalk escarpment there are many villages and towns which have developed on the spring line. These settlements stretch from Bishopstone on the Oxfordshire border, round the Vale of Pewsey to Westbury. To the north and west of this line the clays and rocks of the oolitic formations give towns and villages similar characteristics to those of the south Cotswold area of Gloucestershire and the north-east corner of Somerset. It is in this area that most of the more recent industrial development of Wiltshire has been concentrated, especially in the broad valley of the Bristol Avon and its tributaries.

Agriculture is the oldest and most widely prevalent industry in the county. The chalk uplands have provided excellent sheep walks and cereal crops from early times. The water meadows of the chalk valleys gave rich pasture for dairy cattle and the clay vales to the north of the chalk have produced both arable and pastoral foods.

A consequence of this widespread dependence on agriculture has been the development of industries which process the products of the land. Wiltshire has long been famed for its dairy produce. Defoe describes how cheese and bacon were produced in the county and transported to the London market in the early eighteenth century. Milk processing factories are still important in such towns as Melksham. Calne is dominated by the associated business of processing pig meat. The link between the two industries is the skimmed milk which has long been fed to the local pig population. The railways did much to stimulate the dairy industries and created a substantial trade in liquid milk for the metropolitan region. The collecting depots which were set up for this milk trade still survive alongside the railway lines, for example at Semley.

The drier chalk lands produced the barley which fed the local malt houses and breweries. Defoe also mentions the trade in malt to London but much of it must have been used in the county's own breweries. Although this industry has suffered greatly from the processes of rationalization and mass production for national markets, beer is still brewed in several towns in the county, including Trowbridge, Salisbury and Devizes. Malthouses were at one time very common and a few can be found today. Some of these – such as the Pound Street Maltings in Warminster – are still in production.

Defoe considered that the woollen industry was the principal industry of the county. The prosperity of this industry had been established for 400 years before he wrote. The availability of water power to work the fulling stocks accounts for its earlier success. Many of the surviving watermills are sited where the fulling stocks once worked, but few actual buildings are to be seen. The old mill at West Harnham, near Salisbury, is an exception to this generalization. The development of medleys and Spanish cloths in the late seventeenth century accounts for the growing prosperity which Defoe witnessed. These new fashions increased the need for dyeing facilities, which needed large amounts of water, and the importing of high quality wool from Spain reduced the dependence of the industry on the home product. These changes helped to move the industry's centre of gravity north to the valley of the River Avon and its tributary the Biss. At Trowbridge, Bradford, Westbury, Calne, Chippenham, Malmesbury and several towns in between, factories were built in brick and stone to house the spinning, weaving and shearing machines. The early factories were powered by waterwheels, but increasingly after 1800, steam power was introduced. The woollen factories which have survived provide some of the more dramatic examples of industrial archaeology in the county today. Only one woollen factory still functions in Trowbridge, and elsewhere this once vital industry has disappeared.

A number of successor industries have moved into the old woollen factories. A few were adapted to other textiles, e.g. the manufacture of silk at the Avon Mills in Malmesbury, but the majority have adopted more bizarre processes. These include the processing of milk, the rearing of pigs and the manufacture of rubber goods. The latter was introduced to the county by Stephen Moulton in 1848 when he moved into Kingston Mill at Bradford-on-Avon. Subsequently, other mill sites were utilized at Limpley Stoke and Melksham. In Devizes, Anstie's woollen factory was taken over for the manufacture of snuff.

The clear waters which typify so many of the rivers of Wiltshire led to the development of paper manufacturing – for example, at Slaughterford and Downton. The latter is also noted for its tannery. The processing of leather was an obvious industry to develop in a county with such a dependence on sheep and cattle. Apart from that at Downton, tanneries still operate at Dilton Marsh near Westbury and at Holt.

Unlike the other three counties in this gazeteer, Wiltshire has no coal mines. The lack of this basic industrial fuel helps to explain the difficulties and stagnation experienced by some of the county's industries after 1850. Those industrial centres which were closest to the Somerset and Bristol coalfields were less seriously disadvantaged. Iron ore was worked at Seend and Westbury in the second half of the nineteenth century. At both sites blast furnaces were erected and the ore was smelted close to the quarries. Production at Seend finished about 1900 and although it continued at Westbury until after World War I, very little survives of the iron industry on either site.

Quarrying for building stone and for lime and chalk products was once an important industry and several sites of interest have survived. The stone at Box and Corsham was both mined and quarried. Only one underground works continues in production at Monks Park, Corsham. To the south, in the vale of Wardour, Chilmark stone was also mined. Until very recently it has been also quarried in the Tisbury area. Today, the industry must be studied mainly through the stock of stone buildings which it helped to create.

The lack of good building stone on the chalk lands has left two interesting architectural features – thatched walls and flint buildings. The thatch was needed to protect the cob walls from erosion. Flint was usually split to reveal its shiny surface and incorporated in buildings together with either brick or stone. Chalk was worked for lime and whiting and some quarries, for example at Charnage Down at Mere, are still in production. Sand was excavated from a number of sites in the Melksham area and gravel is worked in the far north of the county near Cricklade. The massive chimney which serves as a better landmark than the white horse at Westbury is part of the cement works which still extract chalk from the hill south of the town.

Wiltshire is well endowed with watermill sites. An ever-increasing number of mill buildings have been converted to private dwellings, but their characteristic design and situation make them fairly easy to recognize. Water power was used in the manufacture of woollen, paper and leather goods, as well as for the more conventional grinding of corn. Windmill sites are much less common, although there is no doubt that they were far more prevalent than the surviving handful suggests. Not one windmill has survived in its original form, but the tasteful restoration of Wilton Windmill by the County Council shows what a far-sighted local authority can achieve. Although generally used to grind corn, a windmill in Devizes was used to grind tobacco for snuff.

Steam power was used quite extensively in the Wiltshire woollen industry but none of the engines has been preserved. The county can justifiably be proud of the restoration of the two pumping engines at Crofton, one of which is now the oldest steam engine produced by the firm of Boulton & Watt which is in working order on its original site. Consequently, the preservation of these engines is of national as well as local significance, and the Crofton Society are to be congratulated on the excellent work which they have performed.

Wiltshire has not escaped the general destruction of local gas generating plants which followed the change-over to North Sea gas. Consequently, the surest guide to previous existence of such plants is the surviving gas holder which has usually been retained to store the new product. However, a few retort houses have survived and that at Salisbury is of particular interest. The county had at least two local bodies which generated electricity with water-powered turbines. The machinery at Downton has only recently been removed, but as at Salisbury's Town Mill, the building and sluices have survived.

Strategically placed across the principal routes from London to the West Country, Wiltshire has many remains of transport systems which go back to prehistoric and Roman times. The road through Marlborough and Chippenham towards Bath is one of these ancient routes and it was one of the first in the county to be turnpiked in the early eighteenth century. By the end of that century many more miles of Wiltshire roads had been similarly organized. Substantial remains of the turnpike age have survived – toll houses, guide posts and coaching houses. Each trust adopted its own design of milestone and there are dozens of examples to be seen. One of the most interesting groups can be seen along the side of White Sheet Hill near Mere, where the old turnpike road has not experienced the mixed blessing of tarmacadam.

Only one river system was taken over by a navigation company in Wiltshire, but the River Avon Navigation Act of 1664 which aimed to make that river navigable from Christchurch to Salisbury, was an early example of this kind of transport enterprise. Little survives today but careful research has positively identified some interesting features – particularly the lock at Britford.

Canals which served predominantly rural areas were rarely profitable but the Kennet and Avon Canal which linked the Avon Navigation at Bath with the Kennet Navigation at Newbury managed to operate successfully into the twentieth century. It was opened throughout its length in 1810 and, thanks to great efforts by enthusiasts and professionals should eventually be restored to full working order. There is so much to see along its length that it is difficult in a short space to mention all the interesting features. The canal passes into the county over the Dundas Aqueduct (see Avon). The Avoncliff Aqueduct is not nearly so splendid but the juxtaposition of buildings and transport routes make this a fascinating site today. The Caen Hill flight of locks at Devizes is probably the most impressive feature of the canal, although the best views appear to be obtained from the air. The summit level above Devizes, with the Burbage Wharf, the Bruce Tunnel and the Crofton Pumping Station is well worth detailed examination.

The other canals which crossed Wiltshire have fared less well. The Wilts and Berks Canal opened in the same year as the Kennet and Avon. It ran from the latter canal at Semington to Abingdon on the Thames. Although not finally abandoned until 1914 it is now derelict over its entire length. However, it remains an attractive route to follow and several locks, aqueducts, wharves and warehouses can be distinguished. Even before the GWR the Wilts and Berks Canal put Swindon on the map. It is from the outskirts of this town that the longest branch was constructed to join the Thames & Severn Canal at Latton, north of Cricklade in 1819. The line of this branch is also derelict, but the southern entrance to the tunnel at Cricklade and the wharf at Latton are well worth visiting. The Thames & Severn Canal just passes through the very north of the county. Opened in 1789, it was finally closed to through traffic in the 1920s. The Wiltshire section is now overgrown but it is possible to trace its course, on which three of the distinctive round lock-keepers' cottages have survived at Cerney Wick, Marston Meysey and Inglesham.

The more rural south-east of the county never supported a successful canal venture. The Southampton and Salisbury Canal Navigation which was started in 1795 was one of the many casualties of the long wars with France. However, a few sections were built and have survived – for example the cutting at Alderbury.

Wiltshire had more success with her railways. It was almost impossible to conceive of a railway line from London to the West Country which did not pass through this county. Indeed, it would appear that a high proportion of the county's lines were so important to the national network that they escaped the cuts of the 1950s and 1960s. The Great Western Railway was completed from London to Bath by 1844. Built on the generous broad gauge advocated by I.K. Brunel, the original route is still used by inter-city trains today. The line has many interesting items of industrial archaeology of which perhaps the most important are Box Tunnel and Chippenham Viaduct. Swindon was one of the first railway towns and the tasteful restoration of the original estate built by the railway company for its employees deserves the highest praise.

The broad-gauge system was extended from the first line at Thingley, south of Chippenham, to Trowbridge and Westbury and then through Somerset and Dorset to Weymouth. This line, operated by the Wilts Somerset & Weymouth Railway Company, was built between 1845 and 1857. A branch from this line was extended from Warminster down the Wylye Valley to Salisbury and opened in 1856. In 1862 a short cut was completed from the Berks & Hants Railway at Hungerford, through Devizes to Westbury. This became increasingly effective with the completion of the

Patney–Westbury line in 1900 and the Castle Cary–Durston line (in Somerset) in 1906. The new through-route thus created proved to be one of the fastest lines between London and Exeter and is still in use today.

The GWR spawned a number of other branch lines, to Calne, Savernake, Cirencester and Malmesbury. Each of these branches has been abandoned but several structures and buildings associated with them have survived. The GWR line from Swindon to Stroud and Cheltenham via Kemble was opened in 1841 and is still used. In 1903 a new line was opened to give direct access to South Wales through the Severn Tunnel – it is still in use.

The principal rival of the GWR was the London and South Western. In 1847 a branch was built from Bishopstoke (Eastleigh) to Milford on the east side of Salisbury. In 1857 the city was linked by a narrow-gauge line to Basingstoke and thence London. An independent line from Salisbury to Yeovil was authorized and in 1859 the line from Milford to Fisherton Street Junction where a new station had been constructed next to the terminus of the broad-gauge line from Warminster. In 1860 the line from London to Exeter through Salisbury was opened and operated by the LSWR. This line is still used today and many of the stations have survived.

In 1882 a cross-country line was built from Red Post Junction west of Andover, to Grafton where it linked up with the Marlborough–Savernake line. In the following year the line was extended to Swindon. Although never a great commercial success, this line served the needs of several military camps on Salisbury Plain. A branch was built from Ludgershall to Tidworth Camp in 1901 and this continued in operation until 1963. By this time the rest of the line from Swindon had been abandoned. A number of the stations have survived as private dwellings, for example at Savernake (Higher Level) and East Grafton. Another short military line was opened in 1906 from Newton Tony Junction to Bulford Camp *via* Amesbury. This line was finally abandoned in 1963.

Today, Wiltshire's industry seems as closely related to the processing of agricultural produce as it was in earlier times. The textile mills are almost all silent, but the factories which produce cheese and butter, bacon and sausages, now serve a wider market than Wiltshire. Swindon, which continues to expand and prosper seems to be as exceptional in the county's economy as it must have seemed when the GWR first developed its engineering works there. So far, the M4 has made no great impact on settlement along its route through north Wiltshire. Should it do so, the imbalance already evident between the industrial north and west and the pastoral south and east will become even more striking. In the meantime there is much to interest the industrial archaeologist who is prepared to travel long distancs and to scour maps and countryside alike for clues of industrial activities.

ALDBOURNE

An old **malthouse** (SU267754) stands on the main road south of the village green. It is a two-storeyed building with a thatched roof. Adjoining it is the drying kiln, marked by the change to the red tiled roof and a distinctive cowl over a round, brick ventilator. The cowl has a fantail in the shape of a man holding a malt shovel. Next to this building is the maltster's house. Opposite this building is a stone **milepost** which records the mileage to Swindon and Hungerford. Further south is a pretty **toll house** at Preston (SU277741). It has a thatched roof overhanging the front porch. The windows are gothic, with shutters. The building is painted white with black imitation pilasters at each corner. On the village green there is an unusual iron **water trough** and **pump** (SU265756). In the Church two 18th-century **fire Engines** are preserved (SU263758).

AMESBURY

This town was once an important route centre and most of the sites of interest relate to road transport. There are a number of fine Coaching Inns, for example, the **George Hotel** (SU154415) and the **Antrobus Arms** (SU153414). **Queensbury Bridge**, designed by John Smeaton, has five segmental arches and a total span of 87 yds (79·55m). The date 1775 is carved on the down-stream parapet (SU151413). A good example of a **milestone** is a carved stone west of the bridge (SU140417). It is dated 1764 and records the miles from London (LXXIX) and from Andover (XIX).

BARFORD ST MARTIN

There were two mill sites on the River Nadder in this village. The **upper mill** (SU054315) has been rebuilt as a residence and only the name Factory Lane records the site of the lower mill.

BISHOPSTONE

Situated on the River Ebble, this pretty village has several **watercress beds** (SU067255) which are so characteristic of the broad chalk valleys. The **lower mill** (SU078263) has a timber building over the millstream. There is a fine, free-standing **dovecote**, built of flint and freestone in alternating bands (SU073256).

BOREHAM

On the River Wylye, near the junction of the B3095 with the A36 is a substantial **mill** building (ST891442). The oldest part is now derelict. It was a three-storeyed building in brick and stone. Modern premises adjoining, also in red brick, are dated 1886.

BOX

This small town on the A4 is famous for its tunnel and for its stone. **Box Tunnel** was built under the direction of I.K. Brunel and the west portal is best viewed from the road bridge (ST829688). The size of this entrance is deceptively large as the bore of the tunnel narrows to half the height for the remainder of its length. The same feature can be seen more clearly on **Little Box Tunnel** to the

west (ST820687). The stone excavated from the tunnel established the extent of these deposits and several stone mines exist in the hill east of the town, e.g. near the Quarryman's Arms (ST834691). On the side of the A4 are the buildings of a **stoneyard** (ST838697). It is a two-storeyed building over seven arches. An interesting square section chimney survives but the crane has been removed. A **brewery** building stands below the A4, at the bottom of the hill (ST826685). The buildings are dated 1864 and now form a private residence. The adjoining premises of an engineering firm are dated 1870. They are two storeys high with a double gable. A four-storeyed stone **mill** stands beside the railway line (ST825688). It is occupied by a manufacturing concern and has been much altered from its original state. **Drewett's Mill** (ST833698) now has a turbine in place of its overshot wheel and functions as a corn mill. There are several good **milestones** belonging to the Bath Trust in the vicinity of Box. One of these (*Plate 53*) (ST842688) claims to be seven miles from Bath and 100 miles from Hyde Park Corner. **Terminus stones** for two routes turnpiked by the Bath Trust are quite close to each other – one on the A365 and the other on the old road from Kingsdown (ST838671). A two-storeyed stone **toll house** stands close to the latter (ST832672). A square, stone **lock up** with a ball finial stands beside the A4 in the centre of the town (ST825684).

BRADFORD ON AVON

This beautiful town derived its prosperity from the woollen industry. Several 18th century buildings which housed the prosperous clothiers of the town and their outworkers have survived. These include Dutch Barton and Druce's Hill House, Middle Rank and Tory. The surviving mill buildings date mainly from the 19th century. **Abbey Mill** (ST826609) was rebuilt in 1874 and although the most handsome in the town it is also the most recent. It is built of stone and rises to five-storeys. Between this and the town bridge is a three-storey range of buildings at right-angles to the river which was known as **Church Street Mill**. Behind **Westbury House**, itself a handsome clothier's residence of the 18th century, is a two-storeyed stone building with segment

53   Box – Milestone

headed windows which formed part of a factory complex (ST824608). On the north bank of the river, above the town bridge, is **Bridge Foot Mill** (ST827609). It consists of a four-storeyed range of buildings dated 1869. It is stone built with a slate roof and the windows are of two lights with flat heads. **Greenland Upper Mill** (ST831606) is a five-storey stone building with an attic and stone framed windows of standard design. The star-shaped ends to the iron tie bars are an interesting feature. Separated by a complex of single-storeyed weaving sheds to the west is **Greenland Middle Mill** (ST830606). Mainly rebuilt after a fire in 1862, this is a two-storeyed building of seven bays at right-angles to the river, below the weir which also provided for the Lower Greenland and **Kingston Mills**. The latter (ST827609), has lost its most interesting features, but several stone factory buildings survive on the site which is occupied by the Moulton Rubber Company. In **Coppice Hill** there are several weavers' cottages with attic windows set in stone gables. At the top of the road there is a **factory** building (ST827611). It is a stone building of three storeys with an attic. It consists of four bays and the windows have stone segment headed frames.

A large **brewery** building stands at the bottom of Wine Street (ST825610). It is five storeys high and built in the local stone. In Silver Street, a two-storeyed building with two loading bays bears the inscription G. & T. Spencer Ale and Porter Store 1884 (ST827610). The tower of a **windmill** stands below Mason's Hill (ST827612) which seems to be an odd site to choose. It is complete up to the cap ring, built of stone and covered with a stone-tiled conical roof. Much of the stone which is incorporated in the buildings of Bradford must have been quarried locally. Stone quarries and mines can be identified between the river and the railway (ST827607). A **gas holder** stands close to a stone building dated 1834 which was presumably associated with it (ST826603). They are sited close to the Kennet & Avon Canal. A typical stone, single-span bridge carries the B3109 road over the canal below the lock gates and **wharf** (ST825602). The Kennet & Avon Canal Trust has its headquarters in the **warehouse** alongside the original dry dock. A single storeyed stone **toll house** stands at the junction of the Westwood and Wingfield roads (ST823595). The Chantry or **Town Bridge** has nine arches, two of which are pointed and the remainder rounded (ST825608). **Barton Bridge** is a pretty packhorse bridge with four pointed arches and three cutwaters on the upstream side (ST822603). This crosses the Avon to the west of the magnificent **tithe barn** (ST823604) which houses a collection of agricultural machinery.

BRATTON

Situated just below the spring line on the north side of Salisbury Plain, this village once had four water-powered mills. North of the B3098 are the two lower storeys of a **Woollen Factory** built in the first decade of the 19th century by Thomas Jarvis (ST917525). It is a brick building with stone segment headed windows. Very little has survived of the two **mills** used by Jarvis further upstream at Stradbrook and Luccombe. The former (ST918523) was originally an edge-tool works before conversion to the woollen industry. A row of cottages was built on its foundations. The ponds built for Luccombe Mill and Jarvis' House are higher up the valley (ST920521). The site of Reeves' Agricultural Works (ST912522) has recently been levelled.

BREMHILL

Hazeland Mill (ST972724) is preserved as a corn mill although it has served as a fulling mill. It is a stone building three storeys high with stone flat-headed windows. **Stanley Mill** (ST956727) is the earliest known fulling mill in Wiltshire. Just above Hazeland Mill, the Calne Branch of the Wilts & Berks Canal is clearly visible. It joins the main line of the canal north of the two arched **aqueduct** across the River Marden (ST960724) and near the remains of the two Stanley Locks. The line of the Chippenham-Calne railway can be seen at right-angles to the Canal to the south of the aqueduct.

BRINKWORTH

The base of a **windmill** survived until recently (SU031853). Little remains on the site although the mill house is occupied.

54 Britford – Lock on the Salisbury Avon Navigation

BRITFORD

This village contains the best example of a **lock** (Plate 54) on the Salisbury Avon Nagivation which involved an artificial cut from below Harnham Bridge (SU148292) to Longford Castle (SU172267). The top gates of the Lock (SU159278) have been replaced by three sluice gates. The central sluice has a stone slab but those on either side were manufactured in iron by V. Armitage of Salisbury. The waterway was constructed and in use between 1675 and 1730. Much of the original masonry has survived although some changes have been incorporated as a result of the subsequent use of the water course for the servicing of water meadows.

BURBAGE

Near the Savernake Forest Hotel is the **Bruce Tunnel** (SU236632) on the summit level of the Kennet & Avon Canal. It is built in red brick and is about 500 yds long. There is no towpath through the tunnel which passes underneath the Savernake Low Level Station on the GWR line. On the east portal of the tunnel there is a stone commemorating the assistance received from the Rt Hon Thomas Bruce, Earl of Ailesbury and Charles, Lord Bruce, his son, dated 1810. The same Earl of Ailesbury was responsible for the establishment of a **wharf** on the canal at Burbage, below the bridge which carries the A346 (SU224635). The site was developed in 1832 and includes a brick **warehouse** and a large wooden **crane** which is being carefully restored to its original state by a small team of enthusiasts. Although the timber has had to be replaced, the ironwork is original.

North of the Bruce Tunnel are the remains of the Savernake Higher Level **Station** (SU237633). This served the Swindon, Marlborough and Andover Railway. The station is a private residence; the signal box and water tower have also been preserved. To the east another **station** is occupied as a private residence at West Grafton (SU248605). It served the same railway as the Savernake Higher Level.

CALNE

The centre of this town is dominated by the **bacon factory** of Harris's (ST998710). The firm's connection with Calne goes back at least 200 years. It was the use of ice to preserve the bacon cured from locally-reared pigs which established the real fortunes of the firm in the 19th century. The present factory buildings are mainly modern. The car-park opposite the factory was the terminus **wharf** of the Calne branch of the Wilts & Berks Canal. The remains of the top **lock** on this canal can be identified (ST997708) although tipping has filled most of the bed. The railway **station** to the south has been taken over by the local bacon factory (ST996707). Another transport site of interest is the **King's Arms**, a coaching house which has retained notices which advertise coaches to Bath, Bristol, Chepstow, Tinterne (*sic*), Monmouth, Hereford, Taunton and Exeter (ST997111).

Calne was an important centre for the manufacture of woollen cloth. There are two buildings on The Green which housed early woollen factories. Nos. 8 and 9 form a building of four storeys with stone-framed three-light windows in five bays. To the north no. 5, a three-storeyed building with two-light windows, five bays and a central arched doorway is known as **Weavers House** (SU000708). **Horsebrook Mill** (SU002706) has been reduced to two storeys but has retained its original segment headed windows and an iron breast-shot waterwheel. **Quemerford Mill** (SU008696) to the south east is a fine example of a late 18th century-woollen factory. It is a four-storeyed stone building with segment headed windows and a square red brick chimney. Originally water-powered, this factory later utilized steam power. To the east of the site are red-brick drying stoves. **Calne Mill** (SU000700) was a grist mill. It is a three-storeyed building of four bays with dormer windows and a slate roof. In the front porch grind-stones are displayed. Below the mill the stream runs into **Doctor's Pond**, named after Joseph Priestly, who, it is claimed, discovered oxygen whilst staying in the town between 1772 and 1779.

CERNEY WICK

The remains of a lock on the Thames & Severn Canal can be identified alongside the lock-keeper's **round house** which is in a very good state of preservation (SU078961).

CHAPMANSLADE

On the south side of the A3098 there are two buildings which housed small **woollen workshops**. The more westerly (ST824478) has recently had its third storey removed. It is a plain stone building with a brick chimney and brick edging to the walls and windows. To the east there is a similar stone fronted building with brick sides and brick-lined windows. It is now occupied by two semi-detached houses (ST827478). To the south at **Corsley Mill Farm** are the lower storeys of a building which served as both a woollen and a grist mill (ST817471).

CHARLTON

A **toll house** of unusual design consists of a two-storeyed building with a round arch which encompasses both floors (ST962889). On each side there are single-storeyed rooms which are protected by one steeply-pitched roof.

CHILMARK

The fine stone which has been mined and quarried in this area was used in many famous Wiltshire buildings, including Salisbury Cathedral. Access to the mines (ST975312) is not permitted.

CHILTON FOLIAT

A red brick corn **mill** (SU316636) stands at the south end of the village. It is a two-storeyed building with a slate roof and a wooden locum on the north gable.

CHIPPENHAM

Situated as it is on the Great West Road and the GWR line from Paddington to Bristol, it is not surprising that Chippenham has a number of important transport monuments. Perhaps the most striking is the **viaduct** (ST918736) which bisects the town centre. It was built to carry Brunel's railway in 1839

55   Chippenham – Maud Heath's Causeway at Kellaways

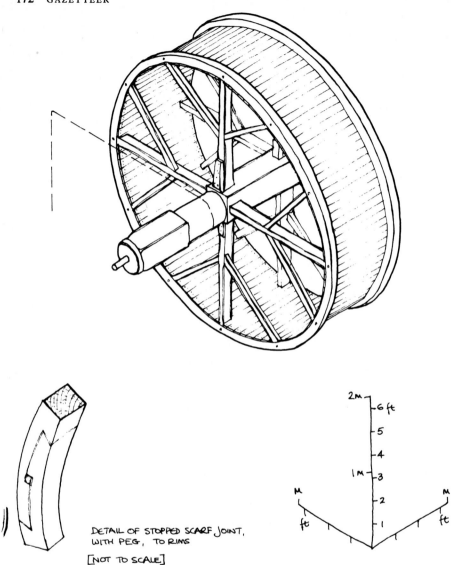

DETAIL OF STOPPED SCARF JOINT,
WITH PEG, TO RIMS

[NOT TO SCALE]

2M
6 ft
5
4
1M 3
M 2 M
ft 1 ft

LOWER UPHAM FARM   CHISELDON   WILTSHIRE

DONKEY WHEEL FOR WATER RAISING.

MEASURED + DRAWN : JUNE 1974 : MARTIN WATTS

Figure 7   Wiltshire: Chiseldon. A rare example of a donkey wheel is shown in this isometric drawing: the donkey walked on treads inside the wheel. Drawn by Martin Watts.

and is best viewed from the north – the side which is faced with Bath stone. The railway **station** (ST921738) is an unexceptional stone building. To the north, across the track is a complex of buildings which appear to have had associations with the railway. They are now occupied by Westinghouse Brake & Signal Co and the Royal Wiltshire Bacon Co. The latter is at the south end of Foundry Lane (ST922738). A spur of the Wilts & Berks Canal ran from the through route (ST939714) into Chippenham. The canal basin is under the present bus station, and little has remained of this transport system inside the town. The line of the abandoned railway to Calne can be identified more easily (ST928739).

Two **toll houses** have survived. On the A420 there is a two-storeyed house built in Bath stone with a slate roof and gothic windows (ST905742). On the A4 to the east there is a single-storeyed house with a stone frontage (ST936723). However, the prettiest survival of the earlier road system is **Maud Heath's Causeway** (*Plate 55*) which was built from Chippenham to Wick Hill where a statue of the lady who financed the project, on the top of a column erected by the Marquis of Lansdowne, looks out over the Avon valley. The most dramatic section is the raised pavement across this flood plain, at Kellaways (ST947757). Here the causeway of Cotswold stone is carried over about 60 brick arches. By the side of the river is a stone column erected in 1698 to explain the history of Maud Heath's Charity. To the north of the causeway is **Kellaways Mill** (ST949758) – a stone building recently converted to a private dwelling. South of the main Town Bridge is a large stone building which housed a **woollen factory** before it was taken over by Nestles as a **creamery** (ST918733). The premises are now empty. They consist of 28 bays on the road side. The floors are supported by cast-iron pillars and a wooden bellcote adorns the roof. To the north across the road are additional factory buildings and the manager's house. The whole site is likely to be redeveloped shortly. On the east bank of the river, below the Town Bridge, there are a number of factory buildings which have the windows typical of the 19th-century woollen industry. At the south end of this range of buildings is a red brick **pumping station** (ST919729) which belongs to the Wessex

Water Authority. To the south of the A4 on the road to the West, is St Andrew's Hospital which is housed in the original **Union Workhouse** (ST919729).

CHISELDON

The only **donkey wheel** (*Fig 7*) on its original site in the county has been retained at Lower Upham Farm (SU208778). It was used to pump water but the well has been sealed. The wheel is 14 ft (4·26m) in diameter. A red brick **windmill** tower stands incongruously in the back garden of a council house (SU190800). It is four storeys high and complete up to the cap ring at which level it has been sealed with a 'lid'.

COOMBE BISSETT

A fine **packhorse bridge** (SU109264) with three pointed arches has survived. It has no parapet and is 6ft wide. Wooden railings have been fitted and the west side has been re-faced with brick. To the west a stone bridge with round arches carries the A354. By the side of this road is a stone **mile post** recording the mileage to Sarum (5) and to Blandford (10). Across the road there is a wooden **watermill** (SU108265), with a broad iron undershot wheel.

CORSHAM

At Monks Park the last working Bath **stone mine** (*Plate 56*) continues to operate (ST877683). Since 1948 the mine has been worked by machinery. Large stacks of mined stone can be seen above the mine workings. Entry to the workings is by means of a sloping shaft which is fitted with steps as well as railway lines.

CRICKLADE

It is possible to trace the route of the North Wilts Canal through the outskirts of the town. The south portal of a brick **tunnel** stands at the north end of a deep cutting (SU095934). The north entrance is now blocked but the tunnel was originally 200 yds long. Near the junction with the Thames & Severn Canal the stone-lined basin of **Latton Wharf** (*Plate 57*) is still impressive (SU087953). The North Wilts Canal entered the basin through a lock which is built over culverts. The lock-keeper's house is derelict. It is a two-storeyed brick building with a semi-hexagonal porch overlooking the lock. At the east end of the basin, a final lock and the aqueduct which carried the canal over the River Churn have both disappeared, but some of the masonry can be detected in the river bank. East of the river, the line of the Thames and Severn Canal can be seen. This proceeds to the south and east across the A419 where Cricklade **Wharf House** stands at the north end of the bypass (SU100945). At the west end of Gas Lane the **gas retort house** is used as a store (SU099938). It is a single-storeyed red brick building. The brightly painted **clock** in the centre of the town was erected in 1897 to celebrate Queen Victoria's Diamond Jubilee (SU101935).

CROCKERTON

The site of a small **brickworks** (ST866423) is now a discount store. A two-storeyed **toll house** stands on the side of the A350 (ST865426).

DAUNTSEY

Where the Wilts and Berks Canal passes under the A420 there is the site of a **wharf** and **lock-keeper's house** (ST995803). At the roadside there is a **weighbridge** made by Bartlett & Son, Bristol. To the east, seven locks raise the canal towards Wooton Bassett. The first of these is at Tockenham Wick, south of the railway bridge (SU024811).

DEVIZES

At the corner of New Park Street and Snuff Street is the earliest **woollen factory** in Wiltshire (SU005615). It was built by John Anstie in 1785, probably to house spinning jennies. It is four storeys high, 11 bays long and built in yellow brick. In the centre is an iron crane on the first floor. The building has sash windows with distinctive round headed frames of three lights at each end and in the centre of the second floor. Like many early woollen factories, these premises have had a chequered industrial history. They have been used for silk throwing, storage and the processing of tobacco. The latter explains the name Snuff Street to the west which contains a terrace of red brick workers' houses. A tapering square brick chimney stands behind and to the south. A collection of early wool-makers' tools is housed in the **museum** (SU008614). Several interesting

56 Corsham – The stone mine at Monks Park

transport facilities have survived in the town. The **toll house** (ST997617) at the junction of the A342 and 361 is a two-storeyed stone building with castellated decorations, known as Shaw's Castle. The most impressive site, however, is the flight of 17 locks which carry the Kennet & Avon Canal up Caen Hill. These are best viewed from the bridge which carries the B3101 over the canal at the bottom of this 'staircase' (ST977615). Although the locks are derelict, restoration work has already commenced. Above each lock there is a large pound for waiting barges; these are generally silted-up. When the locks were being built, a horse tramway was used on the incline which carries the tow path. A few traces have survived and the enthusiast will recognize a section of fish-bellied iron rail – now used as a handrail – near the top of the incline. The Caen Hill locks form the centre piece of the 29 locks which raise the canal 237 ft in less than two miles. South of the road bridge over the canal (SU001616) is a stone **lock-keeper's cottage** which is inhabited.

The town's **gas works** were sited alongside the Canal, but only the gasometer survives. The town **wharf** (SU004617) has retained a number of small warehouses, for example on Commercial Road, where a two-storeyed stone building has an iron hoist. The railway line through Devizes has been abandoned but both entrances to the short **tunnel** which passed under the ramparts of the castle are visible. At the west end the **station** buildings (SU002614) have been almost totally demolished.

The Devizes **Brick & Tile Works** (ST985613) which worked the clay deposits of Caen Hill are now derelict. The square, iron-banded **chimney** of a Hoffman kiln is the only survival of importance. Wadworth's **Brewery** (SU005615) was built in 1885. It is an impressive red brick building which, fortunately for the connoisseur of real ale, is still in production. There are several buildings of a more general interest in the town, including the Corn Exchange (dated 1856), the covered market with its clock tower and **St John's**

57   Cricklade – The lock-keeper's house and wharf at Latton

Alley – a beautiful medieval cobbled street with overhanging, timber-framed buildings (SU005613).

DILTON MARSH

This straggling community grew out of squatters' settlements on common land. Weavers set up small loom shops alongside their brick cottages. Several of these have survived as modern utility rooms or outhouses. A **tannery** has occupied the premises of a late 18th-century **woollen factory** known as Boyers Mill, since 1901 (ST858499). It is a brick building of six bays, three storeys high with stone-framed, square-headed windows of two lights. To the west of the village there is a two-storeyed **toll house** (ST838501) of conventional design with a red tile roof and gothic windows.

DOWNTON

The broad valley of the River Avon, which is straddled by this pretty village, has been watered by a number of artificial channels. Most were cut to serve the water meadows, but it is possible to trace the line of the **river navigation**'s cut from the weir near Charlton (SU179239) via New Court Farm (SU175227) to below the B3080 at Downton. To the east of the village there is a large **tannery** (*Plate 58*) (SU180215) which has been in operation since about 1830. The front of the stone and brick building is covered with ivy. The four storeys are arranged in five bays between gabled sections, each of three bays. These end sections have three light semi-circular windows at the attic level. Behind this façade substantial brick and timber buildings house the various tanning processes. An undershot **waterwheel** with curved blades is used to agitate the vats in which the skins are dressed. To the south, across the road, there are a number of brick buildings which stand above four water courses. Originally, these housed a **paper mill** but more recently have served as a

58 Downton – The Tannery

59   Great Bedwyn – The Crofton Pumping Station

power house equipped with Armfield turbines which supplied electricity to the national grid (SU179214). The turbines have now been removed but the sluices remain.

EAST KNOYLE

The tower of a **windmill** stands on open ground to the west of the village (ST873310). It is a stone building which stands on a walled mound about two ft high. Externally the building is in its original state up to the cap ring, but a modern tiled roof with four dormer windows – now boarded up – has been placed on the top.

EASTON GREY

A **packhorse bridge** (ST880874) with five round arches crosses the River Avon to the south of this pretty stone-built hamlet. It has six cutwaters on its upstream side but has evidently been doubled in width at some stage in its life.

ENFORD

Coombe Mill (SU148505) has a large metal lower-breast shot wheel *in situ*. Originally a grist mill, all internal machinery has been removed. More recently it was used to pump water. It is a two-storeyed building of white painted brick alongside the mill house.

GREAT CHEVERELL

The **water mill** (ST982563) is a red brick building of two storeys which is in the course of being renovated. It was a corn mill. The sluices are intact but only the axle of the waterwheel has survived in place.

GREAT BEDWYN

Within a short distance of this village are two of the most interesting industrial archaeological sites in Wiltshire. At Crofton the **pumping station** (*Plate 59*) (SU264642) was built to house the beam engines used to pump water into the upper pound of the Kennet & Avon Canal. It has now been restored to full working order by the Crofton Society. The red brick engine house contains two beam engines. The oldest was manufactured by Boulton and Watt. It has a cast-iron beam and was installed in 1812. The second engine – a Sims Combined Cylinder Engine – was installed in 1846 to replace one of the original Boulton and Watt engines. Steam to power the engines is produced by two Lancashire boilers which replaced the earlier – but not original – Cornish boilers in the 1890s. The boilers are housed in a building adjoining the main engine house. The latter has three storeys and it is possible to examine the engines from the beams downwards. Outside, the round brick chimney was reduced to its present height in 1958. The engines pump water from a well which is fed by springs and a culvert leading from the canal, which in turn is fed from Wilton Water. This artificial lake was created in 1836 to ensure a regular supply of water. The pumps are of different design. No. 1 pump is a bucket or lift pump which raises water on the up or power stroke. No. 2 pump is a force pump which pushes up the main on the down or return stroke. In 1968 the Crofton Pumping Station was purchased by the Kennet & Avon Canal Trust, and the engines were restored to working order in 1970. The premises are open to the public when the engines are working in steam on selected weekends throughout the year. The day-to-day pumping is performed by a modest electric pump which stands in a small building near the railway. It pumps water straight into the feeder canal through a pipe which is quite conspicuous outside the engine house.

Wilton Windmill (*Plate 60*) stands about 1½ miles to the south (SU276616). This is a red brick tower mill dated 1821 which has been heavily restored recently. The cap, which was originally covered with lead, has been re-covered with aluminium on the original wrought-iron frame. This gives the mill a distinctive appearance which makes it an easily recognizable landmark. The cap is turned by a fantail mechanism and chains, which are operated from the balcony which runs round the tower at first-floor level, and regulate the pitch of the sails. The latter, which have also been restored, consist of a pair which are automatic and a pair designed to carry canvas. The interior of the mill is in the process of being restored. On the first floor there are two pairs of stones – a pair of French Burr and a pair of Peak Millstone Grit. The building now belongs to Wiltshire

60 Great Bedwyn – Wilton Windmill as restored

County Council and is regularly open to the public.

GREAT HINTON

A small **woollen factory** has survived next to the Linnet Inn (ST909591). It is a two-storeyed brick building of 1816. It has a mansard roof and conventional stone segment-headed window frames. It served as a Brewery for the adjoining inn after the woollen machinery had been sold.

GREAT WISHFORD

A pretty red brick **bridge** (SU083355) with five rounded arches carries the road from the village to the A36 across the River Wylye. Local stone has been incorporated for decorative purposes. It has cutwaters on both sides. To the east of the church, in the wall of the churchyard, are stones which record the changes in bread prices between 1800 and 1971 (SU081354). A stone and timber **goods shed** (SU079352) stands on the east side of the railway track.

HEYTESBURY

A three-storeyed red brick **corn mill** (ST932422) stands to the south of the village next to a farm. An octagonal **lock up** stands in the centre of the village on the north side of the A36 (ST925426). A stone-built **malthouse** stands on the south side of the A36 in front of the church (ST924425). The rounded end of the drying kiln is recognizable at the west end.

HOLT

Beavan's **Gloving Factory** (ST861620) developed in the elegant red brick house with stone framed windows, but expanded into a large **tannery** – the principal building of which is three storeys high excluding the attic range. This building has twin gables and a hoist to the third floor. A tall square, brick chimney stands to the rear. To the east J. Sawtell's **Bedding Factory** (ST863621) includes a two-storeyed brick building with a handsome iron hoist. The adjoining three-storeyed stone building with brick rimmed windows was originally built as the Spa which was developed in 1720 by Lady Lisle and

Rev. J. Lewis. At the west end of this building the original water pump survives under an inscription taken from Virgil.

HORNINGSHAM

There are two mill sites in this village. At the Upper Mill there is a clothier's house which incorporates an octagonal **drying stove** as used in the local woollen industry (ST816411). There was once a fulling mill and dye house on this site. Lower Mill was another fulling mill. It was converted to a Gig Mill which provoked its destruction by shearmen in 1767. The surviving mill pond serves a **grist mill** (ST816415). A **roundhouse** for horse gear is incorporated in the wooden barn at Manor Farm (ST822415).

LACOCK

This beautiful old town of timber-framed buildings, now owned by the National Trust, is largely unspoilt by modernization. The Fox Talbot collection of early photographic equipment is housed in Lacock Abbey. Nearby, is the Lackham College of Agriculture which has a museum of agricultural equipment including that used for the working of water meadows (ST922702). **Lacock Bridge** (ST922681) has five arches, three of which are pointed and the remaining two are rounded. The former probably date from the 15th century. The latter date from 1809 and are built on brick vaults with stone string courses. A second bridge beyond the causeway now crosses the River Avon. It has four pointed arches and a cutwater on the upstream side. East of the causeway it is possible to identify the north–south route of the Wilts & Berks Canal.

LIMPLEY STOKE

The **viaduct** (ST781621) of eleven arches built of Bath stone was reputedley built by Thomas Telford. The **mill** (ST783611) is a four-storeyed stone building of seven bays. The stone-framed windows are typical of the local woollen factories which were built in the early 19th century. It is now used by a firm of timber merchants.

LONGLEAT

Some **mileposts** which display the distance to

61 Luckington – The pottery kiln

this important residence have survived. They are cast-iron plates on stone pillars. A two-mile stone (ST806402) and a one-mile stone (ST810415) are good examples. **Stalls Farm** (ST807439) is a good example of a model estate farm of the last century. The stone built out-houses include a square chimney.

LUCKINGTON

West of the village and south of the B4040 is a red brick **bottle kiln** (*Plate 61*) (ST822819). It is approximately 40ft high and appears to be in a good state of preservation. It was one of several kilns which were built to supply bricks and pottery for the nearby Badminton estate.

MALMESBURY

The oldest part of this town is built on a peninsula of land which is outlined on its west and south sides by the River Avon. A substantial tributary delineates the eastern boundary of this peninsula. The town has expanded through a narrow neck of higher ground towards the north west. Unusually, the abbey may claim to have industrial associations. When Leland visited the town in the early 1540s he found that William Stumpe had bought the abbey and recorded that 'every corner of the vast office that belonged to the abbey be full of looms to weave cloth in'. Even earlier than this, in 1020, Oliver of Malmesbury is supposed to have thrown himself from the abbey walls in a primitive display of human aeronautics. He is commemorated by the inn sign for the **Flying Monk** (ST931878). The woollen industry was revived in the town when Francis Hill built **Avon Mill** (*Plate 62*) (ST936869) in the early 1790s. This handsome building started with the wing which stands at right-angles to the river. It is five storeys high and has eight bays with two-light windows and brick-lined arches. This was possibly the first water-powered woollen factory in Wiltshire. Early in the 19th century a wing parallel to the river, in similar style and proportions to the original building, was added. The later transi-

62 Malmesbury – The Avon Mill

tion to steam power is demonstrated by the later block of five storeys which stands to the rear, at right-angles to the river. The red brick, octagonal chimney is still standing. The premises are now occupied by a firm of antique dealers.

Abbey Mill (ST933874) above the pack-horse bridge, was a grist mill. The leat has been blocked but pieces of wooden shafting could be seen recently in the garden. Further upstream there is a complex of red brick buildings, now a council depot, which was a dairy products **factory** (ST929878). Above Avon Mill, alongside the Avon, the old corn mill has been incorporated in the **brewery** (ST932872). It is a four-storeyed building which has been considerably enlarged. A water tower is situated at the roof level and a stone bears the inscription T.L. 1836 and C.R.L. 1865. This refers to the Luce family, whose name is incorporated in the brickwork of the large **maltings**, dated 1887, on the downstream side of the brewery. These premises are occupied by a plastics firm. An older **brewery** (ST933873) stands to the east of the abbey. It is a two-storeyed building with the second floor overhanging a cobbled pavement and supported by wooden posts. The upper storey is partly covered with ivy, but it is possible to distinguish two windows with wooden louvres. The building is dated 1804. The brewer's house – a two-storeyed stone building with a stone tiled roof and attics – stands to the north with a number of out-buildings. A small, red-brick building houses an iron and engineering works in the aptly-named **Foundry Road** (ST929877). There are some unusual cast-iron plates in the town which indicate the street names together with the name of the mayor and his year of office, e.g. Cross Hayes Lane also bears the name of Josh Poole Esq., Mayor 1890–91 (ST934872).

Malmesbury was the terminus for a branch line which ran from the GWR main line near Little Somerford. Although the track has been removed, and the station site levelled, a stone **goods shed** has survived (ST932878). The stone abutments of the bridge which carried this line across the river remain and the **tunnel** under Holloway can be seen on the south side (ST935874).

MARLBOROUGH

This ancient market town has little to offer the industrial archaeologist. Situated on the main road from London to the west before the opening of the M4, it has always been associated with road transport. There are a number of excellent coaching inns, for example the **Ailesbury Arms Hotel** (SU188691). This is a three-storeyed building with a mansard roof and attic windows. It has a fine entrance porch with a wrought-iron balcony. The town's two railway stations are both closed and the railway lines abandoned (SU190684 and 195687). A gas holder and a small two-storeyed brick building stand on the site of the town's **gas works** (SU192691).

MARDEN

A three-storeyed red brick **mill** dated 1842 (SU087582) now uses a water turbine to grind animal feed. The mill house stands next to the mill. Nearby, at Broad Street, a two-storeyed **warehouse** occupied by a seed and corn merchant has retained its locum for the hoist (SU106593).

MARSTON MEYSEY

One of the distinctive round **lock-keeper's houses** stands on the side of the Thames–Severn Canal (SU132962). It is built of stone with a cement rendered cover. Its roof is an inverted cone, like that at Inglesham, which was intended to serve as a rainwater cistern. The parapet wall makes it difficult to recognize this feature from the outside, although the building is now roofless and derelict.

MELKSHAM

This thriving town has retained a number of buildings which were originally associated with the woollen industry. The most remarkable features are the two **drying stoves** which were used after the fulling and dyeing processes. One of these, in Church Street (*Plate 63*) (ST904637), is a circular stone building with stone-framed windows and a stone-tiled roof with a central vent. The other, in Lowborne (ST906638), is octagonal and built in stone. It is now a two-storeyed private residence. The three-storeyed stone building alongside, with three gables and three-light windows was probably an early woollen factory. A more substantial woollen factory is now occupied by the Avon Rubber

63 Melksham – One of the few surviving drying stoves, Church Street

Co (ST903642). It is a four-storeyed building which has retained some of its segment headed windows on the end wall. A clothier's house forms an imposing frontage to the premises. Opposite this factory, below the town bridge is the large **creamery** owned by Unigate (ST903641). This red brick building has a ventilated roof and a tall round chimney, the base of which is edged with blue engineering bricks. The **Town Bridge** itself is a handsome stone structure with four round arches and a stone balustrade. Sand was quarried east of the town at the **Sahara Sand Pit** (ST939647) between 1937 and 1960. The workings still contain some of the quarrying machinery. The Wilts & Berks Canal can be traced to the north and south of the town. At the junction of Calne Road and Forest Road the red brick parapet of a canal bridge can be seen although the bed of the canal has been filled (ST908643). There is an **aqueduct** (ST914655) which carried the canal over the Forest Brook.

MERE

The recently completed bypass has restored some peace to this town which was situated on one of the main routes from the west towards London. The **Ship Hotel** is a good example of a coaching inn and the exquisite wrought-iron frame which supports the inn sign is particularly worthy of note (ST812324).

A four-storeyed **warehouse** dated 1886 stands behind Walton's shop (ST813324). The lower two storeys are built in the local stone, the upper two in brick. It has five bays on the road side and an iron hoist is fitted above the centre bay of the fourth floor. To the east, the premises occupied by a firm of wine merchants has the appearance of a modest-sized **brewery** (ST816324). The buildings are situated by a small stream and include a handsome gatehouse with four dormer windows and a tall square brick chimney. To the east above the A303 there is a **chalk quarry** on the side of Charnage Down (ST837329) which is still worked. To the north the old **turnpike road** cuts from east to west across Charnage Down and White Sheet Hill. On this stretch of road there are some original **mileposts**. They are made of stone, the mileage from Sarum and London is carved into the surface, and they are also dated, e.g. (ST830345) (*Plate 64*).

MILDENHALL

Durnford Mill (SU221695) is a two-storeyed red brick building with an undershot wheel.

PEWSEY

Bucklease Mill (SU164607)is a two-storeyed red brick building with a semi-hipped roof. The wheel has been removed but the adjacent mill house is a private residence. **Pewsey Wharf** (SU158611) on the Kennet & Avon Canal is used for moorings and the two-storeyed brick warehouse has survived. The **workhouse** (SU157603), dated 1836, is still used as a hospital.

PURTON

Collins Lane Gate **toll house** (SU093882) is a two-storeyed stone building with a semi-hexagonal front. It is of particular interest because it has retained its toll-board which, in addition to a list of charges, contains the requirement that 'when any Waggon or Cart shall desend this Hill in this District or Road will either of them be chain locked or Skidpan or Slipper shall be used to the bottom of such wheel draging the whole time of its being locked. By order of the Trustees.' This appears to be the only toll house in the county to retain its board *in situ*. Purton **Brickworks** (SU088887), alongside the railway, is now occupied by a bottled-gas company. The various brick-making buildings appear to have survived, but a rectangular **Kiln** is in the process of being levelled. There are two square chimneys and the clay pit which has been abandoned. The brick hospital to the south of the village was built as the **workhouse** for the Cricklade Union in 1837 (SU085875).

RAMSBURY

Ramsbury Mill is a red brick residence (SU270714). A number of mill stones can be seen in the stream below the mill. **Howe Mill** (SU284715) is a two-storeyed building of brick and flint. In the High Street there is the site of a Saxon **forge** (SU272715) which was excavated in the course of the recent residential development which has taken place on the site.

64   Mere – Milestone on old turnpike road across White Sheet Hill

SALISBURY

Agriculture has always made an important contribution – either directly or indirectly – to the economy of Wiltshire's only cathedral city. The meadows of the Avon and Nadder valleys to the west of the cathedral were systematically flooded to improve the quality of the pastures. The sluices and channels associated with this practice can be easily identified from the footpath which runs south west from Mill Road towards Harnham Mill (SU138299–135294). There are several industrial sites within the city which illustrate the importance of the association with the products of local agriculture. Cheese and corn were sold in the premises which stood behind the splendid façade of the **market house** (SU143301) which now leads into the new library. To the south the **town mill** was originally used to grind corn (SU142300). This is a three-storeyed, red brick building with three bays and a tiled roof. It stands on the site of a mill which was recorded in Domesday and was in use before

the city was even built. Between 1897 and 1973 the water flowing under the mill was used to generate electricity.

The city originally possessed a number of breweries which no doubt prepared malt from the barley which was grown on the well-drained chalk uplands of the surrounding area. In Castle Street only an Inn Sign records the site of the **Avon Brewery** (SU143302). Another **brewery** stood in Rollestone Street (SU147301). A four-storeyed brick building of four bays and an arched entrance are all that remains on this site. The **Anchor Brewery** of Gibbs Mew & Co Ltd (SU147298) is the only active survivor of this industry in the city. It is a large complex of buildings in Gigant Street. The brewery buildings are of brick which has been painted white. Sandwiched amongst them is a small public house which dispenses the local brew. As well as processing the products of local agriculture, Salisbury was also an important centre for the woollen industry. A number of fine clothiers' houses have survived, **John a Porte's** in Queen Street

65 Salisbury – Fulling Mill at West Harnham

(su147299). **Greencroft** (su148302) is all that remains of the open ground on which the woollen cloth was dried and bleached. **Harnham mill** (*Plate 65*) (su135294) at West Harnham was built on the site of an older mill in the late Middle Ages. It is a two-storeyed building, the ground floor of flint, the top of brick and the roof tiled. It stands above the water course which must have powered undershot wheels. The building is now occupied by a craft shop and and café. It was used originally for fulling and more recently for grinding corn and bones as well as for the manufacture of paper. The four-storeyed red brick building alongside the mill was a later addition but probably housed machinery associated with the manufacture of woollen cloth. To the south of this mill are **chalk quarries** (su128288) which were worked at three levels. **Quidhampton Quarry** (su113313) produced chalk for the manufacture of whiting. A large red brick **retort house** (su138306) stands in Gas Lane to the north of the ring road. It has eight bays and the characteristic round opening in the gable end and a ventilated roof. One large gasometer is in use but the frame of an older holder stands to the west. The whole site is a remarkable survival and the gas works, which were established in 1849, deserve a thorough survey before they are demolished.

As a county town, Salisbury has had a long association with transport facilities. There are several coaching houses of importance – e.g. the **Red Lion and Cross Keys Hotel** (su145299), parts of which date to the 13th century. Regular coaching services operated from here in the 18th and 19th centuries. **Harnham Bridge** (su143291) also dates from the 13th century. It is a stone structure of six arches. **Crane Bridge,** (su141299) near the city centre, is also of medieval origin. A **toll house** stands on the A345 at Old Sarum (*Plate 66*) (su143332). It is built of brick and flint with a slate roof and a wall of hung slates to the south. The two-light windows have pointed arches. The Avon below Harnham Bridge was canalized in the

66 Salisbury – The Toll House at Old Sarum

late 17th century following the River Avon Navigation Act of 1664, but the city was never linked with an efficient water transport system. In the road called New Canal there is an excellent three-storeyed red brick **warehouse** (SU145130) with a locum and iron hoist.

The city was a point of contact between the broad-gauge GWR system and the narrow gauge of the LSWR. In 1857 the Basingstoke and Salisbury railway reached Milford and the Company amalgamated with the Salisbury and Yeovil Railway in the same year. This necessitated building a **tunnel** (SU150309) and an embankment to the west to carry the line to Fisherton Street. A station was built with the up-platform east of the bridge over the road, and the down-platform to the west. The white stone building of the latter adjoins the later combined **station** (SU137301) built in a florid red brick in 1902. The up-platform has been incorporated in the marshalling yards to the east, but the entrance gate can be seen by the

bridge on the side of the street. North of this station is the brick and stone façade of the Brunel-designed **terminus** of the GWR which was built in 1856. An interesting extension of the LSWR was the line to the Market House. An Act of 1856 incorporated the Salisbury Railway and Market House Company. Although the line continued to function until the 1960s, only a brick **viaduct** (SU140302) of three arches and an adjoining loading platform survive. The footbridge over the millstream west of the Market House rests on the cast-iron beams of the older railway bridge. To the north, also across the millstream is **Scamell's Bridge** (SU143304). This single-span, iron bridge, with a cast-iron balustrade was manufactured in 1857 to carry the extension of the Basingstoke and Salisbury line across Castle Street. It was removed to its present site in 1898 by Scamell 'without the aid of machinery', and now serves as a road bridge. Finally, it would be wrong to ignore one of the oldest pieces of engineering in Salisbury – the Cathedral **clock**. This dates

67   Seend – Ironworks alongside Kennet & Avon Canal in the 1880s

from the 14th century and its ancient and ingenious mechanism can be viewed in the nave of the Cathedral.

SEEND

This was once an important woollen manufacturing centre. Several imposing clothiers' houses have survived and also a small **factory** (SU941609). The terrace of houses, now known as Weavers' Cottages, was originally called Factory Row. It is a brick terrace of five bays with stone-framed windows on each of the three storeys. At the west end – and built in the same style – is a Wesleyan Chapel, opened by John Wesley himself in 1775. **Seendhead Mill** (ST922599) is on the site of an early fulling mill although it has been used for corn milling since the mid-19th century. A turbine replaced the waterwheel in 1936. **Baldham Mill** (ST927598) was another flour mill owned by J. Noad (who owned Seendhead Mill) and also powered by turbine. Alongside the Bell Inn is a two-storeyed brick building with louvred windows and a ventilated roof which suggests that it was once a small **brewery** (ST939608).

The evidence for **Seend Ironworks** (*Plate 67*) has to be sought by imaginative fieldwork. At the top of Seend Hill there is a quarry (ST937610) – now mainly filled – from which iron ore was worked in the mid-19th century. It is possible to trace the line of a tramway which ran from the quarry to the banks of the Kennet & Avon Canal where three blast furnaces once stood (SU935613). There are several depressions in the field south of the canal and east of the bridge beside the Barge Inn, together with substantial lumps of furnace slag. The tramway continued across the canal, by means of a bridge which has since been demolished, and north towards the railway line. At the beginning of the 20th century this was replaced by an overhead cable system. Overlooking the furnace area is **Ferrum Towers** (SU934611) once the home of the local iron master. Below and above the bridge across the canal there are a number of locks (*Plate 68*) which are being restored to working order.

SEMINGTON

East of the bridge which carries the A350 over the Kennet & Avon Canal is the site of the junction with the Wilts & Berks Canal (ST900610). The lock on the latter canal forms the garden of what was the lock keeper's cottage. South west of the bridge is a wharf with a house on the existing canal. Further west an **aqueduct** carries the Kennet & Avon over the Semington Brook. The line of the Wilts & Berks Canal can be traced north towards Melksham and the remains of a railway **viaduct** over the canal can still be seen (ST901615). The Union **Workhouse** (ST894604) is a distinctive feature on the skyline above the Kennet and Avon Canal. **Littleton Mill** (ST913606) is now a grist mill powered by a turbine. It stands on the site of an earlier woollen mill which was destroyed in the famous riot of 1803. The present building is two storeys high, stone-built with a slate roof.

SEMLEY

One of the first **milk depots** to organize the collection of Wiltshire's milk for the London market was established beside the LSWR line in 1871 (ST873267). The white-painted premises are now occupied by furniture and building firms. Opposite the depot is **Semley Station** (ST874267), a two-storeyed red brick building with a large goods shed standing to the east.

SHREWTON

A **lock up** stands on the west side of the A360 in the middle of the village (SU068438).

SLAUGHTERFORD

Although most of **Rag Mill** (ST839737) has been destroyed, the water courses and a large waterwheel have survived. The latter is 9ft wide and 15ft diameter. It was a high breast-shot wheel with iron buckets and cast-iron rim. The wheel has 12 wooden spokes and the drive was taken from the rim. One furnace boiler, a grindstone and several foundations survive, together with the remains of one iron-framed vat in which the 'stuff' was transported to the lower mill where it was utilized in the manufacture of paper. W.J. Dowdings **Lower Mill** (ST843737) is still producing paper, using the river which once powered both mills to supply the water used

68   Seend – Old locks on the Kennet & Avon Canal looking towards the site of the ironworks beyond the bridge

in the manufacturing process. A small **brewery** (ST839739) stands north of Rag Mill. It is a two-storeyed stone building with a ventilated roof and a square red brick chimney.

SOUTH NEWTON

On the side of the A36, south of the village is a **mill** (SU089339) two storeys high, red brick with red tiled roof and three bays, with a timber barn on staddle stones alongside.

STAVERTON

The former **woollen mill** (ST856609) at Staverton is a shadow of its former stature. Only the lower two storeys of the building constructed in 1824 have survived. The upper storeys were removed in the 1930s and the remainder occupied by Nestles. The three waterwheels were fitted under the building and arches of the water courses can be seen from the road. The chimneys which served the steam engines have been removed. The surviving building is of stone with two-light segment headed windows.

STEEPLE ASHTON

A **lock up** stands on the village green of this picturesque community (ST907568). It is an octagonal stone structure with a ball finial. It stands next to an elegant stone sundial on a column.

STOURHEAD

Below the gardens of this famous 18th century house is an overshot **waterwheel** (ST772338) manufactured at the foundry of E. S. Hindley in Bourton (Dorset).

SWINDON

This is substantially the largest town in Wiltshire. Old Swindon was an ancient borough and market town. New Swindon developed at the bottom of the hill to the north as a result of the construction of the GWR. The decision of the directors of that company to construct engine works alongside their railway at Swindon in 1841 was quickly implemented. The original engine sheds have been completely modernized and little has

survived of the age of steam. The **Railway Museum** (SU153853) in Faringdon Road, has endeavoured to preserve as much as possible of this age. The original **railway station** (SU149853) has also disappeared under modern rebuilding. An unusual **water tower** stands west of the station (SU146849). The original stone terraced cottages built for the employees of the railway company (*Plate 69*) are being carefully restored (e.g. Oxford Street) and re-let. The entire preservation enterprise is a commendable example to other authorities. Other civic buildings associated with this railway community include the **Mechanics' Institute** (SU148849) – founded in 1855 and enlarged in 1892 – and the Medical Fund **Hospital** (SU147848) which was established by the GWR Medical Fund Society for the benefit of their employees and dependents. Even before the arrival of the GWR Swindon was put on the transport map by the Wilts & Berks Canal which ran north of the old town. Although largely destroyed, it is possible to trace sections of this canal today. In Milton Road (SU147845) there is a fine brick bridge with a stone balustrade which once crossed the canal. To the east a large red brick building dated 1894 was a warehouse on the side of the canal. Another bridge takes Cambria Road over the bed of the canal (SU145844). To the east Fleming Way follows the line of the canal, and to the west it can be traced to its junction with the North Wilts Canal which ran north past Moredon **Power Station** (SU122873) towards Cricklade and its junction with the Thames–Severn Canal. The M4 runs to the south of Swindon. Near junction 15, on the outskirts of the town, are the remains of a **brick kiln** (SU189815) which has retained its square brick chimney.

TISBURY

This small town lies off the main east–west routes, although it is still served by the main Salisbury to Yeovil railway line. Near the centre of the town, alongside the Church-yard, is the **Wiltshire Brewery** (ST944292). This three-storeyed building is built in stone on the lower two floors and in brick on the top floor. A stone over the arched gateway records that the building was rebuilt in 1885. The stone malthouse forms the eastern boundary of the churchyard. The water tank

69 Swindon – Railway housing

is housed in the square tower at the east end of the façade. This tower has a steeply angled slate roof with wooden louvred dormers and a flat top. The premises are now occupied by a printing firm. The **tithe barn** at Place Farm (ST952298) is the real show piece of Tisbury. It is a magnificent thatched building dating from the 15th century. It is 200ft long and has a cruck roof structure and stone walls with two gabled entrances on the long sides. At the town end of the road which leads to the barn is a stone erected in 1881 which records that Alfred Morrison Esq built the road 'at his sole expense' (ST945295). To the east is a small red brick **laundry**. Chilmark stone has been worked in this locality and the last source to be worked is at **Tucking Mill Quarry** (ST931291). There is another quarry site to the east (ST935291).

TROWBRIDGE

This busy industrial town which houses the county's administrative offices, developed primarily because of its association with the woollen industry in the 18th and 19th centuries. Although in steep decline since 1900, this industry has left many buildings of importance which now house more modern manufacturing processes.

Courtfield House (ST860578) is a fine example of an early woollen factory. It is a red brick building of two storeys which was built by John Cockes in the 1750s. **Courts Mill** (ST859577) was largely demolished in the 1960s, but one range of three storeys with segment-headed windows which forms the eastern boundary of the park, is now occupied by a youth club. A two-storeyed brick building with a ventilated roof which stands to the south east of the site, served as a **drying house** (ST860577). To the east stands **Ashton Mill** (*Plate 70*) (ST861576). It is a stone building, five storeys high with eight bays. The weaving sheds stand to the north. The premises have retained their tall, brick, octagonal chimney. The pyramid roof of the stair turret at the north-east corner of the main block has been removed quite recently. There is another complex of **woollen mills** on the banks of the River Biss above Cradle Bridge (ST857576). This is made up of **Upper Mill** and **Victoria Mill**. The former is a four-storeyed block of 12 bays. The latter stands alongside Castle Street where a single-storeyed stone building probably housed a stove rack. The premises include the three-storeyed brick building on the banks of the river which has stone framed segment headed windows. The buildings are now derelict. North of Victoria Mill, between Court Street and the river is **Castle Mill** (ST855577) which was built in 1828. It is a five-storeyed brick building with stone segment-headed windows and a truncated square chimney at its south end. Between this and the river is another brick factory, four storeys high with stone lintels and sash windows. It dates from about 1830. To the north is **Brick Mill** (ST855578), another four-storeyed brick factory with stone segment headed windows. **Stone Mill** (ST855578) – once more to the north – is on the site of a 16th-century fulling mill, and was undoubtedly water-powered before a steam engine was installed in 1814. The building, as the name suggests, is of stone. It has flat headed windows set in eight bays in the three-storeyed block closest to the river. It was in the block of four bays at the Court Street end that the steam engine was installed. **Home Mills** (ST856579) stands just round the corner of Court Street. It still houses a firm of woollen cloth manufacturers (Samuel Salter and J. T. Clark) which must be unique in the town today. This four-storeyed building was mainly rebuilt after two devastating fires in 1862 and 1931. The ground floor is built of stone, the other three storeys of brick with decorated window arches. **Studley Mill** (ST854578) stands on the west bank of the River Biss above the town bridge. This factory grew out of the handsome 18th-century clothier's house (Bridge House) and the original workshop building can be seen to the rear. The main block of Studley Mill, built in 1860, is now four storeys high with a square stair tower. Extensive weaving sheds line the bank of the river to the south. Across the river is the now, almost unique, **handle house**, a three-storeyed brick structure with perforated walls, which was used to dry the teasle frames. North of the bridge is **Innox Mill** (ST853580), now occupied by Bowyers Ltd. Behind the Georgian clothier's house is a three-storeyed brick building of 12 bays with stone-dressed windows which dates from 1875. In Shails Lane there is another two-storeyed brick **woollen factory** (ST853583) dated 1877.

70 Trowbridge – Ashton Mill

Trowbridge contains a number of splendid clothiers' houses, of which the best is probably that which is now occupied by Lloyds Bank in Fore Street. There are also a number of weavers' houses, with the elongated top-storey windows which are so characteristic – for example in Castle Street (ST856578) and Yerbury Street (ST860581). Hadens' **Engineering Works** (ST857579) served the local woollen industry by providing steam engines and steam drying stoves. They also supplied central heating systems for Union Workhouses and other large buildings. **Usher's Brewery** (ST855581), situated in the centre of the town, is a five-storeyed red brick building which has extended to newer premises across Church Street. It is still in full production and forms part of the Watneys group. The brickwork is elaborate with yellow brick decorations; the building is dated 1824. Usher's **Maltings**, also part of Watneys, stands at the end of River Way (ST851581). At these premises a brick maltings with kiln and ventilated roof are recognizable. Between River Way and Shails Lane are the remains of the town's **gas works** (ST853582). A long brick retort house, two storeys high with stone framed, round headed windows and a ventilated roof, is now occupied by a transport firm. A short square chimney has also survived alongside a smaller two-storeyed building of five bays which has the traditional round fan hole in the gable end. The **railway station** (ST852579) on the Westbury–Bristol line is operational. It is a single-storeyed stone building with a stone and timber goods shed to the north. Between the railway line and Bythesea Road, in premises formerly occupied by St George's Foundry, is Unigate's large **milk processing factory** (ST853578). A **toll house** (ST873590) stands on the A361 towards Devizes, at the junction with the B3105 at Hilperton. It is a two-storeyed stone building with a stone shelter over the door. On the east side of the town bridge is a square, stone-built **lock up** (ST853580) with a ball finial. The **bridge** has three round arches with two cutwaters on the upstream side. Obviously, Trowbridge is a town with many sites of interest to the industrial archaeologist and well repays a thorough perambulation.

TYTHERINGTON
This is a quaint but scattered village. It contains an interesting red brick building dated 1810 which appears to have served as a barn and dovecote (ST914410). It is built over three small arches which keep its floor above ground level. **Milestone Cottage** (ST914410) has a cast-iron milestone plate set in the front of the building. The **railway station** (ST923419) on the Warminster–Salisbury line, has lost its platform but the single-storeyed stone building has otherwise survived.

WARMINSTER
This is a garrison town which has been a manufacturing centre of some importance, as well as a market town and route centre. Relatively few buildings which obviously relate to the town's connection with the woollen industry have survived. However, a building which housed a **silk factory** stands to the south of the town (ST866447). The older part of the building is of stone with brick-lined windows. The slate roof is surmounted by a bell. The adjacent weaving sheds are in red brick and a round, brick chimney stands on a stone base. More evidence survives of the town's association with the brewing industry. In the last century there were over 20 malthouses operating in Warminster. Only one **malthouse** (*Plate 71*) is in production today, it stands in Pound Street (ST867449). It consists of a two-storeyed stone building with the usual kiln at the end of the wing at right-angles to the road. Over the door in Pound Street is the inscription, 'William Frank Morgan Licensed Maltster'. A close examination of the OS 6in Map for 1886 shows the sites of several more malthouses. Most of these have been converted to other uses, but it is possible to recognize some of them – e.g. north of the High Street between Common Close and Portway (ST873452); in Vicarage Street (ST868451); and in Church Street (ST869453). There is a **toll house** on the south side of the A36 on the east side of the town (ST883446). This is a two-storeyed stone building. A prettier example stands at the end of the lane to Hensfords Marsh Mill (ST878440). This single-storeyed, hexagonal building has been incorporated into a two-storeyed cottage, the thatched roof of which overhangs the toll house. Another single-storeyed **toll house** with an hexagonal

frontage stands at Whitbourne Gate on the A362 (ST839442). The **obelisk** which stands at the junction of the roads to Frome and Bath (ST869451) once carried direction posts, but only pieces of the iron mounts have survived. There are a number of interesting **coaching houses** of which the Old Bell Inn with its handsome colonnaded front is particularly noteworthy (ST878448). Sambourne Hospital (ST868446) was built as the **Union Workhouse** in 1836.

WESTBURY

This manufacturing town which lies under the north escarpment of Salisbury Plain has made extensive use of the locally available water power. The buildings which housed two of the woollen factories of Abraham Laverton are standing and occupied. **Bitham Mill** (ST877513) was built as a water-powered factory in 1803 and and extended to utilize steam power in 1829. The pond which supplied the water for the wheel, and presumably the engine's boiler, has survived.

The mill buildings are ranged round a triangular courtyard. On the south-east there is a three-storeyed brick building with round headed windows adjoining the original engine house. On the north-west side a two-storeyed building, also in brick, has windows with rounded stone lintels and prominent keystones. The south-west side is formed by a three-storeyed building of seven bays with casement windows which has the appearance of a clothier's house of about 1800. A square brick chimney has also survived. The original beam engine continued in use until 1939 and the factory only ceased producing woollen cloth in 1969. **Angel Mill** (ST873512) was also operated by Abraham Laverton & Co until 1969. The factory building dates from 1806. This was probably the first factory to be built in Wiltshire with the intention of using steam power. The main block is five storeys high and consists of 10 bays. It is built in red brick with stone framed segment headed windows and a central pediment over the central four bays. In 1856 a matching wing of eight bays

71 Warminster – The maltings in Pound Street

72 Westbury – The Angel Mill

was built at right-angles to this earlier block. On the gable end of this later wing it is possible to read the advertisement, 'Laverton's Famous Worsted and Woollen Cloths'. The main entrance to the courtyard is under a magnificent stone archway with a highly decorative pediment (*Plate 72*). The mill occupies an island site and it is easy to confuse some of its buildings with those of the **Public Baths** which were erected in 1887.

Hawkridge Mill (ST867534) was used for grinding corn, fulling and other processes associated with the woollen industry in the 19th century. It is a four-storeyed building of seven bays, covered with grey cement rendering. The original water course which powered an overshot wheel has been diverted. The base of the chimney which served a steam engine survives but the building is generally in poor condition and now houses pigs. Like Warminster, Westbury was also a centre for malting and brewing. A large **malthouse** stands alongside the Frome Road at Westbury Leigh (ST863500). It is a stone building of two storeys which is set at right angles to the road. At the road end there are two large drying kilns with steep-sided pyramidical roofs of slate, capped with square ventilators. The **Oak Brewery** (ST871509) is typical of the early, small breweries which were attached to the public houses which marketed their produce. The brewery is the red brick building behind the Oak Inn. The stone malthouse and kiln (dated 1896) to the west have recently been renovated. A similar early brewery stands beside the Railway Hotel (ST865519). Very little has survived of the iron industry in Westbury except for the exhausted and flooded working near the **railway station** (ST862519). The latter is still an important junction on what was the GWR line. Some interesting buildings associated with the millowner A. Laverton are still occupied. **Prospect Square** (ST875511) consists of 39 houses set round a piece of open ground used for allotments; it was built to consolidate Laverton's political fortunes. The **town hall** (ST874511) built in the mixture of brick and stone which characterized his mills bears the lettering 'A. Laverton's Institute 1873'.

WEST LAVINGTON

Robbers' Stone (SU008513) on the east side of the A360 to Shrewton records one of the hazards facing road travellers in 1839. Mr Dean was attacked and robbed by four highwaymen but the latter each received his due deserts.

WESTWOOD

There is an interesting concentration of industrial sites in the gorge of the River Avon to the north of the village. Across the river at this point is an ancient weir which has supplied water power to mills on both banks. As early as 1791 this power was being used to drive woollen machinery at Avoncliffe. Two storeys have survived of this **woollen mill** (ST805600). It is a much restored stone building which is a private residence called Weavers Mill. The arch over the mill leat is clearly visible. Alongside is a square brick **chimney** with stone quoins. On the Bradford side of the weir is a building which has served as a grist and a flock **mill** (ST805601). It is a stone building with three storeys on the river side. A large corrugated iron excrescence has been built over the large iron breast-shot wheel. The narrow river valley contains the original GWR railway between Bradford on Avon and Bath, but the most remarkable transport feature of this site is undoubtedly the stone **aqueduct** (ST804600) which carries the Kennet & Avon Canal across the Avon. Although not as elegant as the Dundas Aqueduct, this important structure is being renovated. It has three arches although the settlement of the centre arch and the indiscriminate patching of the stone facing with bricks, has spoilt its overall appearance. However, there are several good masons' marks to be seen on the underside of the south archway. The canal on both sides of the aqueduct has been dry for many years but the whole section is being re-lined and restored.

WILTON

Now famous for the Royal Carpet Factory which was founded in 1699 (SU100314), Wilton was once a centre for the manufacture of woollen cloth. The present carpet factory occupies the site of an earlier woollen mill at Burdensball which was destroyed by fire in 1799. Rebuilt soon afterwards, water power was used to drive spinning and fulling machinery until the 1830s when the manufacture of carpets was started. Although most of the existing buildings date from the time of carpet manufacture, the three-storeyed brick building with mansard roof and dormer windows was probably part of the original water-powered factory. **Crow Lane Mill** (SU096313), a two-storeyed red brick building with attic and eight bays of segment-headed windows, is occupied by a firm which has been manufacturing felt for pianos and other purposes since the original building was destroyed in the riots of 1830. In North Street there is an interesting red brick terrace of workers' cottages called **Weavers Guild Terrace**, dated 1892, with a coat of arms (SU098314).

WINGFIELD

This parish is situated on the county's boundary with Somerset and includes two surviving wool-manufacturing sites on the River Frome. **Stowford Mill** (ST812577) stands on the site of the 15th-century fulling mill. The present building is three storeys high with an attic range. It and the adjoining farm house and out-buildings are built in the local stone and have been described as 'the best preserved clothing hamlet in the County'. **Langham Mill** (ST806551) was also a fulling mill in the 16th century and continued to be used as such until the mid-19th century.

WINSLEY

A recently re-discovered **wharf** on the side of the Kennet & Avon Canal (ST796605) was linked by iron rails *via* an inclined plane to the Canal Company's **quarries** at Murhill. The site of the stone quarries and mines can be seen in the grounds of the Winsley Chest Hospital. The incline worked on a counter balancing principle. Although most of the stone blocks which carried the rails have now been covered with asphalt, a few sections of fish-bellied cast-iron rails 2ft 6ins long have been uncovered. The stone facing of the wharf has a raised section which was presumably designed to support a crane. To the east the **Conkwell Incline** (ST786625) was a similar structure designed to link the stone

quarries with the Kennet & Avon Canal at the east end of the Dundas Aqueduct.

WINTERBOURNE GUNNER

A red brick **mill** (SU179355) which is three storeys high with a slate roof stands to the west of the River Bourne. Outside there is a millstone and an antiquated petrol pump. There is an attractive timber and thatched building alongside, as well as the brick mill house. **West Gomeldon Windmill** (SU176363) stands in a dense copse. It originally had four floors but these have all collapsed. The brick and flint structure is shown where the external cement rendering has fallen off. The walls are complete up to the cap ring, and pieces of timber and iron gearing can be identified. There are two broken millstones on the floor of the mill.

WOOTTON BASSET

Vastern Wharf (SU052816) is on the side of the Wilts and Berks Canal south west of the town. There is a timber yard on this site.

WORTON

A large corn **mill** (ST966575), built in the 1850s worked until recently. It was powered by an undershot wheel. It has been converted to a private residence but it remains an imposing red brick building of three storeys with stone-framed double light windows.

WYLYE

The new bypass which takes the A303 traffic to the west has restored some peace and calm to this pretty village. The **mill** (SU008378) is a three-storeyed building of three bays. The ground floor is built of stone, the upper floors of brick. A hoist at the rear is fitted to the top storey. Wooden sluices and the brick arch over the leat indicate its original power source. Next to The Bell is a three-storeyed stone **malthouse** (SU008377) which is in the process of conversion to a private residence.

Bibliography

AVON COUNTY

Being a new county, there is not as yet much literature devoted specifically to Avon. But there is a large amount on Bristol, and the relevant sections from the Victoria County Histories of Somerset and Gloucestershire are well worth consulting. Readers of this book will find the following works amongst the most useful if they wish to pursue their enquiries further:

Buchanan, R.A., and Cossons, Neil, *Industrial Archaeology of the Bristol Region*, David & Charles, Newton Abbot, 1969.
Buchanan, R. A., and Cossons, Neil, *Industrial History in Pictures: Bristol*, David & Charles, Newton Abbot, 1970.
Buchanan, R. A., *Industrial Archaeolgy of Bath*, Bath University Press, 1969.
Atthill, Robin, *The Somerset & Dorset Railway*, David & Charles, Newton Abbot, 1967.
Clew, Kenneth R., *The Kennet & Avon Canal*, David & Charles, Newton Abbot, 1968.
Clew, Kenneth R., *The Somersetshire Coal Canal and Railways*, David & Charles, Newton Abbot, 1970.
Latimer, J., *Annals of Bristol*, Kingsmead Press, Bath, reprinted in 3 volumes, 1970.
Wells, C., *A Short History of the Port of Bristol*, Bristol, 1904.
Neale, W.G., *At the Port of Bristol*, Port of Bristol Authority, 2 vols, 1968 and 1970.
Ison, W., *The Georgian Buildings of Bristol*, Faber, London, 1952.
Ison, W., *The Georgian Buildings of Bath*, Faber, London, 1948.
Day, Joan, *Bristol Brass: The History of the Industry*, David & Charles, Newton Abbot, 1973.
Walker, Frank, *The Bristol Region*, Nelson, London, 1972.
Brace, Keith, *Portrait of Bristol*, Robert Hale, London, 1971.

The volumes of historic photographs assembled and published by Reece Winstone, *Bristol as it was*, etc are well worth browsing through. The publications of the Bristol Industrial Archaeological Society, and especially *BIAS Journal* which celebrated its tenth issue in 1978, are highly topical: they are available through the Society, at Bristol City Museums.

GLOUCESTERSHIRE

The county has rarely been short of writers to sing the praise of the Forest, Vale and Wold, and there has been a spate of recent books. Amongst the works aimed largely at tourists are:

Finberg, Josceline, *The Cotswolds*, Eyre Methuen, London, 1977.
Hadfield, Charles and Alice Mary, *The Cotswolds*, Batsford, London, 1966.
Brill, Edith, *Portrait of the Cotswolds*, Robert Hale, London, 1964.
Brill, Edith, *Old Cotswold*, David & Charles, Newton Abbot, 1968.
Ryder, T.A., *Portrait of Gloucestershire*, Robert Hale, London, 1966.
Still an excellent survey, although now somewhat dated is:
Finberg, H. P. R., *Gloucestershire: an Illustrated Essay on the History of the Landscape*, Hodder & Stoughton, London, 1955.
But by far the most useful two books for the industrial archaeological explorer are:
Tann, Jennifer, *Gloucestershire Woollen Mills*, David & Charles, Newton Abbot, 1967, and
Hart, Cyril, *Industrial History of Dean*, David & Charles, Newton Abbot, 1971.
Also of interest are:
Parr, H.W., *The Severn & Wye Railway*, David & Charles, Newton Abbot, 1963.
Chatwin, Amina, *Cheltenham's Ornamental Ironwork*, Cheltenham, 1975.
Bick, D.E., *The Gloucester & Cheltenham Railway*, Oakwood Press, 1968.

Bick, D.E., *Old Leckhampton*, Newent, 1971.
Handford, M.,*The Stroudwater Canal*, Moonraker, Bradford-on-Avon, 1977.
Household, H.G.W., *The Thames & Severn Canal*, David & Charles, Newton Abbot, 1964.
Maggs, C.G., *The Bristol & Gloucester Railway*, Oakwood Press, 1964.
Maggs, C. G., *The Midland & South Western Junction Railway*, David & Charles, Newton Abbot, 1967.

The publications of the Gloucestershire Society for Industrial Archaeology include Newsletters from 1964 to 1970, and a Journal since 1971. The illustrated guide, *Industrial Archaeology in Gloucestershire*, published by the GSIA in 1973, is a very useful introduction. The Hon Secretary is Miss A Chatwin, of 6 & 7 Montpellier Street, Cheltenham.

SOMERSET

Allen, N.V., *The Waters of Exmoor*, Exmoor Press, 1978.
Atthill, R.,*Old Mendip*, David & Charles, 1971 ed.
Atthill, R., *The Somerset & Dorset Railway*, 1971 ed.
Belham, P., *The Making of Frome*, Frome Society, 1973.
Binding, H., and Stevens, D., *Minehead – a New History*, Exmoor Press, 1977.
Brooke, L., *The Book of Yeovil*, Barracuda Books, 1978.
Buchanan, R.A., and Cossons, Neil, *Industrial Archaeology of the Bristol Region*, David & Charles, 1969.
Bush, R., *The Book of Taunton*, Barracuda Books, 1977.
Chard History Group No.1 *The Chard Canal*, 1967.
　　　　　　　　　　　 No.2 *The Roads of Chard*, 1968.
　　　　　　　　　　　 No.4 *The History of Chard*, ND.
Clew, K.R., *The Dorset & Somerset Canal*, David & Charles, 1971.
Coulthard, A.J., and Watts, M., *Windmills of Somerset*, Research Publishing Co, 1978.
Couzens, P., *Bruton in Selwood*, Abbey Press, 1968.
Down, C.G., and Warrington, A.J., *The History of the Somerset Coalfield*, David & Charles, 1971.
Farr, G., *Ships and Harbours of Exmoor*, Exmoor Press, 1974.
Farr, G., *Somerset Harbours*, Christopher Johnson, 1954.
Gough, J.W., *The Mines of Mendip*, David & Charles, 1967.
Hadfield, C., *The Canals of South-West England*, David & Charles, 1967.
Hamilton, J., and Lawrence, J.F., *Men and Mining on the Quantocks*, Town & County Press, 1970.
Harris, H., *The Grand Western Canal*, David & Charles, 1973.
Knight, F.A., *The Heart of Mendip*, Chatford House Press, 1971.
Lawrence, B., *Coleridge and Wordsworth in Somerset*, David & Charles, 1970.
Maber, R., *Martock Memories*, Norman, Maber & Associates, 1977.
Orwin, C.S., and Sellick, R.J., *The Reclamation of Exmoor Forest*, David & Charles, 1970.
Rogers, K., *Wiltshire and Somerset Woollen Mills*, Pasold, 1976.
Sellick, R. H., *The West Somerset Mineral Railway*, David & Charles, 1970.
Sellick, R.J., *The Old Mineral Line*, Exmoor Press, 1976.
Slader, J.M., *Days of Renown – Mining on Exmoor*, West Country Publications, 1965.
Thomas, D.St.J.,*A Regional History of the Railways of Great Britain, Vol I, The West Country*, David & Charles, 1966.
Wedlake, A.L., *A History of Watchet*, Exmoor Press, 1973.
Williams, M., *The Drainage of the Somerset Levels*, C.U.P., 1970.

More detailed information on the industrial archaeology of Somerset will be found in the Journals of the Bristol Industrial Archaeological Society and of the Somerset Industrial Archaeological Society. The publications *Industrial Archaeology* and *The Industrial Archaeology Review* also contain some material relevant to this county.

WILTSHIRE

Backinsell, W.G.C., *The Medieval Clock in Salisbury Cathedral*, SWIAS, 1977.
Backinsell, W.G.C., *The Salisbury Railway & Market House Company*, SWIAS, 1977.
Buchanan, R.A., and Cossons, N., *Industrial Archaeology of the Bristol Region*, David & Charles, 1969.
Clew, K.R., *The Kennet & Avon Canal*, David & Charles, 1973.
Corfield, M.C., (ed), *A Guide to the Industrial Archaeology of Wiltshire*, Wilts. County Council and Wilts. Arch. & Nat. History Society, 1978.
Cross, D.E., *Salisbury Town Trails*, Wessexplore, ND.
Dalby, L.J., *The Wilts & Berks Canal*, Oakwood Press, 1971.
Defoe, D., *A Tour Through the Whole Island of Great Britain*, Everyman, 1962.
Harris,D., (ed), *Crofton Beam Engines*, Crofton Society, 1975.
Hudson, K., *The Industrial Archaeology of Southern England*, David & Charles, 1965.
Household, H., *The Thames & Severn Canal*, David & Charles, 1969.
Major, J.K., *Animal Powered Engines*, Batsford, 1978.
de L Mann, J., *The Cloth Industry in the West of England 1640–1880*, Oxford, 1971.
Ponting, K.G., *The Woollen Industry of South-West England*, Adams & Dart, 1971.
Ponting, K.G., (ed), *The Industrial Archaeology of Wiltshire*, Wilts. Arch. and Nat. History Society, 1973.
Rogers, K., *Wiltshire and Somerset Woollen Mills*, Pasold, 1976.
Russell, R., *Discovering Lost Canals*, Shire, Publications, 1975.
White, H.P., *A Regional History of the Railways of Great Britain, Vol 2 Southern England*, David & Charles, 1969.
More detailed information on the industrial archaeology of Wiltshire will be found in the journals *Wiltshire Industrial Archaeology*, *Industrial Archaeology*, and *The Industrial Archaeology Review*.

Index

Sites, Industries, and Persons mentioned in the text excluding the Introduction. Railways and Canals listed under their titles. Numbers in italics indicate an illustration.